JOHN CATT'S
Which School? for Special Needs
2019/20

28th Edition
Editor: Jonathan Barnes

JOHN
CATT
EDUCATIONAL
LIMITED

Published in 2019 by
John Catt Educational Ltd,
15 Riduna Park, Melton
Woodbridge, Suffolk IP12 1QT UK
Tel: 01394 389850   Fax: 01394 386893
Email: enquiries@johncatt.com
Website: www.johncatt.com
© 2019 John Catt Educational Ltd

**A CIP catalogue record for this book is available from the
British Library.**

ISBN: 978 1 912906 27 7

Contacts
Editor
Jonathan Barnes

Advertising and School Profiles
Tel: +44 (0) 1394 389850
Email: sales@johncatt.com

Distribution/Book Sales
Tel: +44 (0) 1394 389863
Email: booksales@johncatt.com

Contents

How to use this guide

Here are some pointers on how to use this guidebook effectively

Which School? for Special Needs is divided into specific sections:

1. Editorial
This includes articles, written by experts in their fields, explaining various aspects of special needs education. There are also case studies and other interesting articles.

2. Profiles
Here the schools and colleges have been given the opportunity to highlight what they feel are their best qualities in order to help you decide whether this is the right school for your child. They are presented in sections according to the needs they specialise in:

- social interaction difficulties (autism, ASC & ASP)
- emotional, behavioural and/or social difficulties.
- learning difficulties (including dyslexia/SPLD)
- sensory or physical impairment

Within these sections, schools and colleges are listed by region in alphabetical order.

3. Directory
Here you will find basic up-to-date information about every independent or non-maintained special needs school and college, and further education colleges, in England, Northern Ireland, Scotland and Wales, giving contact details, size of school and which specific needs are catered for. (You will find a key to the abbreviations at the start of each directory section) The directory is divided into four sections:

- social interaction difficulties (autism, ASC & ASP)
- emotional, behavioural and/or social difficulties.
- learning difficulties (including dyslexia/SPLD)
- sensory or physical impairment

Within these sections, each establishment is listed by region in alphabetical order and those that have entries in the profiles section are cross-referenced to allow you to find further detailed information. Against each entry you will find a number of symbols indicating any SEN speciality, including an icon to indicate if the school is DfE approved.

4. Useful associations and websites
In this section we provide a list of useful organisations and websites relevant to special educational needs, which may be useful to parents looking for specific help or advice.

5. Maintained schools
Here we have included basic details of all maintained special schools in England, Northern Ireland, Scotland and Wales. They are listed according to their Local Authority.

6. Index
Page numbers preceded by a D indicate a school appearing in the directory, those without will be found in the profiles section.

How to use this guide effectively

John Catt's *Which School? for Special Needs* can be used effectively in several ways according to the information you are looking for. For example, are you looking for:

A specific school? If you know the name of the school but are unsure of its location simply go to the index at the back of the guide where you will find all schools listed alphabetically.

A particular type of school? Both the profiles and directories are divided into sections according to the type of provision. **See also the appendix on page 169**, which lists specific special needs and the schools that cater for them.

A school in a certain region? Look first in the relevant directory. This will give you the basic information about the schools in each region, complete with contact details and which specific needs are catered for. More detailed information can be found in the profiles section for those schools that have chosen to include a full entry.

More information on relevant educational organisations? At the end of the directories you will find a list of useful organisations and websites relevant to special educational needs.

Please note: regional divisions

To facilitate the use of this guide, we have included the geographical region 'Central & West'. This is not an officially designated region and has been created solely for the purposes of this publication.

One final thing, below you will find a list of commonly used SEN abbreviations. This list can be found repeated at various points throughout the guide.

Abbreviations – a full glossary can be found at page 303

ADD	Attention Deficit Disorder	LD	Learning Difficulties
ADHD	Attention Deficit and Hyperactivity Disorder	MLD	Moderate Learning Difficulties
		MSI	Multi-sensory Impairment
ASC	Autistic Spectrum Conditions	OCD	Obsessive Compulsive Disorder
ASD	Autistic Spectrum Disorder	PD	Physical Difficulties
ASP	Asperger Syndrome	PH	Physical Impairment
AUT	Autism	Phe	Partially Hearing
BESD	Behavioural, Emotional and Social Difficulties	PMLD	Profound and Multiple Learning Difficulties
		PNI	Physical Neurological Impairment
CCD	Complex Communication Difficulties	SCD	Social and Communication Difficulties
CLD	Complex Learning Difficulties	SCLD	Severe to Complex Learning Difficulties
CP	Cerebral Palsy	SEMH	Severe Emotional and Mental Heath Needs
D	Deaf		
DYS	Dyslexia	SEBN	Social, Emotional and Behavioural Needs
DYSP	Dyspraxia	SLD	Severe Language Difficulties
EBD	Emotional and Behavioural Difficulties	SLI	Specific Language Impairment
EPI	Epilepsy	SPLD	Specific Learning Difficulties
GLD	General Learning Difficulties	SP&LD	Speech and Language Difficulties
HA	High Ability	VIS	Visual Impairment
HI	Hearing Impairment		

National
Autistic
Society

Tailor-made, innovative education

for students
aged 4 -22

UK-wide day and residential
placements for autistic young
people. Book a visit to one of
our nine specialist
schools today.

Contact us:

www.autism.org.uk/school

Gather information, ask questions – why your involvement is so important

SEND consultant and author David Bartram, Director of Prescient Education, introduces the new edition...

All children and young people should expect to receive an education that enables them to achieve the best possible educational and wider outcomes, and become confident, able to communicate their own views and ready to make a successful transition into adulthood. The choice of school for your child is central to these aims and will be one of the most important decisions you make as a parent.

Identifying the school that will best meet the needs of your child will mean gathering as much information about the school as possible. This might include finding out about the school's curriculum and how it is taught, how the school prepares its learners for the next stage in their education, employment and independent life, and importantly how the school ensures there is a culture of high aspiration for all of its learners.

This Guide offers the opportunity for you to make an informed choice. It will provide you with information on the wider national context and the current legislation as it applies to SEND, and act as a resource to support your decision-making, allowing you to see the range of schools and provision available. It will give you an insight into the school, including its vision and approach, so that you can then use your knowledge of your own child to make the decision on whether this is the right school for your family.

The Guide should also give you the confidence to ask questions of the school before you make your decision. For example:

- How has the school created a culture and ethos that welcomes and engages parents and carers of learners with SEND?

- How do systems at your school allow parents and carers to meaningfully contribute to shaping the quality of support and provision?

- How do you work with families to support effective transition for children and young people?

This focus on family, and the school's approach to working with families, is important. The Lamb Inquiry (2009) concluded that there was a lack of aspiration and focus on securing good outcomes in the school system for children with special educational needs and disabilities. It found that parents, children and young people's views were not properly listened to and acted on and highlighted the need for schools to communicate openly, honestly and frequently with families.

To address these issues, the Children and Families Act 2014 sought to put parental and learners' involvement at the heart of achieving better outcomes. This is then linked to ensuring better outcomes in the Department for Education's 2015 Code of Practice which recognises that effective engagement with parents and carers has a clear impact on children reaching their potential.

This Guide will give you an insight into the school, including its vision and approach, so that you can then use your knowledge of your own child to make the decision on whether this is the right school for your family.

We're one of the UK's leading independent providers of residential services, schools and colleges supporting people with autism and complex needs.

Our highly trained staff provide the highest quality, person-centred approach. Giving those who use our services the support, skills and tools they need to be as independent as possible.

Our unique **Hesley Enhancing Lives Programme (HELP)** is a big part of this.

Combining the latest techniques and practices, HELP is our successful value-based positive behaviour support programme. Based on the principles of Therapeutic Crisis Intervention which is accredited by the British Institute of Learning Disabilities, HELP reduces the need for high-risk interventions by taking an empathic and proactive approach. We focus on how our actions can positively shape the emotional well-being of all those who use our services. It's why all our staff are given HELP training to make sure it works in practice as well as theory.

Find out more about our schools and colleges visit www.hesleygroup.co.uk or call 0800 0556789.

Embedding parental involvement is based on extensive but often ignored evidence that greater parental involvement has a dramatic impact on progression, attainment and wider outcomes as well as improved attendance and behaviour. This is especially relevant for children and young people with SEND who are already vulnerable learners. High quality parental involvement needs planning and focus. Parental engagement needs to be part of a whole-school approach and there should be clear leadership of parental engagement within the school.

Five years on since the introduction of the Children and Families Act, there remains considerable variation between schools in how they ensure greater parental confidence and better partnership with families. In schools where this is working well, the child is at the centre, with the school and the family working together to secure improved outcomes.

There are great examples of independent and non-maintained special schools working in partnership with families, many of which are contained within this Guide. All of the schools listed are fully registered and regularly inspected by the Office for Standards in Education (OfSTED) and by the Care Quality Commission. Many are centres of excellence with high levels of expertise that specialise in addressing specific learning needs, and in curricular areas which are innovative and distinctive. This Guide will help you navigate the range and choice of school available, supporting you to identify best practice and allowing you to select the most appropriate provision so that you make the right choice for your child and your family.

For more information about Prescient Education, see www.prescienteducation.co.uk

*David Bartram OBE is the editor of **Great Expectations: Leading an Effective SEND Strategy in School**.*

This book features leading educationalists and school leaders with a track record of improving outcomes for children and young people with additional needs discussing and highlighting the significant role that school leaders play in shaping effective practice in SEND.

Available for £15 from www.johncatt.com

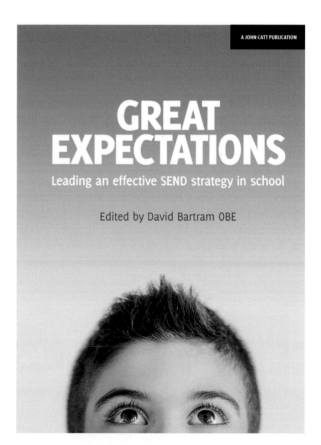

A JOHN CATT PUBLICATION

GREAT EXPECTATIONS

Leading an effective SEND strategy in school

Edited by David Bartram OBE

Round and round we go

Douglas Silas, of Douglas Silas Solicitors, gives an overview of the latest develoments in the SEND sector

One of the fortunate things for me, as someone who has been dealing with SEND issues for so many years, is that I have the advantage of sometimes seeing 'new' issues, which are really just 'old' ones presenting themselves slightly differently this time around.

In the past year, I have also been lucky enough to hear a number of experienced SEND professionals. On the one hand, there are those people who feel we are now in the middle of a SEND crisis, whilst other people feel that we are just still experiencing initial difficulties, as a result of the move to a new SEND framework, brought into effect by the Children and Families Act 2014, some five years ago now.

Those who talk about a 'SEND Crisis' point out that:

- There was the report in October 2017, from the Local Government and Social Care Ombudsman (LGSCO), where the outcome of 80% of the first 100 investigations about SEND were upheld, compared to a figure of 53% in other areas they investigate;

- There was the Ofsted Annual Report for 2017/18 looking at a number of areas of LAs showing weaknesses in the identification of children/young people with SEND; variation in quality of Education, Health and Care (EHC) Plans (including non-implementation of agreed support) and poor SEND provision provided to young people from 19-25. This includes a lot of children and young people with SEND being excluded or 'off-rolled;

- Almost half of all local area SEND inspections conducted by Ofsted/CQC (the Care Quality Commission) in recent years have required 'Written Statements of Action' and there have also been a number of Judicial Review cases brought by parents and carers against their LAs;

- Schools and colleges feel that there is an underestimation of children and young people's needs in EHC Plans, a lack of support from LAs and Educational Psychology services, not enough staff and teaching assistants being available and generally insufficient support being there; and

- There has been a significant increase of appeals brought to the SEND Tribunal, particularly in recent years, when it was just over 3,500 in 2011/12, but in the last year it was over 5,500.

Those who say there are really only initial difficulties point out that:

- There are a number of things to celebrate, in relation to 'co-production', 'compliance with statutory duties', 'increased satisfaction with local services' and 'timely identification of SEND';

- LAs have had to do a lot of work in the last few years in relation to transfers from Statements to EHC Plans and dealing with increasing requests for EHC Needs Assessments, as well as the increasing number of EHC Plans themselves (which was up last year over 11% from 2016), without additional resources and insufficient funding, or the now extended responsibilities in relation to the 19-25 group;

- There have been other challenges in the delivery of the SEND reforms, including high staff turnover, training and the pressure on school places, including the increased amount of demand for special school places and the need to keep mainstream schools onboard, (i.e. successful inclusion);

Everyone thinks that there is not enough funding in the SEND system, and this has fallen over many years, whilst trying to implement a new system, particularly for the post-16 section

- There has been 'improved attainment' for those children and young people with SEND where there has been stronger focus on SEN support and where more young people are going onto post-16 education, training and employment. There just needs to be more focus on successful implementation, particularly in relation to cultural shifts, the legal framework and better accountability; and

- There has been improved parental confidence in a number of areas and they are encouraged by early evidence of the impact of the implementation of the SEND reforms and how they have improved the lives of children and young people, but they also recognise the challenges and that there is much more work to do in order to achieve consistency across the country.

I have found myself sometimes taken back to 2005/2006 and the Education Select Committee's Inquiry, where they found that parents were really unhappy and that the SEN system was not working, because there were too many exclusions, too many Tribunals, etc. I have also noticed a number of similar themes though, for example:

- Many people feel that, whilst the principles of the new SEND Code of Practice were quite good in identifying and meeting all the needs, it was implemented at the time of limited budgets, schools turning into academies and changes to school assessments, so that it has probably been a bit overshadowed;

- There seems to now be a much greater demand for more special schools places, which seems a bit ironic, as there was so much drive towards inclusion in the first few years after the change in the law to strengthen mainstream inclusion in 2001;

- There are now some mainstream schools who now seem to be SEND 'magnets', that attract many children with SEND, as they are more inclusive – either because parents want their child with SEND to go to that school, as it is more welcoming, or because other mainstream schools tend to refer children with SEND to them;

- Everyone thinks that there is not enough funding in the SEND system, and this has fallen over many years, whilst trying to implement a new system, particularly for the post-16 section; and

- Although there are still problems, we must be careful not to only focus on the difficulties and recognise that there have been some improvements and there are many people who would now not want to go back to the old system. However, there is still a lot of work to do and there are still a lot of LAs and schools not doing things right.

Ultimately, we need to change the culture of the system to achieve better outcomes for children and young people with SEND and remember that, often, parents will choose for their child to go to a school that is welcoming, rather than one that is not. There are also a number of things that we can do, like investing in schools and colleges, including giving more training to frontline staff; listening to parents and young people more, including building more effective relationships between parents, schools and young people; looking at more strategic development with LAs; etc. (to name but a few).

There also needs to be better guidance from the Department for Education (DfE), more possibilities for 19-25 year olds, more advice and support for parents of young people, improved joined-up working and, of course, more funding!

I guess that you will make up your own mind, but one thing I am fairly sure of is that SEND issues will not go away and will probably just go round and around...

For more information visit www.specialeducationalneeds.co.uk

Nothing but the best!

Jenny Hooper, a professional SEN advocate with over 30 years of practical experience, explains how you can get the best education for your child

Many times, as a parent myself, I have questioned my choices in relation to parenting. I have been told, by those who have gone before me, 'there is no rule book for bringing up children'. Each one of us muddles along, learning from other parents and remembering what things were like when we were children. However, when you have a child with additional needs, you require more than a rule book. You need a suit of armour and the energy to go into battle again and again. You will be expected to have extensive, immediate knowledge of the specific needs of your child, so that you can successfully access the right educational environment for them (and you) to fulfil their dreams and aspirations.

And here's where it gets difficult. It's a minefield out there. Does your child need a Statutory Assessment that should lead to an Education Health Care Plan? What help can you expect from your Local Authority? What mainstream and specialist schools are there in your catchment area or can you consider schools elsewhere? How can you find your way through complex legislation to ensure you get everything your child is entitled to by law?

Your biggest battle may be finding the right school. Once told that their child has a learning disability, parents have to accept that they should set aside their own expectations and put the needs of their child first. Your child is an individual with needs, 'special' or otherwise, that must be identified before you start looking for a school. The better you know what these are, the easier it will be to ask the right questions and the clearer your choice of school will become.

Choosing the right school when your child has an Education Health Care Plan is never easy, especially when the Local Authority is not in a position to help you. Every Local Authority is legally bound by the Code of Practice of the Children and Families Act 2014 to have a 'local offer', which includes a list of schools in that area. But that is really as far as it goes.

The onus is on parents to ask their Local Authority to consult with the schools of their choice. But the Local Authority cannot advise you on which schools to choose. It will send the schools the Education Health Care Plan along with the reports which support it. Then the special educational needs coordinator at each school will decide if they can meet your child's needs. You then

Your child is an individual with needs, 'special' or otherwise, that must be identified before you start looking for a school. The better you know what these are, the easier it will be to ask the right questions and the clearer your choice of school will become.

have the choice of the schools which have said they can meet your child's needs. The final choice is down to you.

There are some government supported schemes which can advise parents on schooling, but none of these can create the bespoke package that an independent SEN consultancy can do. It is essential to understand a child personally, to have close knowledge of their additional needs and an understanding of the education offered in varying environments so that they can prosper. In these fast-moving times, where parents are pulled in all directions, there is little time to scout around the local area or sometimes further afield looking for the right school. Why not let somebody else do the ground work for you?

There are many things to consider and many parents feel more comfortable with an expert guide on their side. Someone they can confide in, someone who can hold their hands through the complex and often lengthy process, someone who is totally dedicated to getting the best for their child, someone who is not afraid to ask the right questions. For instance, many mainstream schools now cater for mild and moderate difficulties. But it is hard to know exactly how good these departments are without asking some searching questions, and many parents worry that by revealing their child's difficulties, they might be risking their chances of getting in.

But information is out there. At each school, it is vital that you speak directly to the SEN coordinator, and if the support seems impressive, then try to establish how well it is communicated throughout the school by talking to some teachers.

But then again, are you, like most parents, convinced that you want your child to go to a mainstream school – to lead 'a normal life'? Does it not concern you that, with the universal pressure on education budgets, many mainstream schools just do not have the resources to fully meet the needs of children with additional needs? In mainstream schools, children sometimes feel stigmatised when withdrawn from class for extra help. It is by succeeding in a smaller specialist environment, sometimes for the first time in their lives, that children will develop self-esteem and confidence. Confidence and self-esteem play an integral part in a child's learning and it is vital that they do not lose such confidence.

Most of experts believe that mainstream schools could learn a huge amount from the individualised approach to education offered by specialist schools, with small class-sizes and teaching strategies designed to accommodate children with additional but varying needs. Proof is in the fact that many specialist schools outperform the mainstream schools with their results. Most teachers are sympathetic to parents coming to terms with their children's difficulties and try to gently encourage parents along the right route. But making the decision between mainstream and special ultimately has to be the parents', and perhaps the child's, decision.

Many parents find the prospect of making such decisions quite terrifying, particularly if they feel they have not received independent advice. If you feel that I might be able to help you as an experienced and sympathetic guide, just e-mail (jennyhoopersenconsulting@gmail.com) or phone me on 07720 898394 for a free, no obligations chat.

For more information about Jenny Hooper SEN Consulting Ltd visit www.jhoopersenconsulting.com

A parent's guide to understanding your child's spiky learning profile

Julie Taplin, Chief Executive of Potential Plus UK, looks at the considerations for children with Dual or Multiple Exceptionality

Does your child have some areas where they learn with ease? Perhaps they have expertise in one specific area of interest. Or they have exceptional visual or auditory memory? At the same time there are other areas where they really struggle. Perhaps they have difficulty keeping on track and finishing a task? Or they are frustrated by their inability to transfer their thoughts clearly onto paper?

In the UK, this kind of spiky learning profile is called Dual or Multiple Exceptionality and is often shortened to DME. It is used to describe children who have one or more special educational needs or disabilities and also have high ability (which Potential Plus UK calls high learning potential).

A minority within a minority
The majority of children in the UK do not have a special educational need or disability (SEND). The majority of children in the UK do not have high learning potential. Therefore, those children who have both high learning potential and have one or more special education needs

or disabilities are a distinct minority within a minority. This is an important point for parents to consider, as finding an appropriate educational setting for these children is clearly very important and is made more difficult by the fact that they have very complex educational needs. Their abilities are advanced in some areas, but significantly lagging in others.

Characteristics and consequences of a spiky profile
These characteristics should help parents understand their child's learning profile. Not all of these characteristics will relate to all DME children, but any combination is likely to create a spiky profile.

Intellectual strengths:

- Ability/expertise in one specific area
- Active imagination
- Extensive vocabulary

- Exceptional comprehension
- High performance in tasks requiring abstract thinking
- Excellent visual or auditory memory
- Creativity outside school

Academic difficulties:

- Poor handwriting
- Poor spelling
- Difficulty with phonics
- Inability to do seemingly simple tasks, whilst completing more complex ones
- Success in either mathematics or language subjects, but challenges in the other
- Difficulties in completing tasks with a sequence of steps discussions
- Inattentive at times

Emotional indicators:

- Confusion about abilities
- Strong fear of failure
- Sensitivity to criticism
- Experiences of intense frustration
- Low self-esteem
- Feelings of being different from others
- Poor social skills

Behaviour:

- Disruptive in class
- Often off-task
- Disorganised
- Impulsive
- Creative when making excuses to avoid tasks they find difficult
- Frustrated, sometimes spilling over into anger or aggression
- Withdrawn at times

Dependent on how these characteristics are recognised and understood in a school setting DME children are likely to share some common traits.

1. Children whose high learning potential is recognised but whose special education needs or disabilities are unrecognised often share the following traits:

- Compensate for their special needs through the use of their advanced abilities. This can lead to their learning difficulties being hidden.
- As they grow older, their special needs cause an increasing discrepancy between their expected and actual performance in school.
- The overall impression they give of being 'very able' is often contradicted by poor performance.
- Ability enables them to 'get by'.

When high learning potential compensates for a special educational need or disability, they frequently are not identified as having SEND. Neither are they deemed suitable for receiving extra support or provision. For example, a high potential learner with dyslexia might develop coping strategies within a classroom, perhaps by relying upon verbal proficiency to get through lessons.

2. Children whose special educational needs or disabilities are recognised but whose high learning potential is unrecognised can share the following traits:

- Often noticed for what they cannot do, rather than what they can do.
- Special educational needs and disabilities affect their achievement to a great extent and their strengths in other areas are not recognised.
- Restrictions are placed on the extended learning opportunities on offer in school.
- Often fail to achieve their potential in school.

For some DME children their special educational needs or disabilities are seen as their sole distinguishing feature. Such children are at greater risk of not being identified as having high learning potential and thereby lose out on support to develop their abilities. These children then miss out on opportunities for challenge and enrichment, which are the basis of good provision within the education system. This can be a very demoralising situation for high learning potential children to be in, as they are not given a chance to reach their own potential, but are instead set much lower targets (for them) across the board; irrespective of their individual strengths or weaknesses.

3. Children for whom *both* high learning potential *and* special educational needs or disabilities are unrecognised can share the following traits:

- High learning potential masks their special educational needs or disabilities, and their special educational needs or disabilities mask their high learning potential

OUR SERVICES FOR SCHOOLS

SCHOOL PARTNERSHIP BENEFITS

- Online teacher resources
- Best practice sharing
- Discounts on CPD Training and Parents' Workshops
- Support for all parents of identified pupils:
  - Online parent resources
  - Monthly updates
  - Access to online community
  - Discounts on national events

CPD TRAINING
Topics include:

- Identifying Able, Gifted & Talented Learners
- Classroom Strategies to Provide Challenge
- Tackling Underachievement
- Fostering Resilience in the Classroom

PARENTS' WORKSHOPS
Topics include:

- Parenting an Able, Gifted & Talented Child
- Creative and Critical Thinking
- Extending Your Child's Learning at Home
- Supporting Your Child's Social and Emotional Needs

UNDERACHIEVEMENT ASSESSMENTS

We provide assessments to identify reasons for underachievement in seemingly able children covering cognitive ability, working memory, processing, sensory issues and social/emotional issues.

Potential Plus UK | Discover. Nurture. Succeed.

Potential Plus UK works with schools and parents to support able, gifted & talented children and help them achieve excellence. We can help you identify able learners, understand their capabilities, tailor provision to ensure they make progress, support underachievers and Dual or Multiple Exceptional learners (those who have high ability and a learning difficulty).

FOR MORE INFORMATION

go to **www.potentialplusuk.org**
call us on **01908 646433**
or email **amazingchildren@potentialplusuk.org**

CHARITY REGISTRATION NO 313182

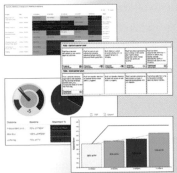

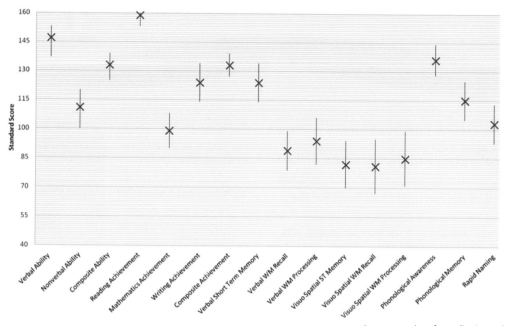

An example of a spiky learning profile

- Intellectual abilities have to work harder to compensate for perceived weaknesses associated with an undiagnosed special need.

- True abilities may only surface when they are given an opportunity to unlock their area of talent.

- This is the group which is most at risk of under achievement.

When DME in its entirety (that is the strengths as well as weaknesses) is not recognised and supported there can be severe implications, not only with regards to consistent underachievement, but also for these children's self-esteem, mental health, emotional well-being, aspirations, further education and career prospects.

4. Children for whom *both* their high learning potential *and* special educational needs or disabilities are recognised are the lucky ones:

- More likely to feel understood and supported both at home and at school.

- Often feel comfortable enough to voice concerns regarding any difficulties related to their special educational needs or disabilities.

- Academically or creatively challenged on a regular basis.

- Access to learning support aids/provision if necessary.

These DME children are most likely to fully achieve their true high potential. The experience of a consistently supportive education will positively influence their self-esteem and self-confidence, enabling them to seek further challenges and new experiences, which should in turn lead to positive learning and wellbeing outcomes.

What next?

Having an understanding of why your child might have a spiky learning profile is the first step to ensuring that they are in a school that can provide appropriately for their educational, social, and emotional needs. Potential Plus UK is an educational charity that supports children with high learning potential, including DME learners. By providing information, advice and training to parents and to schools we aim to improve educational and wellbeing outcomes for DME children. There is more information on our website including free advice sheets on DME: www.potentialplusuk.org/index.php/advice-sheets

For more information about Potential Plus UK, see www.potentialplusuk.org

From Isolation to Independence

TCES Group schools provide LA funded education for pupils aged 7-19 years whose Social, Emotional or Mental Health needs (SEMH) or Autism Spectrum Condition (ASC) plus complex co-morbid needs has made it difficult for them to achieve success in a mainstream school. Pupils often have undiagnosed speech, language and communication needs (SLCN), sensory difficulties or learning difficulties, which can create barriers to learning that must be addressed before the pupil can settle into education. Our integrated approach to education, health and care takes each pupil on an individual journey of change that encourages a love of learning. We offer two options according to the needs of the pupil:

Day School Provision

For pupils with SEMH needs or an ASC for whom the expectation is that they will be able to thrive in and integrate easily into a small group learning environment, which would include an internal induction period as standard. Once in school full time, the pupil would be supported by TCES Group's Team Around the Child approach.

There may be exceptional circumstances where a pupil needs additional support over a specified period to ensure they are able to engage with and thrive in their placement.

Day school services are delivered and managed by the leadership teams in each of our schools – Head and Deputy Head of School and Inclusion Managers – in conjunction with Head of Clinical Services, Clinical and Therapy Team and our School Improvement Team.

Create Service

For pupils with SEMH or an ASC for whom integration into a class-based school placement is not indicated, which may be for a number of reasons. At best they will need a graduated programme into a small group learning environment. They may need 1:1 support in the medium to long term in tandem with TCES Group's Team Around the Child approach.

Also for pupils with SEMH or an ASC who either present high risk to themselves or others or who are extremely vulnerable and are therefore at high risk. Pupils' complex and additional needs (across education, health and care) negate their ability to be educated in any group setting.

Create Service is delivered and managed by the Head of Service and Case Co-ordinators, teachers and tutors as a parallel service to that of our schools, in conjunction with our Head of Clinical Services, Clinical and Therapy Team and School Improvement Team. Therapeutic education, assessment and monitoring is delivered through a highly specialised case co-ordination model. Pupils may attend one of Create's Therapeutic Hubs, be educated in safe community spaces or, in some cases, their own homes.

East London
Independent School

North West London
Independent School

referrals@tces.org.uk
www.tces.org.uk
020 8543 7878

Essex Fresh Start
Independent School

Create Service
Personalised Therapeutic Education

School life without labels; from social exclusion to school inclusion

Thomas Keaney, CEO and Schools' Proprietor of TCES Group, celebrates 'the art of the possible'

In its purest form inclusive practice means the complete inclusion into mainstream classrooms, with the correct level of support for the pupil with Special Educational Needs and Disabilities (SEND) to be successful. To be truly inclusive, the school must wrap itself around the child's special education needs or disabilities and not expect the child to adapt to the school.

However, there are a number of barriers to inclusion. In reality, mainstream school staff often do not feel they have the training, skills or expertise to support pupils with the most complex needs. Inclusion studies show that further concern has arisen from schools who feel that their performance might be damaged – either in reality or in the way their outcomes are reported publicly – if they are to become 'too' inclusive.

Much of society and some mainstream schools are not yet ready to accept hidden disabilities like autism or social, emotional and mental health (SEMH) needs, especially if they come with behavioural issues as one of the symptoms. These are the ways SEND pupils communicate their disabilities and their symptoms whilst awaiting much needed support, but they lead to significant disadvantage through being marginalised or excluded by society and schools due to this manifestation of their disability.

Sadly, if autistic or SEMH pupils are a challenge for a mainstream school they are either moved to an on-site learning support unit, off-site to one-to-one outreach programmes, an alternative provision like a pupil referral unit (PRU), or they become part of a managed move to another school, avoiding the 'permanent inclusion' tag.

If none of the above options are available, then the pupil is excluded from mainstream, often with a condemning and exaggerated negative report. This 'paperwork passport' usually indicates enough labels and high-end needs to make the most inclusive Head Teacher run a mile.

There has been a general buzz lately condemning the number of permanent exclusions that mainstream schools and academies are making, highlighting the high level of risk this can place on a pupil. This is especially true of pupils with SEND, who are up to six times more likely to be permanently excluded. Despite pressure from external sources such as the Department for Education or Ofsted regarding 'off-rolling', pupil exclusions are rising significantly.

SEND pupils, those in KS4 embarking on their GCSE programmes and pupils from low-income families are particularly affected. Sadly, it is also affecting 'care experienced' pupils, who are facing the problem of a 'school-to-prison' pipeline.

Parents of children who have been excluded or are labelled as too overly complex for mainstream education look to specialist schools as the last option. Usually these schools further 'segregate' pupils into two separate groups – 'autism spectrum condition' (ASC), or 'SEMH needs'. General opinions of these schools in the past indicate that they should be separated – however, the 2015 SEND Code of Practice reveals significant similarities in these pupils' needs.

The art of the possible

At TCES Group, we believe that a school should be an inclusive place for all pupils, and not just an exclusive place for some pupils.

Being inclusive can work extraordinarily well in the most challenging of circumstances. After 20 years of working with SEND pupils with some of the most complex, challenging and co-morbid needs, we have never excluded a pupil.

Our schools aim to be truly inclusive, and we work extremely hard to remove labels, promote mutual respect and a general acceptance of everyone. We prepare our pupils for life after school, and have high expectations for our pupils with SEND as both UK and global citizens. Exposure to diversity creates resilience in our pupils, reduces prejudices and makes them more employable and emotionally healthy.

While working with some of the most complex pupils with ASC and SEMH, our first step is to deliver a message

of inclusion. We explore and agree our values with the whole school community – pupils, staff, parents and carers – and share the elements of each school that make us most proud, displaying them around the school as reminders.

This helps to signal to all pupils that they are accepted into the school community, that they are understood and will be supported. We ensure that they know their school is a place for all abilities, and remove the sense of feeling that SEND pupils are a problem. Our children are not damaged, deranged or dangerous – they simply need our support to engage them. We help them believe that they are important and can succeed in whatever they do.

Child Psychologist Bruno Bettleheim's view that *"Children don't care how much you know until they know how much you care"* is an important first step for our staff. Every child needs an adult figure in their life who is willing to go the extra mile for them, even if this is against the prevailing culture of a school.

Our pupils are encouraged to deliver 'all about me' presentations to each other, which allow them to talk about their strengths, talents, families, disabilities, triggers, likes and dislikes in a way that ensures that each pupil's differences are celebrated. These pupils with SEMH and ASC are then educated together in the same classrooms. They 'get' each other, and accept each other.

The only labels that we tolerate are those which describe our pupils as gifted, talented, or in a position of leadership. Many of our pupils have withstood issues in their lives that would knock down most adults. Issues they have encountered early in their lives can develop hidden talents, like resilience and humour – the job of a good school is to support them in evolving these talents and turning them into positive strengths.

Thomas Keaney has 25 years' experience of educating children and young people with the most complex and wide-ranging special educational needs. He is CEO and Schools' Proprietor for TCES Group, which operates three independent schools in London and Essex, plus Therapeutic Hubs for its parallel service, Create, for young people with multiple overlapping and complex needs who need more intensive adult and clinical support in a range of non-school settings.

For more information about TCES Group see page 60

A 24-hour curriculum for communication

I CAN provides the best possible care and education for children with speech and language communication needs (SLCN). This article outlines why residential care is so important and the innovations I CAN uses at both its schools to improve all areas of our children's lives.

At I CAN our vision is of a world where all children have the communication skills they need to fulfil their potential. At our schools, this doesn't just end at 3.30pm.

For children with the most complex SLCN, they need extra support to improve their speech and language development but also their social, behavioural and emotional development too. This is where our Residential Services come in.

At both our schools, residential planning is expertly tailored to each individual's needs. A detailed induction into the school ensures students are able to settle quickly and staff work tirelessly to ensure that pupils settle into school life quickly and have their individual needs met.

The residential teams at both Dawn House and Meath contribute to the delivery of a 24-hour curriculum that builds confidence, resilience, self-esteem and positive attitudes towards life. In addition, learning is continued through implementing daily routines and a wide range of leisure pursuits on site and in the local community itself.

The residential teams work closely with parents, teachers, therapists and members of the well-being team to support students in overcoming the challenges they might face in accessing educational opportunities whilst gaining new experiences in managing transitions and relationships; in person and with the use of technology.

This enables both their education and their social skills to develop hand-in-hand, giving them the life-skills and independence they need for the outside world.

Residential at Dawn House School

Our Dawn House school in Nottinghamshire provides specialist education, therapy and care for children and young people aged 5-19 years with the most complex speech language and communication needs (SLCN).

The current residential provision comprises of two adjoining houses; Rufford is home to the pre-sixteen

I CAN – The children's communication charity

Our vision is a world where all children have the communication skills they need to fulfil their potential.

1.4 million children in the UK have severe communication difficulties, and in some areas over 50% of children start school with delayed language.

We work directly with the people who educate, care for, support and advise children, young people and families.

Help us ensure no child is left out or left behind because of a difficulty speaking or understanding.

www.ican.org.uk

students from Monday to Friday whilst Newstead houses their neighbours from the post-sixteen provision.

The weekly boarders are also joined at different points throughout the week by peers accessing extended days and occasional overnight stays. After-school clubs for day students include a drama group that showcase their talents with performances at Christmas and at the end of the summer term, as well as 'play dates,' 1:1 guitar tuition and a weekly aqua-fit/swim party.

The impact of after school clubs has been significant. They have facilitated friendships across the school, giving students the confidence to try new things and access leisure opportunities independent of their family members. For one student who follows an individualised programme in the quieter educational setting of Chimes, attending drama club enabled him to participate as part of a group in the main school building for the first time.

The Residential Service Manager consults with students and parents to develop additional extra-curricular activities to meet specific interests and needs and can offer guidance on the application process to secure funding for short breaks. Parents can also pay directly for an evening's activities and may use childcare vouchers or personal budgets to do so.

Individual programmes of care are planned and implemented that support young people to pursue their own interests, develop increasing independence and achieve personal goals. Learning in this area is underpinned by the completion of a nationally recognised qualification (The Aim Award) for which external accreditation is achieved.

In the academic year 2018-19 all Sixth form residential students achieved accreditation, alongside one pre-sixteen student who already has one completed unit in their Aim Award Portfolio.

This year the progress of all residential students will be measured against Aim Award assessment criteria. Areas for focused work include: Domestic Cooking Skills, Domestic Skills, Using Public Transport and Responsible Road Vehicle Ownership and Use.

Ofsted reported that residential staff "know all pupils very well" and "care for them as a good parent would." They concluded that at Dawn House "Residential provision enhances pupils' education and their recreational and social lives. Educational outcomes improve because of the impact of residential care."

An extensive programme of refurbishment to the residential building has been planned and is well under-way!

Students are invested in the residential provision and parents have said that the opportunities it provides their children have made them flourish.

Residential at Meath School

At our Meath School in Surrey, they too offer their own tailored Residential Services plan. For children aged 4-11, this is provided via individual care plans and collaborative approaches – ensuring the health, safety and welfare of all their pupils.

The Child Care Department provides a waking curriculum which can enhance the progress pupils make via a range of out of classroom activities including:

- Before and After School Clubs (including external pupils)
- Sports, adventure playground and swimming on site
- Trips to shops, leisure centres and country pursuits
- Arts and crafts, cooking, games, reading and imaginative play
- Cubs and Brownies, Girls and Boys Brigade
- Joining local youth clubs and gyms

The school also offer a Holiday Club Week (residential or day) for a limited number of pupils in the first week of the summer holiday.

Specialist teaching, therapy and care are also provided by the school, with parents having the option to pay for individual overnight stays, either through childcare vouchers or personal payments.

Students are invested in the residential provision and parents have said that the opportunities it provides their children have made them flourish; daily living skills are developed and enhanced and opportunities for increased independence and the chance to practise social interactions in a supportive environment help them achieve their potential.

The ultimate goal is for them to be happy, confident individuals that contribute to society.

For more information about Dawn House School see page 99
For more information about Meath School see page 104

Supporting autistic pupils for over 50 years

Explaining the National Autistic Society's approach to education...

Autism is a development disability that affects people for their whole lives from childhood through to adulthood. If you're autistic, you might experience the world differently and can sometimes find communicating and relating to others challenging. It's like you're getting too much information and it can make daily life overwhelming. There are around 700,000 people including children in the UK living with autism – that's more than 1 in 100.

An estimated 140,000 school-aged children in the UK are on the autism spectrum. It affects each child differently and can make school life very difficult. For instance, some children are so sensitive to light or sound that a bright overhead light or humming computer can be physically painful and make it almost impossible to follow a lesson. For others, a small change to the day's schedule, like the school bus turning up late or a sudden change to the seating plan, can feel like the end of the world.

The National Autistic Society is here to transform lives, challenge perceptions and build a society that works for autistic people. We started providing autism-specific education over fifty years ago in 1965, we have developed our education offer into a diverse network of independent and free schools, and programmes which are relied upon by hundreds of people across the UK. There are eight thriving National Autistic Society autism-specific schools all which are highly rated. Ofsted has rated the majority of our schools in England as 'Good' or 'Outstanding'. Vanguard School will be our ninth school opening in January 2020. Vanguard School will cater to students aged 11-19 from Lambeth and neighbouring boroughs in Greater London.

"The principal, governors and trust (at Church Lawton) have, in a short space of time, created an inclusive and caring ethos. The principal and staff are passionate about making a difference to the lives of pupils." National Autistic Society Church Lawton School Ofsted report

We are specialists providing support and education for young people on the autism spectrum and we are focused on their progress. MyProgress® is the name of the overall strategy for working with your child that the National Autistic Society's schools offer. With MyProgress®, your child will have the best start in life because every aspect of their care and education will be tailor-made for them.

Everything our schools does is centred on your child, we make sure that our curriculum meets their specific needs and our multidisciplinary team will closely support their learning in communication, social, behavioural, emotional, sensory, physical and self-help skills.

MyProgress® will comprise of:

- A MyAbility Profile, which provides a summary of the initial assessment showing the young person's strengths and areas for development.

- MyProgress® meetings identify what the school and family can do to build on the young person's strengths and interests. Achievements are celebrated, progress is evaluated and targets are recommended for any areas for development. Collaboration with parents is central to improving outcomes for young people. Induction sessions are provided for all parents of new students to explain MyProgress®. Personalised goals are developed collaboratively between the young person, their parents, commissioners and the school through MyProgress® meetings soon after the placement starts.

- MyProgress® plans set out academic, social and independence targets and say how the curriculum and timetable are going to be tailored to meet the student's needs. A student's MyProgress® plan is the cornerstone of the personalised educational programme tailored to meet the specific needs of an individual student.

- MyProgress® file provides evidence of achievement of key milestones. The evidence may be a piece of work or a photo with the date and objective.

- MyProgress® Report provides a brief highlight of what's working well and action plan to address areas not working so well. The report also clearly present progress against targets agreed in the MyProgress® Plan. The report is sent to all stakeholders ahead of the termly MyProgress® meeting.

MyProgress® guarantees that your child will use approaches that we have tried and tested over many years: we know that they make a difference.

"The National Autistic Society's MyProgress system tracks what children can do. This helps to celebrate their achievements, such as taking part in small group activities and joining in with lessons." National Autistic Society Robert Ogden School Ofsted report

In addition to running eight specialist schools, we challenge society's perceptions by campaigning nationally and working with businesses and policy-makers to change laws and deliver services that work better for autistic people.

In November 2017, the National Autistic Society and the All Party Parliamentary Group on Autism published a report on autism and education. It found that autistic children and young people in England are being let down and held back from achieving their potential by the education system. Together with Ambitious About Autism, we have launched our Held Back campaign. We want the Government to make sure no children are held back from meeting their potential because they're autistic.

The National Autistic Society has a pioneering, innovative and flexible approach to education. When delivered by our experienced staff and tailored to each person's needs, we can transform a young person's life.

"My child is extremely happy at the school. I think the teachers genuinely care about the development of every single child in the school. My child has progressed very well. I cannot praise the school enough." Parent

Our unique education provision is facilitated by our passionate and highly trained staff, who take great care to create a path for each pupil, helping them through their early years on to secondary school, higher education and beyond. Find out more about our strategy and our schools here www.autism.org.uk/schools.

For more information about NAS schools,see page 58

Preparing for Adulthood at Queen Alexandra College (QAC)

Based in Birmingham, Queen Alexandra College (QAC) is a national specialist residential college that supports a diverse range of student abilities and needs. The College provides education, training and routes to independent living and employment. Class sizes are small and support levels high.

QAC is a stepping stone to your future life. Whatever your ambitions, QAC staff will provide support and assistance when leaving College based around your needs and aspirations to progress on to meaningful provision such as further education, higher education, supported internships, employment and supported living.

Regular Annual Reviews will be held with you, your family, College staff and other relevant professionals. Following the review a person-centred plan will be created and your Education, Health and Care (EHC) plan will be updated to reflect your needs.

Charlie, Hannah and Jess, three former QAC students, share their experiences of preparing for adulthood:

Charlie

"Hi, my name is Charlie. On leaving QAC I entered paid employment with The Albion Foundation – the charity of West Bromwich Albion Football Club.

"I really enjoyed my time at QAC and successfully completed a BTEC Level 2 in Sport. The College provided the structure that I needed and offered me the opportunity to complete an external work placement with The Albion Foundation during my first year.

"Initially my work placement was over a four week period, but it went so well it became ongoing during my time at College with staff supporting me. With the help of QAC I was able to fulfil my long-term goal of securing paid employment.

"I love my job, the responsibility and various tasks that I have to complete. I have also recently passed my driving test; I can now drive into work independently using my own car!"

Hannah

"Hello, my name is Hannah. I completed a BTEC Level 3 in Health and Social Care at QAC and represented the College as a Student Ambassador. I am now studying a BSc (Hons) in 'Special Educational Needs, Disability and Inclusion' at the University of Wolverhampton.

"My time at QAC really helped to prepare me for University as it gave me the confidence and independence I needed to get me to where I am today. I gained a lot from the additional support I received at QAC, particularly the travel training sessions which have enabled me to travel independently to and from University.

"I am enjoying all aspects of University life, the students and lecturers are really kind and are always there if I need help or advice.

"Next year, I am going to apply to live in halls where I can continue to develop my independence and get more involved in University life!"

Jess

"Hi, my name is Jess, During my time at QAC I gained a Level 3 IT qualification and lived in one of the residential houses on campus. As a residential student I gained the skills and confidence which enabled me to live semi-independently and now I am living in my own supported living flat.

"I love having my own flat because I have my own space and more freedom to do what I want. Since living on my own I have continued to grow in confidence and feel I am able to live independently without relying on my family. I still have access to support and the staff are brilliant! I have made really good friends with another girl through my support worker and we go out into the local community together and do lots of fun activities.

"QAC has assisted me to get where I am today! I am also looking forward to starting a work placement, where I will be volunteering for a local charity."

During 2017/18, 95% of QAC students achieved their main learning aim on accredited qualifications with progression outcomes for students (84 leavers including Charlie, Hannah and Jess) as follows:

- 15% Employment
- 8% General FE
- 4% HE Institution
- 5% Independent Specialist College
- 38% Other (including Adult Social Care)
- 25% QAC Supported Internship/Other
- 5% Work Based Training

Kerry Lowe, QAC Transitions Officer, commented: "During your time at QAC you will receive support, information, advice and guidance based around your needs and aspirations to explore your future options. My role is to help you make positive plans for what will happen when you leave QAC."

If you would like more information about transitions at QAC you can contact Kerry on 0121 428 5086 or klowe@qac.ac.uk.

For more information about QAC, see page 82

The same high ambitions for all children

How do you create an educational environment where children who are deaf or have complex communication difficulties, sensory issues and autism spectrum conditions can succeed and what does that success look like? How can we help deaf children achieve in line with their hearing peers? Ann Bradbury, Head Teacher at St John's Catholic School for the Deaf, explains how creating the correct learning and support environments is vital for supporting young people for whom mainstream school settings can be too challenging...

Young people who find it difficult to focus, who struggle to communicate or make themselves understood and those who may have sensory difficulties too often find the mainstream educational system does not meet their needs.

Classes are too large, too noisy and the child may experience sensory overload. Teachers have many children to support and peers may not always understand the additional needs the young person has. They may feel increasingly isolated and anxious. Their ability to learn effectively suffers, and their chances of achieving success academically, and indeed socially, shrink.

In 2018, deaf children were reported to be achieving more than a whole grade less at GCSE than their hearing peers. Further figures revealed that more than 55 per cent of young deaf people in England did not achieve more than one A-Level by the age of 19. It was a year when students with no SEN were shown to have opened up the biggest attainment gap – almost 25 per cent – over their deaf peers since 2012.

While deafness brings its own difficulties, it is not a learning disability and should not be treated as such. In principle, there are few, if any, reasons why, with the right support in place and understanding of their needs, a deaf young person could not achieve in line with a hearing child.

Here at St John's we support young people who are deaf in our school, and weekly-boarding residential service, through offering an environment which benefits children for whom learning is a challenge due to their communication or sensory difficulties and for whom mainstream settings do not work.

When they come through our doors they find an environment which is spacious and peaceful, where teaching and care staff are used to finding bespoke communication methods to support children and where children learn, play and socialise with supportive and understanding peers each day.

Class sizes are small, classrooms are designed to create calm learning spaces and teachers and care team staff are specialists and experienced in supporting young people who may find learning difficult. This additional and specialist support – such as speech and language input, auditory equipment and support, note takers, transport or specialist placements in schools and sixth forms – is a key part of creating an environment where a child can succeed.

However, we must not underestimate the importance of other factors – mental health, a child's self-confidence and sense of self and their environment are all crucial for young people to flourish.

Mental health support and understanding of emotional development is key. At the outset, all concerned need to recognise that these young people may be more vulnerable to experiencing mental health difficulties, before we look at what we can do to provide appropriate and timely assistance.

We all have a vital role to play in identifying early signs in the deaf child that they may be struggling with their mental health. Working with the local deaf child and adolescent mental health service (DCAMHS), creating a relationship with these services, is also extremely important, as is supporting families to understand the difficulties their child may be facing.

Creating this environment where the child can learn is the first step to helping them have good mental health. They need a place where they are part of a group of children with whom they can communicate. As with all children, they need a place where they can learn, play and feel safe and happy – where they can make friends and foster friendships.

Physical health is also a factor. Learning can be disrupted with physical health difficulties – some children who are deaf also have additional physical difficulties which can impact on their learning either due to mobility, discomfort or pain.

Just being aware of them as factors in a child's ability to learn can make all the difference. Offering comfortable seating, regular breaks, note takers, phased

transitions back to school, outreach and again, having a school nurse who understands the issues, can all help a child stay in school and be ready to learn.

We understand that success is not just passing exams (although our children do that, with each child achieving between 8 and 12 qualifications each and 100% going on to further education, training or employment) but that learning to be part of a group, gaining skills for independence and how to be resilient are all important too.

Perhaps most importantly of all, we are hugely ambitious for our young people. We know they can succeed, that they can achieve – no matter the difficulties they experience. We expect great things from them and for them – and when they come back to visit, we see they achieve all that we wish for them.

We should have the same high expectations for deaf children as we have for all children; if we believe they can succeed, they will believe it too and that really is the first step towards encouraging good mental health and to achievement which closes the gap.

St John's, in Boston Spa, West Yorkshire, provides day and weekly-boarding placements for young people who are deaf and hearing impaired, those with complex multi-sensory impairment, those with communication and sensory difficulties and children with an autism spectrum condition. Our teaching approaches focus on producing confident communicators with both spoken and written communication skills.

Visits from parents, children and families are welcome. To make an appointment call 01937 842144.

For more information on St John's Catholic School for the Deaf see page 124

A barista training course gave LVS Hassocks students a chance to learn skills to benefit their futures.

The benefits of supported work experience and learning practical skills

By Sarah Sherwood, Director of SEN at LVS Oxford and LVS Hassocks

Why practical learning is so effective

For many individuals with a diagnosis on the autism spectrum, learning through practical tasks holds more meaning than conceptual learning within a traditional classroom situation. Tasks such as making a drink, cooking a meal, changing a bicycle wheel or upcycling a piece of furniture have a sequence of steps with a defined ending. As an initial stage in teaching a new practical skill, a task analysis needs to take place, so that each component part of the task is isolated and can be taught as a single skill. Some students prefer to do the last element of the task, with staff completing the initial parts. This is known as back-chaining. Forward-chaining is where the student completes the first element of the task, with staff completing the remainder. Whichever form of 'chaining' is used, over time the individual with ASD is supported to complete the full sequence to achieve task completion from beginning to end.

How therapy can boost practical skills work

Therapy input is essential for students undertaking practical skills. At LVS Hassocks and LVS Oxford, occupational therapists assist the young person with ASD in organising the resources required for the task, whilst speech and language therapists advise on the wording and graphics required for a task instruction sheet. A task instruction sheet takes the individual through the task step by step, enabling them to achieve independence in completing the task.

Careers focus

Engaging students with future opportunities is a great way to get them thinking about what direction they wish to take through their qualifications and ensuing work experience. Careers Week at LVS Oxford gave students of all ages a chance to learn about possible future employment in a very interactive way. Visitors from sports coaching programmes, local hotels and pubs demonstrated roles available, whilst plumbing and electrical trade sessions allowed them to try their hand at manual roles. Careers advisors also visited to help students prepare their CVs and practise interview techniques. At LVS Hassocks a Careers Day saw visitors from technology, media and sporting professions run workshops that left students enthused and ready to consider their futures.

Work experience within school

LVS Hassocks and LVS Oxford also offer students supported work experience. As work experience can be daunting, this initially takes place on site, either in the café or student reward shop at LVS Hassocks, in tending for chickens, or as part of the Junior Estates Team. This gives students the opportunities to gain a taste for work experience in an environment they are familiar with and more confident in. A barista course at LVS Hassocks recently gave a number of students the chance to learn transferable employment skills and earn a qualification for their CVs that will help them to live independent lives in the future. The bespoke course gave training on making a whole range of drinks

and built soft skills like confidence and interaction with the public. The certificate the students earned in Foundation Coffee Skills is a qualification that could lead to a job in a coffee shop.

Links to local employers create opportunities

Once the students have the confidence to use their task instruction sheets independently to complete a task, the schools secure them work experience with local employers. Initially, the students are fully supported by school staff, ensuring they understand the requirements of the job they are to do. Additional task instruction sheets can be drawn up if required, to ensure that the young person is able to complete the task with minimal supervision. As the student becomes more confident, staff are able to fade their support, until the student is able to work independently. This model has proved extremely successful, as the schools have students gaining work experience at venues from Blenheim Palace and local gyms to retail outlets and cafes to give them the skills they need to live independently as adults.

For more information go to www.lvs-oxford.org.uk or www.lvs-hassocks.org.uk
Read more about LVS Oxford on page 68 and LVS Hassocks on page 74

LVS Oxford's link with Blenheim Palace allows students to gain valuable work experience there.

Upgrading facilities to extend provision

Kisimul Schools provide an update on recent developments

Kisimul Schools work with a large number of local authorities to provide education for learners with severe learning disabilities and autism. Learners typically come to be placed within the schools when placements elsewhere are unable to provide the specialist input necessary to manage the complex profiles and behaviours that cause challenge.

Within Kisimul Schools there is a focus on functional learning skills rehearsed within a largely semi-formal curriculum offer, using an experiential and practical skills approach, alongside therapeutic input within specialist environments for young people with severe learning difficulties. In order to achieve this, there is a need to adapt the environment and facilities to meet the various challenges and special educational needs of the learners.

Alongside this, there is a dual focus on a physical and outdoor orientation, which serves to meet the sensory regulation needs of young people, promote healthy lifestyle choices, and enable learners to apply learnt skills within real life contexts.

In order to support this provision, the schools have undertaken recent project developments to further upgrade their facilities and support this core curriculum offer. Careful planning and needs analysis was undertaken to support the implementation of new buildings. This included reconfiguring existing spaces to better facilitate learning, consider the movement of footfall throughout the school, and create more adaptable teaching opportunities across the education accommodation.

The addition of 7 new classroom spaces within the schools provision in Lincolnshire has provided this additional flexibility. These classrooms have been carefully planned to include a flow of natural light and access to outdoor learning spaces. Curved walls have been installed within corridor and communal spaces, providing some break out spaces and to better manage transitions through the building. A small soft play room with ball pool and sensory lighting and music provides a flexible space to provide a fun experience and assist regulation for young people who need to be able to

There is a dual focus on a physical and outdoor orientation, which serves to meet the sensory regulation needs of young people, promote healthy lifestyle choices, and enable learners to apply learnt skills within real life contexts.

move in and out of classrooms in short periods to engage more successfully with learning challenges.

Classrooms include integrated storage so that the focus of the learning intention is not distracted by other resources within the teaching space. Each classroom comes equipped with interactive teaching boards, and are colour co-ordinated to give each space an individual identity. Modular table arrangements and seating in some rooms enables a flexibility for various group sizes or individual support as required.

To reinforce and extend the focus on vocational and life skills acquisition as a learner progress through the school to post 16 education, every other classroom comes equipped with a fully integrated kitchen space. This enables a focus on functional learning skills (Maths and English), as well independent living skills to be used in context within cooking sessions. The outdoor vocational learning element is being developed further within the next planned phases of development, so the horticulture and animal husbandry provision in place at our Acacia Hall school site can be replicated at our other schools and college.

The addition of a theatre room, with integrated interactive floors and walls, sensory lighting and modular seating, has extended the curriculum to include creative arts and drama opportunities, and support functional communication and reciprocal interaction. This supplements the other elements of the environments in both the school sites to facilitate interactive learning within the smaller immersive rooms.

The addition of a swimming pool and gym within the Surrey school campus has provided both the opportunity for physical input and interactive games, as well as the sensory and regulatory benefit of having a pool facility onsite. This has enabled flexible access both as a tool to directly support confidence and sensory input, and supports with engagement in wider learning and input for more classroom based learning opportunities.

As part of the physical curriculum, having the benefit of an onsite gym area means that there is immediate access to a safe area to provide physical input and stimulation for learners in the school. This benefits both social interaction in the provision of group work and team building, and also enables individuals who require a more regular physical outlet with the space to do so regardless of the weather. The gym space can also be flexibly used to facilitate enrichment activities and further group opportunities such as visiting theatre or dance groups.

The swimming pool can likewise be used flexibly – as a motivational tool, for sensory input and to encourage reciprocal communication during water play and games. The development of better water confidence can be better facilitated by accessing an onsite facility, where there are less time restrictions or reservation requirements – if learners would benefit from accessing the pool a number of times during the week, this can be more readily facilitated.

These recent developments are part of phased plans to extend the education provision across the KGL sites, and reinforce the benefit of having multiple group provisions whereby curriculum innovations and successes in one school can be shared across other settings. This ensures reciprocal benefits for children and young adults placed within our education settings, and bears testament to our commitment for having first class and sector leading learning facilities across the schools and college.

For more information about Kisimul Schools see page 56

A whole school approach – curriculum delivery and the EHC Plan

Principal Dr Gill Barrett explains The Loddon School's integrated offering

The Children's and Families Act 2014 and The Special Educational Needs and Disability Code of Practice 2014 introduced the Educational Health and Care Plan. A plan replacing the Statement of Special Educational Needs and for the first time incorporating the provision for one child, for their Educational needs, Health needs and Social Care needs. Educational provision was also redefined: "*Health care provision or social care provision that educates or trains a child or young person is to be treated as special educational provision instead of separate Health care or social care provision.*" The overarching aim was to deal with each child holistically, a single team around the child, providing provision to fully meet their needs. For children with highly complex needs the new EHCP is essential.

The new Ofsted framework places greater emphasis on the curriculum, how it serves the school population and prepares the students for the next stage of their learning journey or adulthood. Outstanding schools, it could be argued, have always had this as a key focus and one reason for the high rates of progress, by having rich and broad curriculums, catering well for the specific requirements of their cohort. "*Pupils thrive at Loddon. They make exceptional progress in all aspects of their learning. Consequently, they are very well prepared for life beyond school.*" (Ofsted 2018) The new framework requires the school to have designed their curriculum stating clearly the knowledge and skills that will be gained at each stage. School leaders need to be able to articulate and demonstrate the intent of their curriculum, how it is implemented at all key stages, and to have evaluated what has been gained by each individual (the impact) against the desired expectations (Ofsted 2019).

The educational and social care legislation strives towards providing a holistic package that is seamless, focused completely on the individual, meeting their education, social and health needs and preparing them well for their next step in life; however, in practice this is not always the case. At The Loddon School®, our aim is to do just this, providing a totally integrated approach. The school has an integrated day with students educated from their home base, rather than having to travel to separate classrooms. The team around the child are: Learning and Care workers, the teacher and the Children's Service Manager, the therapists and nursing team, providing a fully integrated approach. *"Children benefit from the integrated, multi-disciplinary approach to education and care. The entire team focuses on the needs of each child, communicating across the disciplines so that there is a consistent approach."* (Ofsted 2018)

The PLLUSS® curriculum is unique providing the essential skills required for the lives of students with specific special needs. The six roots of the curriculum – communication, access to learning, relating and interacting, independence, transitions and leisure & well-being – link directly to the Framework for Adulthood. This alignment to this framework provides cohesion and consistency for a curriculum which is outside the national curriculum. The PLLUSS® curriculum has an ethos which is rooted in all that the school does and links directly with the elements of the child's EHCP, placing their individual targets into one of the six areas. The intent of the curriculum is to provide a platform to practise and develop the linked skills firstly in a familiar environment with physical, gestural or verbal prompts, practising the skills until they become routine before learning to generalise in new environments, with different support staff, and with reducing support. For example – being able to manoeuvre a wheel barrow in the stables (access to learning), using both hands and steering it will help with steering a tricycle (transitions), and pushing a shopping trolley through a supermarket (Independence). The curriculum deals holistically with the child's skill progression taking full advantage of opportunities to experience the wider community beyond the school grounds ensuring robust skill and knowledge development for adulthood and a rich quality of life.

The PLLUSS® curriculum is implemented with learning taking place throughout the total waking day. Staff use all activities as a vehicle to extend the learning of each child in the school. The day is shaped to help each child to deal with their sensory processing needs; individual timetables are built so that there are regular sensory learning activities throughout the day to allow the child to remain calm and focused and ready to learn. Teachers carefully plan highly creative and playful learning experiences embracing the sensory diet of the

The fully integrated recording system completes the total integration approach and simplifies the sometimes-cumbersome bureaucratic paperwork that is attached to children with special educational needs.

child. This approach keeps the child highly engaged in a calm but alert state able to utilise new learning and build upon previous learning experiences. Personal learning targets which focus around the six elements of the PLLUSS® curriculum also align fully with their EHCP targets in this integrated whole approach. The Access to Learning sphere of the PLLUSS® curriculum provides a platform for termly themed learning, opening the child up to knowledge-based learning experiences related to aspects of the world around them, culture, scientific learning and historical events and is a rich vehicle to embed early reading, writing and mathematics.

The fully integrated recording system completes the total integration approach and simplifies the sometimes-cumbersome bureaucratic paperwork that is attached to children with special educational needs. Within one document – the EHCP review – Health matters, social care issues, progress with PLLUSS® targets incorporating PEP targets, progress with Early Reading, Writing and Mathematics, therapies, the Engagement Profile, transition plans and photographic evidence to demonstrate impact of provision are recorded. Progress is reviewed every five months with a progress review and annual review meeting every year. The Pre-review meeting held one month before allows the multidisciplinary team to discuss progress and set up new targets. All paperwork is available to the LA, parents and school staff via a portal two weeks before the meeting.

The PLLUSS® curriculum is a whole approach delivering fully all aspects of the EHCP in a totally integrated way and results in young people *"who thrive and are well prepared for life beyond school".*

For more information about The Loddon School, see page 108

A real-world approach to work-related learning

Dr Graeme Athey is Director of Education at Fairfield Farm College, which specialises in providing study programmes for young people with SEND, focusing on work-related learning as an alternative to the traditional work experience model.

Approaches to work experience, are, in the main, future looking insomuch as they expect young people to predict a future employment market and then to identify their role within it. This demand on young people requires insights that are often decontextualized, overly ambitious and increasingly mismatched to a competitive world of work of the future. How can young people prepare for a future that does not yet exist? Such snap-shot perspectives on 'work experience' do little to develop significant understanding in the wider context of work and are often compounded by rigid or inflexible ways of thinking, limited opportunity and rudimentary considerations of employment.

The concept of work is challenging at the outset. It is infinite, ever-changing and variable, which does little to set a conceptual understanding in our learners. The

idea that you need to be able to visualise and predict a desired field of work, or furthermore, a specific career and then back-chain to the present day is problematic, for many reasons.

There is a practical tension vis-à-vis teaching and learning, principally between preparing students for an uncertain future whilst continuing conventional approaches to education and an understanding about work. Employment rates are greater among young people with qualifications than those without (OECD, 2013); therefore, it may seem prudent to assume that from this perspective it pays to be educated. Yet, 48% of adults with disabilities are unemployed compared to 19% of those without disabilities (House of Commons, paper 7540 Nov 2018) which represents a substantial conflict between the intention behind work experience and the realistic outcomes. This further supports the difficulties that the world of work presents for people with disabilities.

The conceptual challenges associated with futuristic predictions of the world of work, the employment sector in general and the conflicting information continues to be problematic. The World of Work approach at Fairfield Farm College offers an alternative perspective. Most school leavers have a memory of going to work at a family business, or at the offices of a friend of their parents, which generally involved undertaking menial duties, running errands and supporting others in their work. In most cases, the role was not part of a planned approach, did little to identify and build on existing skills, aspirations and desires but simply offered a tick in the box for 'work experience completed'.

Recognising a range of models and approaches to work-based learning within a setting provides a variety of opportunities to engage with the world of work, regardless of ability, academic achievement or learning disability. This approach also pulls the world of work into the present and contextualises the here and now, a skill that young people with SEND often find challenging. A central theme that adds value to Fairfield Farm College's approach is an understanding of differing types of work-related learning. A distinction that puts the work at the centre of its learning opportunities.

Understanding that everything the students undertake at college is related to work, is a simple but significant shift in understanding by the learners and staff alike. The wise W. C. Fields, once said 'never work with animals or children'. But for the staff at Fairfield Farm College, this is a daily occurrence. Opportunities for the development of work-related learning comprise a 26-acre working farm, equine studies and stable management, animal management, reception and customer service, hospitality and catering, a 15-acre animal park, two cafes and a farm shop.

Fairfield Farm College takes a broad approach to curriculum. All of the young people follow a personalised programme of employability skills, which permeate all areas of college life and leaning. Working alongside real animals, dealing with real-life customers, budgeting for, planting and propagating real plants for sale in our farm shop and serving hundreds of customers a week provides for a myriad of opportunities to understand how our young peoples' skills and areas for development can lead to employment.

Regardless of diagnosis or academic achievement, all of the young people are engaged with a work-related

learning programme. At the earliest phase, this could be focusing on the prerequisite skills that underpin all work, such as turn taking, following instructions, recognising a sequence or understanding when a task is complete. At the other end of this continuum are young people running a professional catering kitchen, cafes that serve over 350 customers a week and grooming, feeding and caring for Highland cows, emus or alpacas!

The key to any approach is consistency, but for us we have a commitment to making explicit how each activity, skill and opportunity can contribute to an overall understanding of the world of work. Communication, number skills, relationship building, problem solving and IT all feature prominently in the craft of the tutors and job coaches. Planning and assessment focus on transferability and consolidating skills development. Empowering our learners to understand their skills-set and how this applies to work, rather than a specific role, gives our graduates the best opportunity as they move from education into the supposed 'real-world'.

For further information regarding Fairfield Farm College's approach to work-related learning, go to www.ffc.ac.uk or call us on 01373 823028.

Read Fairfield Farm College's profile on page 98

Building blocks towards an exciting future

New College Worcester (NCW), a school and college for blind and vision-impaired young people, teamed up with The LEGO Foundation and LEGO Group for a trial of ground-breaking LEGO Braille Bricks.

New College Worcester, a national residential school and college for young people age 11-19 who are blind or vision impaired, has taken part in a revolutionary, global project with The LEGO Foundation and LEGO Group to help blind and vision impaired children learn through play.

LEGO Braille Bricks is a concept which was first proposed in 2011, and since then has been further shaped in close collaboration with New College Worcester along with other blind associations from Denmark, Brazil and Norway.

With a dedicated Braille department and expanded core curriculum, New College Worcester jumped at the opportunity to test the prototype and show the potential of learning with LEGO Braille Bricks in the classroom, which has so far included Mathematics, English and Spanish.

Speaking of her passion for the project, Susan Lock, Head of Mathematics at New College Worcester, said: "Braille gives vision impaired children and adults absolute independence. Without it, how will children learn grammar, or how to spell? The ability to read and understand Braille can be life changing for many of our students and can present very many opportunities, which is why we were so thrilled to be involved in the project.

"I'm passionate about both the Braille Bricks and teaching at NCW because we have the opportunity to transform children's lives. LEGO Braille Bricks is doing that because it is making subjects far more accessible than they ever were before."

Daniel, a Year 8 student at New College Worcester, explains: "I started learning Braille when I was 5. It empowers me and enables me to do things I would have never been able to do before, such as entertainment, education and music.

"I started learning Braille when I was 5. It empowers me and enables me to do things I would have never been able to do before, such as entertainment, education and music."
Daniel, Year 8 student

"LEGO is so much fun, but it's versatile and allows me to have something tangible that I can rearrange in so many ways."

LEGO Braille Bricks will be moulded with the same number of studs used for individual letters and numbers in the Braille alphabet, while remaining fully compatible with the LEGO System in Play. To ensure the tool is inclusive allowing sighted teachers, students and family members to interact on equal terms, each brick will also feature a printed letter or character. This ingenious combination brings a whole new and playful approach to encourage blind and vision impaired children to engage with learning Braille, enabling them to develop a breadth of skills needed to thrive and succeed in a fast-paced world.

Prior to the launch of LEGO Braille Bricks, many teachers of blind and vision impaired students made their own resources to assist with the learning of Braille, and off-the-shelf products are few and far between.

Braille Bricks is a game changer in the vision impaired world – for both learning and teaching.

John Goodwin, CEO of The LEGO Foundation, said: "Blind and vision impaired children have dreams and aspirations for their future just as sighted children. They have the same desire and need to explore the world and socialise through play, but often face involuntary isolation as a consequence of exclusion from activities. In The LEGO Foundation, we believe children learn best through play and in turn develop the breadth of skills, such as creativity, collaboration and communication that they need. With this project, we are bringing a playful and inclusive approach to learning Braille to children. I hope children, parents, caregivers, teachers and practitioners worldwide will be as excited as we are, and we can't wait to see the positive impact."

The product is currently being tested in Danish, Norwegian, English and Portuguese, while German, Spanish and French will be tested later in 2019.

The final LEGO Braille Bricks kit is expected to launch in 2020 and will be distributed free of charge to select institutions through participating partner networks. It will contain approximately 250 LEGO Braille Bricks covering the full alphabet, numbers 0-9, select math symbols and inspiration for teaching and interactive games.

For more information about New College Worcester, see page 123

Planning your next steps?

Toni Hodges, Placement Administrator at QEF's Independent Living Service, talks about the questions parents frequently ask when considering next steps for their son or daughter as they turn 18+ and leave full time education.

At QEF we offer specialist residential care for young adults with complex disabilities. Our aim is to provide a person-centred approach that reflects each person's needs, whilst supporting the development of life skills and enabling people to live as independently as possible.

Lots of parents and potential residents have the same types of queries and below are some of the questions we are asked most frequently.

When do we need to start planning our next steps?
We suggest people start thinking about what the next steps could be at least a year before their current placement ends, so the summer term of your penultimate year – if not before.

What areas do you specialise in?
Different places may have different areas of expertise. Do you need medical support maybe? What therapy support would your son or daughter require? Does this need to be available in-house? At QEF for example we have a lot of experience supporting people with complex needs arising from Cerebral Palsy, Spina Bifida, or Duchenne Muscular Dystrophy. We have in-house physiotherapy and expertise in managing dysphagia and PEG feeding, as well as supporting people with communication aids.

Are you a home for life?
Are there any restrictions on the length of time a person can stay with that provider, or can they live there as long as their funding allows? For example, we only have residents who are 18+, although there is no upper age restriction.

How do residents fill their day? What leisure activities are available?
Look at notice boards and ask other residents what type of activities are available for them to get involved in. Are there a good variety of activities, games, sports and trips? Are residents encouraged to get involved with delivering some of these activities if they have relevant skills? We have a team of life coaches/activity coordinators to ensure a varied programme of activities including games, art and craft, drama productions and live music

events. Residents also have weekly programmes which can be attached to their wheelchairs so they know what their activities are each day.

Is there medical support/therapy available on site?
This will depend on your son or daughter's individual needs as to what level of medical support is required. At QEF our residents are generally registered with a local doctor and a district nurse visits regularly; we also have physiotherapy and speech and language expertise on site. However, we do not have nursing support on site, so this is an important factor to explore.

Is there transport for medical appointments?
Getting to medical appointments is important. What facilities are in place to ensure your son or daughter can attend these? At QEF we have drivers and wheelchair accessible vehicles available that can help residents attend planned appointments, as long as they are within a reasonable distance.

What level of training do the staff have?
A commitment to supporting staff and their training is important. All Support Workers at QEF undertake The Care Certificate which is an agreed set of standards that sets out the knowledge, skills and behaviours expected in the social care sector. They also have the opportunity

to complete Level 3 Diploma in Adult Care or undertake apprenticeships. As well as mandatory training, QEF offers more bespoke training such as Dysphagia management.

Can people personalise their rooms?
This is an important aspect to ensure residents feel very much at home. At QEF people can decorate their rooms as much or as little as they want. They can even bring their own furniture if they want to, as long as it is fire approved.

Are dietary requirements/religious beliefs supported?
Food is important to all of us and supporting dietary requirements can be essential. Find out what current residents think of the food available. Do they like it? Is there a good variety? Also are there people of different faiths already living there and are their dietary needs supported?

Is there any support for managing money?
Managing benefit payments and personal spending money is something that residents, with support from their families or carers, can decide how they would like to approach. It's a good idea to find out if there is anyone available to assist residents on a day-to-day basis as support may be needed to manage bank accounts and/or cash. You need to discuss how you are going to keep personal funds safe but accessible.

Access to any wider facilities?
Are there any additional services or facilities that the centre has access to beyond that specific location? At QEF our residents can explore additional opportunities such as volunteering in our charity shops, potentially learning to drive at our mobility centre, and our partner charity MERU also regularly supports residents with individual needs for bespoke equipment.

What does the referral process involve?
From June/July in your penultimate term, research next step options that suit you and arrange informal visits so you can ask questions.

Once you decide which location you prefer, contact the providers and your social worker and let them know you would like to arrange an assessment. At QEF we then contact your current placement and request your up-to-date reports. These are then reviewed by our Multi-Disciplinary Team to assess whether we could support each potential resident's needs.

The next step is to arrange an assessment, which for us takes place over 3 days and 2 nights. You are asked to bring all equipment you need for your usual care routine and you will have 1:1 support throughout the visit. Assessments usually takes place in Jan/Feb of your last placement year.

Assessment feedback is then collated and reviewed. If everyone is happy then reports along with QEF's suggested costings are sent to social services for funding approval. If this is approved, then a place can be offered and we agree a start date that suits you, whether that's straight from college or a different date that works for you.

About QEF
Queen Elizabeth's Foundation for Disabled People is a UK charity based in Surrey with national reach, supporting over 5,000 disabled people a year. Our specialist services all focus on helping people to maximise their independence. QEF Independent Living Services is a specialist residential care service supporting young adults with complex disabilities. In Spring 2020 we are moving to a bespoke new centre with modern, comfortable facilities and assistive technology in the bedrooms.

www.qef.org.uk

Can classrooms be sensory rooms?

Kevin Wheatley, of Ambispace, looks at latest technological possibilities

Sensory rooms have been a part of the special school tool kit for many years now and are generally seen as a highly valued and well used resource. Awareness of the positive impact they can have on the lives of young people with SEND is currently spreading rapidly and I am finding I am being approached by a much wider range of clients. This includes mainstream schools looking to support SEND pupils in a more rounded way.

This is a very positive expansion, but it does present a problem for some schools. They may want to increase their sensory provision to support pupils as others are doing, but they simply don't have the room to do it. Lack of physical capacity is often a challenge for special schools, too, who find the sensory room is oversubscribed due to the number of children in their care. It is a greater issue when a pupil is heading towards a crisis that could be intercepted by a session in the sensory room, only to find it is already in use by someone else in equal need.

The challenge therefore is twofold. How do you reduce the need for sensory room access and how do you increase the availability of sensory support tools without giving up existing teaching and learning facilities?

As a specialist sensory designer, I believe the answer to these two puzzles is a single one: make the current classrooms more sensory proactive environments.

So how do you do this without turning them in to light or dark rooms? You use available technologies in an innovative way to make practical adjustments to existing classrooms. Doing this will make them adaptable and accessible to personal and group needs. It will extend the timespan pupils with SEND can stay in what are otherwise challenging environments. It will boost concentration levels for longer periods and reduce the incidence of challenging behaviours.

Here are a few examples, drawn from my years of experience designing sensory spaces, of what could be done to create sensory proactive classrooms. Some are simple affordable adjustments, others more complex.

Lighting
We are predominantly visual creatures and therefore light has a major influence upon our mood. Blue lighting

introduced to Japanese railway stations reduced suicide rates by 74% between 2000 and 2013 in an academic study. This is because of the calming effect it has upon the brain. Red is much more stimulating and increases alertness. Using zone control colour change LED lighting the classroom can become an adaptable mood influencing environment.

Bio-adaptive lighting systems automatically control artificial lights using intelligent software to match the needs of our circadian rhythms as we move through the day. This can greatly improve wellbeing and behaviour management.

The replacement of standard white panels with scenic picture panels is a simple way to make the classroom a more comfortable and inviting place.

Noise

In a recent online survey by the Autism Academy, 76% of respondents said noise was the most overwhelming factor in public places. Classrooms can be made more tolerable by adding sound-absorbing panels to walls and ceilings. These practical additions are a great opportunity to add design styling in to the room too. Thick carpets reduce noisy footsteps and prevent sounds from bouncing around the room.

A useful addition straight from the sensory room is an interactive LED light tube. These multiprogram light displays include a two-colour light effect that rises and falls in direct response to noise levels. It provides a clear visual indicator to pupils as a group, helping them moderate their own behaviour to the benefit of SEND classmates. Light tubes have the additional benefit of being a focus point to aid meditation.

AV Technology

A more accessible alternative to the interactive whiteboard is an interactive touchscreen. These large format screens provide HD to 4K quality images and graphics that do not become obscured by shadow when someone moves close to them. The antiglare screens ensure visually impaired pupils can see them more clearly from any angle. Many have the benefit of being supplied with educational software suites preloaded to make full use of the touch interaction. This provides a literal hands-on opportunity for pupils to engage with the learning materials.

A number of these systems include collaboration technology that enables a pupil to connect their own

tablet or laptop to the main screen so they can contribute to the group learning process without having to move to the front of class. This can reduce anxiety, overcome physical barriers and ensures pupils working with support are included on equal terms.

The ultimate sensory classroom can be created using large format wall and floor projections to create immersive scenes that transport pupils anywhere in the universe. The addition of sensory effects such as wind, scent, vibration, sounds and lighting make learning highly inclusive and engaging for pupils of all abilities. It is important that these sophisticated tech heavy rooms are simple to control and interact with, so the learning process is a smooth and flexible one. Pupils can not only learn from experience in these spaces but also practise everyday situations under controlled conditions to help desensitise them to the challenges of the wider world.

Sensory Nooks

An easy way to take pressure off the sensory room and increase availability of proactive support in or near to the classroom is the use of mobile sensory nooks or pods. This sort of unit was originally developed to create personal space within open plan offices where people can hold meetings with a degree of privacy and find a place to concentrate on important tasks. These nook pods dramatically reduce noise levels and with the addition of sensory technology create a protective oasis that can be moved to wherever it is needed with ease.

Broader integration of sensory technology in to everyday environments provides benefits for everyone's wellbeing. For people with SEND it can make a huge difference to life quality and the opportunity to engage with the learning processes they are entitled to.

Kevin is an award winning sensory and immersive specialist who designs rooms and pods to deliver technology driven experiences for special needs and education. He has previously taught young people with SEN and successfully recovered from the debilitating condition ME, an experience that strongly influences his work today.

Introducing CReSTeD

Exploring the work of The Council for the Registration of Schools Teaching Dyslexic Pupils

Introduction

The Council for the Registration of Schools Teaching Dyslexic Pupils (CReSTeD) is a charity set up to help parents and those who advise them choose schools for children with Specific Learning Difficulties (SpLD) of which the main difficulty is dyslexia. There is however a general recognition that dyslexia rarely exists in isolation and latest research demonstrates a high level of co-occurrence with other difficulties. These include Dyspraxia, Dyscalculia, ADD, as well as Pragmatic and Semantic Language Difficulties.

CReSTeD acts as a source of information which can help parents making a placement decision about a child with SpLD. CReSTeD is a valuable resource for parents, educational advisers and schools.

CReSTeD was established in 1989 and publishes and maintains a list of schools and centres accredited for their SpLD provision – the Register – annually. The schools and centres listed within the Register cover all levels of provision for SpLD pupils and include both state and independent provision. The vast majority of schools on the Register are mainstream, offering a wide range of teaching styles, environment and facilities.

The Register

CReSTeD's main activity is to produce and supply to parents, free of charge, a Register of schools and centres which provide for pupils with one or more SpLD. The levels of provision is divided into six broad categories: five for schools – Dyslexia Specialist Provision (Category DSP), Specialist Provision Schools (Category SPS), Dyslexia Unit (Category DU), Withdrawal System (Category WS) and Maintained Sector (Category MS) – and one for centres: Teaching Centres (Category TC). Children have different

requirements and personalities; the categories are a way of helping match each child to the type of provision at the school or centre. A report from an educational psychologist or a specialist teacher who holds an Assessment Practising Certificate should offer guidance as to the level of provision relevant to the child.

A child at the severe end of the dyslexia spectrum may require a Dyslexia Specialist Provision school, whereas a child with, for example, only some slowness in spelling skills may be suitably provided for in a school from Category Withdrawal System. The categories offer this guidance. Note that the maintained sector is only open to local authority schools and not to independent schools.

The Register is published annually and is obtainable from the CReSTeD Administrator or via the CReSTeD website: www.crested.org.uk The website also includes links to all registered schools and centres as well as to other websites that may be of assistance to parents of children with one or more SpLD. There is also a checklist to help parents decide if a school or centre can meet their child's education needs in relation to SpLD at crested.org.uk/documents/parentschecklist.pdf

CReSTeD Criteria and Visits

Every school and centre on the CReSTeD list has been independently verified for SpLD provision by CReSTeD consultants which is not the case in all other lists.

The first stage of any registration is for the school to complete the CReSTeD registration form and to provide supporting documentation, such as policies for dyslexia. This form covers staff development, admission policy, organisation of the school week, specific arrangements for SpLD pupils, examination results for the whole school and for SpLD pupils in particular, resources and a list of parents' names so that the consultant may check parents' feelings about the school or centre.

These criteria include the provision of relevant and high quality information technology resources, Joint Council for Qualifications (JCQ) approved training qualifications for teachers, awareness of the needs of dyslexic pupils by the non-specialist staff, and arrangements to obtain and provide special provision for examinations.

Consultants, who look to see if this information is accurate and that the school or centre meets the criteria set by CReSTeD Council for the particular category, visit the schools.

Schools and centres are visited on a three yearly cycle, with possible earlier visits if there are substantial changes, which should always be swiftly communicated to CReSTeD. If the Head of a CReSTeD school changes, we require the school to inform us and ask the new Head

to confirm that the school intends to continue with the SpLD provision in accordance with the criteria set by CReSTeD (at the agreed category level). This enables us to retain the school's details in the Register without the need for an extra visit.

CReSTeD Council will initiate 'responsive' visits if it has any cause for concern about a particular school.

CReSTeD Council

Council includes representatives from a wide area of SpLD provision including Dyslexia Action, the British Dyslexia Association, Helen Arkell Dyslexia Charity, the Dyslexia-SpLD Trust and schools.

Categories

Categories are used to explain the type of provision given by a school. One category should not be seen as 'better' than another, but as a guide to the provision required by the student. There are six categories within our criteria according to the type of provision:

- Dyslexia Specialist Provision (DSP) schools established primarily to teach pupils with Dyslexia.
- Dyslexia Unit (DU) schools offer a designated unit that provides specialist tuition on a small group or individual basis, according to need.
- Maintained Schools (MS) – local authority schools able to demonstrate an effective system for identifying pupils with dyslexia. This category also includes the British Dyslexia Association's Dyslexia Friendly Quality Mark Schools.
- Specialist Provision (SPS) schools are specifically established to teach pupils with dyslexia and other related specific learning difficulties.
- Teaching Centre (TC) designated centres provide specialist tuition on a small group or individual basis, according to need.
- Withdrawal System (WS) schools help dyslexic pupils by withdrawing them from appropriately selected lessons for specialist tuition.

Conclusion

CReSTeD was founded to help parents. It has had, and will continue to have, influence on the standards of provision for pupils with SpLDs. Council is grateful for the support of the British Dyslexia Association, Dyslexia Action, Helen Arkell Dyslexia Charity, the Dyslexia-SpLD Trust, the schools on the Register and parents.

For further information contact us via email: admin@crested.org.uk

Or visit our website: www.crested.org.uk

Highlighting best practice

OnwardsandUpwards.com is an innovative system that provides analysis of SEND pupils' progress

OnwardsandUpwards provide a tailored performance management system that tracks the progress of learners in a variety of schools, especially those with SEND pupils. Originally designed to assess the progress of larger organisations, the model has been adapted to track and collate learner progress. They collaborate closely with each user to tailor the model to their requirements and have a strong relationship with Pendle Community High School and College, who have assisted further developments to ensure the system effectively meets the needs of SEND pupils. As national curriculum levels have been stripped back and curriculums have become more individualised, they are developing a universal scale for comparison between schools. Mark Robinson founded the company and explains their change of focus...

When we were established in 2004, we were constructing a real-time performance management system that was designed to be flexible enough to be used by any organisation, no matter their size. At its heart was a strategy map that showed the highest goal of the organisation. The concept of our Escendency system was to connect everyone involved with this highest purpose and allow the organisation to assess their progress towards this goal in real time. The original goal would be broken down into second-level strategic objectives, which would then be further subdivided. Each objective would be weighted in terms of its overall contribution. Eventually, these subdivisions could be measured in the real world through performance indicators. These web-based indicators were assigned to people in the organisation, which gave them the ability to self-manage, as they could constantly see their own progress. Beyond this, they could also assess their contribution to the wider organisation as a whole.

A change of focus

While we were doing this, we were approached by a school specifically for SEND pupils. Current school management information systems are built around whole classes and the age-related expectations of the national curriculum. In an SEN environment, there is a much greater need to monitor individualised progress, in terms of not only academic achievement but also social, emotional and behavioural development, working towards independence and employability.

Special schools have tried to do this by acquiring several different commercial systems to cover these areas, supplemented with in-house spreadsheets. The result is high cost and hours of senior teacher and management time interpreting systems that don't talk to each other. They cannot get a "real-time" overview of each learner's progress against their respective expected "flight paths" or indeed the whole school performance or any cohort in-between. Without knowing how learners are doing in real time, it is impossible to know what to focus on next to close the gap towards expected progress.

The technological challenge was to create a holistic, customisable database system that could be mapped to the exact needs of each school's curriculum and individual learning outcomes at an affordable cost. This was not a trivial task and had never been done before.

The knowledge did not exist in any one place and was not understood by any one individual. We had to carry out research, consulting a myriad of different schools across the UK and then mapping their answers against ongoing and future changes in SEN assessment and government analysis requirements. This then, in turn, had to be measured against worldwide available development frameworks and database technologies that could be utilised to provide a comprehensive solution, securely hosted, at an affordable annual cost.

The major progress that has been made is the ability to provide a customised system for each school that would, if designed and built individually, cost many tens of thousands of pounds each and so be unaffordable for a special school. Every school is unique, every learner is unique. Our new generic cloud-based system, OnwardsandUpwards.com, is upgraded centrally and includes support and ongoing upgrades.

Removing rigid curriculum structures

The biggest uncertainty was to establish if it was even possible to create a single system and database design that could meet the needs of the full range of special schools. Such schools have an infinite number of curriculums and learning outcomes and widely differing rates of learning, starting points and future expectations. The other uncertainties were financial. It was unclear whether it was possible to create a system at a price that would recoup the development costs over time with an annual subscription cost that the market could bear.

During the course of 2016, the needs of a wide range of special schools, catering for all types of SEN at all ages, were sought by us from across the UK. We created a technological system and database design and married it to the most advanced cutting-edge development frameworks available in the world. Many design iterations were tried and tested by our "beacon" schools, such as PCHS, whose critical feedback has led to further refining of this process to maximise overall impact. As national curriculum levels were abolished, we created a new national database of state-of-the-art learning outcomes to be shared by all OnwardsandUpwards.com schools to save "reinventing the wheel". We currently have 56 special schools and one mainstream school using OnwardsandUpwards.com Version 20. Over 250 schools are needed to cover ongoing operations. The system is now ready for a national roll-out, and there are virtually unlimited international sales opportunities, as systems like this do not exist anywhere else in the world.

The need for schools to work collaboratively

While individualisation can be a benefit, schools need to collaborate more. Schools that are working in an identical manner are working independently and could benefit from conversing with one another. To help to achieve this, we have inserted a library of learning outcomes checklists within the system and have asked users to contribute their own. Permission can then be sought to borrow these lists. This allows schools to access any best practices performed by similar institutions.

The other challenge we face is ensuring that schools are utilising a holistic system, uniting different metrics of pupil progression. Different assessments must interact to give a full picture of progress while saving each school time and money. We are collaborating closely with our users to help them to achieve this.

We have been working with over 50 schools in the past year to refine our model and ensure that it functions at the highest possible level. We hope to increase our current volume of users and ensure that each of our users has a model that allows them to track, identify and improve learning outcomes for all of their students.

For more information visit www.onwardsandupwards.com

School groups

Hesley Group

**Central Services, Hesley Hall
Tickhill, Doncaster, DH11 9NH
Tel: +44 (0)1302 866906
Fax: +44 (0)1302 861661
Email: enquiries@hesleygroup.co.uk
Website: www.hesleygroup.co.uk**

Autism | Learning Disabilities | Complex Needs

Fullerton House College

Tickhill Square, Denaby, Doncaster, South Yorkshire DN12 4AR
Tel: 01709 861663
Fax: 01709 869635
Email: enquiries@hesleygroup.co.uk
Website: www.hesleygroup.co.uk
FOR MORE INFORMATION SEE PAGE 85

Fullerton House School

Tickill Square, Denaby, Doncaster, South Yorkshire DN12 4AR
Tel: 01709 861663
Fax: 01709 869635
Email: enquiries@hesleygroup.co.uk
Website: www.fullertonhouseschool.co.uk
FOR MORE INFORMATION SEE PAGE 84

Wilsic Hall College

Wadworth, Doncaster, South Yorkshire DN11 9AG
Tel: 01302 856382
Email: enquiries@hesleygroup.co.uk
Website: www.hesleygroup.co.uk
FOR MORE INFORMATION SEE PAGE 85

Wilsic Hall School

Wadworth, Doncaster, South Yorkshire DN11 9AG
Tel: 01302 856382
Email: enquiries@hesleygroup.co.uk
Website: www.wilsichallschool.co.uk
FOR MORE INFORMATION SEE PAGE 88

I CAN

**31 Angel Gate (Gate 5), Goswell Road
London EC1V 2PT
Tel: 0845 225 4073
Fax: 0845 225 4072
Email: info@ican.org.uk
Website: www.ican.org.uk**

helps children communicate

I CAN'S Dawn House School

Helmsley Road, Rainworth, Mansfield,
Nottinghamshire NG21 0DQ
Tel: 01623 795361
Fax: 01623 491173
Email: enquiries@dawnhouse-ican.notts.sch.uk
Website: www.dawnhouseschool.org.uk
FOR MORE INFORMATION SEE PAGE 99

I CAN's Meath School

Brox Road, Ottershaw, Surrey KT16 0LF
Tel: 01932 872302
Fax: 01932 875180
Email: meath@meath-ican.org.uk
Website: www.meathschool.org.uk
FOR MORE INFORMATION SEE PAGE 104

Kisimul

**The Old Vicarage, 61 High Street, Swinderby, Lincoln, Lincolnshire LN6 9LU
Tel: 01522 868279
Email: enquiries@kisimul.co.uk
Website: www.kisimul.co.uk**

Cruckton Hall

Cruckton, Shrewsbury, Shropshire SY5 8PR
Tel: 01743 860206
Fax: 01743 860941
Email: admissions@kisimul.co.uk
Website: www.cruckton.com
FOR MORE INFORMATION SEE PAGE 80

Kisimul School

The Old Vicarage, 61 High Street, Swinderby,
Lincoln, Lincolnshire LN6 9LU
Tel: 01522 868279
Email: admissions@kisimul.co.uk
Website: www.kisimul.co.uk
FOR MORE INFORMATION SEE PAGE 100

Kisimul School – Woodstock House

Woodstock Lane North, Long Ditton, Surbiton, Surrey KT6 5HN
Tel: 020 8335 2570
Fax: 020 8335 2571
Email: admissions@kisimul.co.uk
Website: www.kisimul.co.uk
FOR MORE INFORMATION SEE PAGE 102

Kisimul Upper School

Acacia Hall, Shortwood Lane, Friesthorpe,
Lincoln, Lincolnshire LN3 5AL
Tel: 01673 880022
Fax: 01673 880021
Website: www.kisimul.co.uk

LVS Hassocks and LVS Oxford

West Sussex and Oxfordshire
Tel: 01344 884440
Email: admissions@lvs-hassocks.org.uk

LVS Hassocks

London Road, Sayers Common, Hassocks, West Sussex BN6 9HT
Tel: 01273 832901
Email: info@lvs-hassocks.org.uk
Website: www.lvs-hassocks.org.uk
FOR MORE INFORMATION SEE PAGE 74

LVS Oxford

Spring Hill Road, Begbroke, Oxfordshire OX5 1RX
Tel: 01865 595170
Email: enquiries@lvs-oxford.org.uk
Website: www.lvs-oxford.org.uk
FOR MORE INFORMATION SEE PAGE 68

NAS

393 City Road
London EC1V 1NG
Tel: +44 (0)20 7833 2299
Fax: +44 (0)20 7833 9666
Email: nas@nas.org.uk
Website: www.nas.org.uk

NAS Anderson School

Luxborough Lane, Chigwell, Essex IG7 5AB
Email: theandersonschool@nas.org.uk
Website: www.autism.org.uk/andersonschool
FOR MORE INFORMATION SEE PAGE 69

NAS Church Lawton School

Cherry Tree Avenue, Church Lawton, Stoke-on-Trent, Staffordshire ST7 3EL
Tel: 01270 877601
Email: church.lawton@nas.org.uk
Website: www.autism.org.uk/churchlawton
FOR MORE INFORMATION SEE PAGE 79

NAS Daldorch House School

Sorn Road, Catrine, East Ayrshire KA5 6NA
Tel: 01290 551666
Fax: 01290 553399
Email: daldorch@nas.org.uk
Website: www.autism.org.uk/daldorch
FOR MORE INFORMATION SEE PAGE 87

NAS Daldorch Satellite School

St Leonards, East Kilbride, South Lanarkshire G74
Tel: 01355 246242
Fax: 01290 553399
Email: daldorch@nas.org.uk
Website: www.daldorchhouseschool.org.uk
FOR MORE INFORMATION SEE PAGE XXX

NAS Helen Allison School

Longfield Road, Meopham, Kent DA13 0EW
Tel: 01474 814878
Email: helen.allison@nas.org.uk
Website: www.autism.org.uk/helenallison
FOR MORE INFORMATION SEE PAGE 75

NAS Radlett Lodge School

Harper Lane, Radlett, Hertfordshire WD7 9HW
Tel: 01923 854922
Fax: 01923 859922
Email: radlett.lodge@nas.org.uk
Website: www.autism.org.uk/radlettlodge
FOR MORE INFORMATION SEE PAGE 70

NAS Robert Ogden School

Clayton Lane, Thurnscoe, Rotherham, South Yorkshire S63 0BG
Tel: 01709 874443
Fax: 01709 870701
Email: robert.ogden@nas.org.uk
Website: www.autism.org.uk/robertogden
FOR MORE INFORMATION SEE PAGE 84

NAS Sybil Elgar School

Havelock Road, Southall, Middlesex UB2 4NY
Tel: 020 8813 9168
Fax: 020 8571 7332
Email: sybil.elgar@nas.org.uk
Website: www.autism.org.uk/sybilelgar
FOR MORE INFORMATION SEE PAGE 71

NAS Thames Valley School

Conwy Close, Tilehurst, Reading, Berkshire RG30 4BZ
Tel: 0118 9424 750
Email: thames.valley@nas.org.uk
Website: www.autism.org.uk/thamesvalley
FOR MORE INFORMATION SEE PAGE 78

NAS Vanguard School

Lollard Street, Kennington, Lambeth, London, SE11 6UJ
Website: www.vanguardschool.org.uk
FOR MORE INFORMATION SEE PAGE 72

RNIB

105 Judd Street
London WC1H 9NE
Tel: 0303 123 9999
Email: helpline@rnib.org.uk
Website: www.rnib.org.uk

R N I B

See differently

RNIB College Loughborough

Radmoor Road, Loughborough, Leicestershire LE11 3BS
Tel: 01509 611077
Fax: 01509 232013
Email: enquiries@rnibcollege.ac.uk
Website: www.rnibcollege.ac.uk
FOR MORE INFORMATION SEE PAGE 118

RNIB Three Spires Academy

Kingsbury Road, Coundon, Coventry, West Midlands CV6 1PJ
Tel: 024 7659 4952
Email: threespires@rnib.org.uk
Website: threespires.rnib.org.uk/

RNIB Sunshine House School

33 Dene Road, Northwood, Middlesex HA6 2DD
Tel: 01923 822538
Fax: 01923 826227
Email: sunshinehouse@rnib.org.uk
Website: www.rnib.org.uk/sunshinehouse
FOR MORE INFORMATION SEE PAGE 119

TCES Group

**Park House, 8 Lombard Road, Wimbledon
London SW19 3TZ
Tel: +44 (0)20 8543 7878
Fax: +44 (0)20 8543 7877
Email: referrals@tces.org.uk
Website: www.tces.org.uk**

East London Independent School (ELIS)

Welfare Road, Stratford Marsh, , London E15 4HT

Tel: 020 8555 6737

Email: referrals@tces.org.uk

Website: www.tces.org.uk

FOR MORE INFORMATION SEE PAGE 91

Essex Fresh Start Independent School (EFS)

1 Wellesley Road, Clacton, Essex CO15 3PP

Tel: 01255 225204

Email: referrals@tces.org.uk

Website: www.tces.org.uk

FOR MORE INFORMATION SEE PAGE 90

North West London Independent School (NWLIS)

85 Old Oak Common Lane, Acton, , London W3 7DD

Tel: 020 8749 5403

Email: referrals@tces.org.uk

Website: www.tces.org.uk

FOR MORE INFORMATION SEE PAGE 92

School profiles

Schools and colleges specialising in social interaction difficulties (Autism, ASC & ASP)

Prior's Court School

(Founded 1999)

Hermitage, Thatcham, West Berkshire
RG18 9NU
Tel: 01635 247202/245914
Fax: 01635 247203
Email: mail@priorscourt.org.uk
Website: www.priorscourt.org.uk
Director of Education and Learning:
Sue Piper

Appointed: September 2011
School type: Independent Special School
Age range of pupils: 5–19
No. of pupils enrolled as at 01/01/2019: 65
Boys: 54 *Girls:* 12 *Sixth Form:* 22
No. of boarders: 63
Fees per annum as at 01/01/2019:
On application

Prior's Court School is an independent special school for young people with autism aged from 5 to 19 years. The School offers day, weekly and termly places with 38, 44 and 52 week options. All the students have severe autism, with moderate to severe learning difficulties and complex needs. They may have additional associated diagnoses; some students exhibit challenging behaviours, and many are non verbal. All are working within P scales to lower national curriculum levels.

The School was opened in 1999. It is managed by Prior's Court Foundation, a registered charity which also runs a young adult provision and specialist autism training centre on the same site.

As an autism-specific school, Prior's Court is able to focus on meeting the specific needs of its students in the most effective and consistent way to support their learning:

• A meaningful and functional curriculum with individualised learning programmes used throughout the

waking day is built around students' interests and skills.

• The environment is adapted to meet students' needs – it is highly structured, calm, low-arousal, safe and secure with space and physical exercise a key feature providing opportunities to learn, exercise, socialise and relax onsite. Set in over 50 acres, facilities include a stable yard and paddocks for animal husbandry, a walled garden with greenhouse and polytunnel for horticulture, sensory swimming pool,

families and professionals to create a co-ordinated and consistent programme of education and care whose success is recognised worldwide.

By combining autism expertise and best practice with a person-centred approach, the school aims to achieve the highest level of progress for each individual enabling them to self-manage behaviour, communicate, manage transitions, develop independent living and social skills, make choices and advocate and progress to building vocational skills and undertaking work-placement activities.

Skills are taught onsite and applied out in the community during regular offsite trips, enabling students to work towards inclusion as far as possible.

"We were often told by professionals that our son, Brandon, was the most challenging and severely autistic child they had ever met. Since Brandon has started at Prior's court, we have seen him achieve milestones that we thought to be impossible. Brandon is now able to communicate with PECS, and at times, language. His anxiety levels have dropped and, consequently, so have the levels of challenging behaviour. The times we now spend together as a family are very positive." Parent at Prior's Court School.

trampolines, trim trail, zip wire, swings, activity track and outdoor gym.
- A strong focus on training and expertise amongst staff members is a key factor. Our approach is based on TEACCH methodologies – world renowned for its effectiveness in supporting those with autism.
- A large onsite multi-disciplinary team including Occupational therapy, Speech & Language therapy, Clinical Psychologists and Nurses as well

as dedicated horticulture, animal husbandry, swimming, activities and ICT instructors provide support throughout the school day and in residential settings as well as out in the community where appropriate. All staff (education, residential, night, multidisciplinary and therapeutic team) are trained from induction onwards ensuring the highest levels of knowledge and expertise. These dedicated staff work closely with

Swalcliffe Park School

(Founded 1965)
Swalcliffe, Banbury, Oxfordshire OX15 5EP
Tel: 01295 780302
Email: rpiner@swalcliffepark.co.uk
Website: www.swalcliffepark.co.uk
Principal: Mr Rob Piner

CEO: Mr Kiran Hingorani
School type: Boys' Residential & Day
Age range of boys: 10–19
No. of pupils enrolled as at 01/01/2019: 55
Fees per annum as at 01/01/2019:
Available on request

At Swalcliffe Park, we believe that different thinking is needed to improve the lives of our students and their families. So, we take a Quality of Life (QoL) approach to our work and this drives everything we do.

We want all of our students to be happy, healthy and empowered young people. So, we think it is essential to ask them about what matters to them, what makes them happy and what they would like to do with their lives. We listen to what they tell us and we support them to work towards their personal goals.

We also think it is important to work closely with families. So, we ask them about the impact of autism on family life, about what they would like to do but currently can't and about what is important to them. We listen to what they tell us and try to find ways to help.

We know that working together in this way leads to brighter futures and a better QoL for our students and for their families. This is why we do what we do.

All our students have a primary diagnosis of ASD, are of broadly average ability and have an Education, Health and Care Plan (EHCP) identifying their needs.

The school and residential facilities are set within 20 acres of parkland with a fishing lake, woods, and sports fields. We actively promote physical well-being and our students particularly enjoy spending time outdoors on our bike trail, zip wire, outdoor fitness facilities and play equipment.

Students feel safe and take advantage of the tranquil school grounds to relax, self-calm and have fun.

Our school building has been refurbished with advice from specialists and our students, to ensure it provides an autism-friendly learning environment. We have a range of specialist classrooms including a Science lab, Art studio, DT workshop, Food Tech kitchen, ICT suite, Gym, Library, Sixth Form centre and separate Expressive Arts studio. There is a central café area with indoor and outdoor seating which our students use for relaxing, socialising, and entertaining guests and visitors.

We have a fully equipped Occupational Therapy room including a climbing wall and sensory integration resources. Some students prefer to work in individual working-bases, which are situated in amongst the classrooms within the school building.

Resident students live in one of five autism-friendly houses based within the grounds and are supported by a dedicated group of staff assigned to each house. Students have their own bedroom with en-suite facilities and digital key access. The kitchens and lounges in each house are designed to encourage independence and social living.

Our integrated therapeutic model with inputs from Speech and Language Therapy, Occupational Therapy, Clinical Psychology and Massage provides holistic support for developing students' knowledge and skills and for improving their well-being and QoL. All our therapists are registered with the Health and Care Professions Council (HCPC).

We offer a range of courses leading to GCSE, BTEC and Functional Skills accreditation. Our flexible approach allows students to be entered for formal qualifications when they are ready rather than at prescribed times determined by age. We also have links with four local FE colleges and schools to provide additional vocational options, apprenticeships and further breadth to our curriculum. Class sizes remain at a maximum of 6 throughout a student's time at the school.

In the residential setting, students are supported by a dedicated team of experienced and highly qualified residential staff. The waking day curriculum offers all students a range of experiences and opportunities for them to develop attitudes, values, knowledge

and skills that they will find most helpful in dealing with daily life situations and in preparing for their futures.

Students are able to work towards certification in such things as the Duke of Edinburgh award, driving, swimming, climbing, sailing, football coaching and cycling. After school and weekend activities are open to day students as well as residential students.

The school is developing a local, national and international reputation for its innovative, evidence-based practice and is committed to sharing best practice with like-minded organisations, through our QoL network. The school has been consistently judged to be 'Outstanding' by Ofsted for both education and residential care, and has been awarded Advanced Level Autism Accreditation.

In addition to providing school places, we offer a range of services for parents, professionals and organisations. These include:

• Training
• Outreach advice and support
• Resource sharing
• Autism assessment and diagnosis

Swalcliffe Park is a Charitable Incorporated Organisation (CIO), which means all income generated by the school is used for the sole purpose of supporting our students and their families.

LVS Oxford

Spring Hill Road, Begbroke,
Oxfordshire OX5 1RX
Tel: 01865 595170
Email: enquiries@lvs-oxford.org.uk
Website: www.lvs-oxford.org.uk

Head Teacher: Mrs Louisa Allison-Bergin
School type: Coeducational Day
Age range of pupils: 11–19
No. of pupils enrolled as at 01/01/2019: 68

LVS Oxford is an SEN school providing a unique, positive education for young people on the autism spectrum aged 11 to 19.

A bespoke curriculum includes therapy and academic interventions, helping students make fantastic progress with their academic achievements. Crucially, we also see their self-confidence grow as they build up the life skills that will equip them for the future, including moving on to college, employment or assisted employment.

To enable our students to be happy and active we have created a curriculum underpinned by our three areas for development: Learning, Growing, Achieving.

Learning
At LVS Oxford, our students learn a range of relevant academic and vocational skills in a vibrant and stimulating environment. We help the learning process by focusing on their emotional wellbeing and physical health, as well as ensuring they develop the skills to manage stress and anxiety.

Growing
Pupils are supported by excellent pastoral care and we encourage independence, well-being and healthy lifestyles with students learning life skills outside of the classroom in a safe and secure environment. Students can access a range of vocational qualifications in areas such as ICT, cookery, furniture restoration, health and social care, and business. We aim to provide our students with a 'tool box for life' – a variety of qualifications, skills and coping mechanisms that they can take with them for the future.

Achieving
Students work towards a variety of academic qualifications – A Levels, GCSEs, Entry level qualifications and BTECs. Exam results in 2018 included an 8 (high A grade) in English language to maintain the school's 100% A* C record in the subject since it began offering GCSEs in 2016. For the second consecutive year pupils achieved 100% attainment in all BTEC courses.

We also aim to prepare young people with autism for life in the workplace so that when they leave us they have the skills and knowledge to get a job and sustain work. Our students are given the opportunity to engage in work-based training providing experience in their chosen area.

Whilst we have a criteria and policy for admissions, we also recommend you contact us to discuss the individual's needs, or attend one of our open days.

Anderson School

NAS Anderson School
Luxborough Lane, Chigwell, Essex, IG7 5AB
E: theandersonschool@nas.org.uk
www.andersonschool.org.uk

Principal: Gary Simm

School type: mixed free school with day placements for children and young people on the autism spectrum

Catchment area: Essex, East London and neighbouring authorities
Age range: 11-19
Capacity: 78
Established: 2017

Anderson School opened in September 2017 to children and young people on the autism-spectrum.

It is part of the National Autistic Society's Enterprise Campus situated on a 13-acre site, the campus hosts an Enterprise Centre and the National Inclusion and Development Centre. This is in addition to our sixth form centre, workshop and training facilities and indoor and outdoor sports facilities.

Our ambition is to transform the lives of autistic young people with the aspiration that all students leave the school ready for further education, employment or training.

As with all the National Autistic Society schools, the pedagogy of Anderson School is informed by the National Autistic Society's **MyProgress®** methodology. This has been developed through over 50 years' of experience and research to ensure best practice in teaching young autistic people. The school works in partnership with our other seven schools and the wider organisation to strengthen and develop expertise and innovative thinking.

MyProgress® guarantees that children will use tried and tested approaches that we have developed and used in our network of schools over many years: we know they make a difference. In addition to this we will take opportunities to pilot new and innovative interventions to facilitate the development of social understanding, resilience and independence.

Placements are funded by your local authority.

National Autistic Society

"My ultimate aim for this campus is that every child that leaves school will go into meaningful paid employment or other activity."

Mark Lever, CEO, National Autistic Society

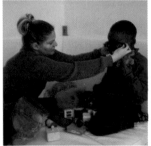

NAS Radlett Lodge School
Harper Lane, Radlett, Herts WD7 9HW
T: 01923 854 922 | F: 01923 859 922
E: radlett.lodge@nas.org.uk | www.radlettlodgeschool.org.uk

School type: mixed independent school with day, weekly and termly residential placements for children and young people on the autism spectrum

Catchment area: national
Age range: 4-19
Capacity: 55
Established: 1974

At Radlett Lodge School, we are driven by our determination to provide the highest quality education to the children in our care and do the best we can for their families. Ofsted have recognised our pursuit for excellence by rating us Outstanding for education and Good for care for a number of years.

We get to know every pupil well, ensuring every element of their school life is personalised to them. We use the principles of the National Autistic Society's **MyProgress®** strategy to help your child to learn, develop and prepare for adult life to the very best of their ability – and we celebrate every achievement.

Radlett Lodge School caters for early years, primary, secondary and post-16 pupils. The school and our residential lodge are located on the same site, which supports a close-knit environment and easy transitions. Strong ties with our local community mean pupils apply their learning to the outside world, particularly when approaching adulthood in our post-16 unit. We also offer flexi-boarding to our pupils, and outreach support to external pupils.

In a structured and supportive learning environment and with the help of friendly, approachable staff, students develop social relationships and receive a broad and balanced education.

Placements are funded by your local authority.

"The care and welfare of pupils is at the heart of the school's work."

Ofsted, 2017

Sybil Elgar School

NAS Sybil Elgar School
Havelock Road, Southall, Middlesex, UB2 4NY
T: 020 8813 9168 | F: 020 8571 7332
E: sybil.elgar@nas.org.uk | www.sybilelgarschool.org.uk

Principal: Chloe Phillips

School type: mixed independent school with day, weekly term-time and 52-week residential placements for children and young people on the autism spectrum

Catchment area: national
Age range: 4-22
Capacity: 90
Established: 1965

As the first autism-specific residential school in the world, Sybil Elgar School is a pioneer in autism education. Having paved the way in autism education for over 50 years, we have the knowledge and experience to apply the tailored education and care each young person who learns with us will receive.

We have a highly specialised curriculum, and our dedicated staff closely support the learning of each pupil in communication, social, behavioural, emotional, sensory, physical and self-help skills. Our extensive performing arts curriculum complements this. Students can discover a new passion or enhance learning in other subjects through music, art and dance. They might play the drums in the school band and even perform at an international arts festival.

Our welcoming environment extends across our three school sites, which include a post-16 department and our year-round children's home, where all staff work together to ensure the safety, wellbeing and progress of all our students.

We follow the principles of the National Autistic Society's **MyProgress**® strategy to ensure each of our students has an experience with us that is truly personalised to them, their strengths, weaknesses and ambitions. And we recognise every achievement, helping our students value their successes and celebrate them.

Placements are funded by your local authority.

National Autistic Society

"The curriculum is creative, innovative and progressive. Pupils love learning and make outstanding progress."
Ofsted, 2018

Ofsted
Good
Provider

Vanguard School

Vanguard School
Lollard Street, Lambeth, South London
www.vanguardschool.org.uk

Executive Principal: Jo Galloway

School type: mixed free school with day placements for children and young people on the autism spectrum

Catchment area: Lambeth and neighbouring authorities

Age range: 11-19
Capacity: 78
Established: 2020

Vanguard School will open in January 2020 to students aged 11-19 on the autism spectrum from Lambeth and neighbouring boroughs in Greater London. The specialist autism school will eventually cater for up to 78 students. The school will grow gradually, with a phased intake of students, starting with years 7 and 8.

We've run autism-specific schools for over 50 years and continue to innovate all the time; we now have a thriving employment offer too, helping 1,000 employers last year to understand autism better.

We are committed to developing outstanding schools that improve outcomes for young people on the autism spectrum.

The pedagogy of Vanguard School is informed by the National Autistic Society's **MyProgress®** methodology. This has been developed to ensure best practice in teaching young autistic people. The school will work in partnership with our other eight schools and the wider organisation to strengthen and develop expertise and innovative thinking.

MyProgress® guarantees that children will use tried and tested approaches that we have developed and used in our network of schools over many years: we know they make a difference.

We want every student who leaves Vanguard school to have developed real life skills and emotional resilience, helping them step seamlessly into meaningful paid employment, further education or enterprising work.

Placements are funded by your local authority.

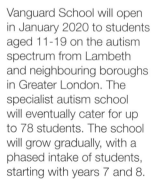

National
Autistic
Society

West Kirby School and College

WEST KIRBY SCHOOL AND COLLEGE

(Founded 1881)

Meols Drive, West Kirby, Wirral,
Merseyside CH48 5DH
Tel: 0151 632 3201
Fax: 0151 632 0621
Website: www.wkrs.co.uk
Head of Day School: Mr Pete Smith

School type:
Coeducational Day & Weekly Boarding
Age range of pupils: 5–19
No. of pupils enrolled as at 01/01/2019: 87
Fees per annum as at 01/01/2019:
On application

Changing Children's Lives, Building Better Futures

WKS is a Non-Maintained Special School for pupils with a wide range of social, communication difficulties often linked with conditions such as Autism and additional complex learning needs.

We have the option of day only provision or flexible boarding provision with pupils staying between one and four nights per week. Residential units include three houses in the locality and all are maintained to a high standard, with individual bedrooms and common areas for dining and recreation.

The school prides itself on being able to help some very complex young people access the National Curriculum and work towards appropriate accreditation in all subjects including Open Awards, GCSEs and A Levels. Staff are highly skilled in the understanding of the social and emotional needs of the pupils, as well as being able to personalise the academic work accordingly and provide high levels of support.

We believe the views of the pupils are paramount to success and the school offers opportunities for this through School Council, Pupil Voice and individual discussion. Every pupil has an 'individual support plan' which they and staff contribute to. Differentiation and small classes with high levels of adult support have proven successful. We have excellent facilities, particularly for arts, sports, drama and other practical subjects.

The school has its own Clinical Service team which provides additional 'therapy' and educational support often necessary for the pupils to access the National Curriculum and fulfil their academic and personal potential. This department consists of: Speech and Language Therapists, Occupational Therapy team, Therapeutic Support Service team, Behaviour and Reading support specialists/teams, a Learning Mentor, a Family Liaison Officer and Pastoral Care Team.

Post 16 is bespoke provision on-site. Each pupil has a study programme tailored to their individual needs, involving academic study, vocational and employability skills and further development of social and communication skills. The college has recently established supported Internships to facilitate access to college and work.

Staff are experienced at assisting pupils in the difficult process of transition from school to adult life. All pupils benefit from the strong pastoral ideal that runs through the school, to be aware both of themselves as individuals and within a group, increasing their respect for others, their self-esteem, emotional regulation and self-awareness.

Our staff are well qualified, experienced professionals. Recruitment procedures are rigorous with exemplary professional development available for all. Continued professional development is supported through an extensive range or partnerships with local schools, universities and other agencies.

A rounded curriculum with enrichment activities are an important part of our school experience to develop pupils' social, emotional and life skills. Pupils are regularly involved in community projects, Enterprise activities, offsite arts and culture trips, alongside being a direct licensed Duke of Edinburgh centre.

'This school remains outstanding' (Ofsted 2016).

WKS is a registered charity no. 207790.

LVS Hassocks

London Road, Sayers Common, Hassocks, West Sussex BN6 9HT
Tel: 01273 832901
Email: info@lvs-hassocks.org.uk
Website: www.lvs-hassocks.org.uk

Head Teacher: Ms Jen Weeks
School type: Coeducational Day
Age range of pupils: 11–19
No. of pupils enrolled as at 01/01/2019: 48

LVS Hassocks is an SEN school providing a unique, positive education for young people on the autism spectrum aged 11 to 19. To enable our students to be happy and active we have created a curriculum underpinned by our three areas for development: Learning, Growing, Achieving.

Our students access a structured environment and high levels of targeted intervention and differentiation throughout the school day. We anticipate that they will gain a range of GCSEs and vocational qualifications at the end of Key Stages 4 and 5.

Learning

At LVS Hassocks, our students learn a range of academic and vocational skills in a vibrant and stimulating environment. Therapists work with teachers to ensure that the learning environment minimises the sensory challenges that many of our students experience.

Growing

Students are supported by excellent pastoral care and we encourage independence, well-being and healthy lifestyles with students learning life skills in and outside of the classroom in a safe and secure environment. There are on-site Speech & Language and Occupational Therapists, school nurses and other therapists (as identified in the EHC Plan) supporting our students. We aim to provide our students with a 'tool box for life' – a variety of qualifications, skills and coping mechanisms that they can take with them for the future.

Achieving

Students will work towards a variety of recognised academic qualifications – A Levels, GCSEs, entry level qualifications and BTECs. In 2018, 82% of our GCSE papers were graded A*–E or equivalent, with 47% graded A*–C or equivalent across ICT, maths, English language, art and statistics.

We aim to prepare young people with autism for life in the workplace so that when they leave us they have the skills and knowledge to get a job and sustain work. Our students are given the opportunity to engage in work-based training on site, for example working in the grounds and kitchens, as well as off site for experience in their chosen area such as businesses, fitness centres and local retail outlets.

Whilst we have a criteria and policy for admissions, we also recommend you contact us to discuss the individual's needs, or attend one of our open days.

Helen Allison School

NAS Helen Allison School
Longfield Road, Meopham, Kent DA13 0EW
T: 01474 814 878
E: helen.allison@nas.org.uk | www.helenallisonschool.org.uk

School type: mixed independent school with day and weekly term-time residential placements for children and young people on the autism spectrum

Catchment area: London, South East and East Anglia
Age range: 5-19
Capacity: 77
Established: 1968

At Helen Allison School we deliver a high quality, relevant and enjoyable education and use our expert knowledge of autism to find the best possible way for each student to learn to the best of their ability.

Following the principles of **MyProgress**®, The National Autistic Society's strategy for working with autistic students, we ensure they get the best start in life with an education tailored to them.

We believe in preparing our students for fulfilling adult lives, so our main curriculum is enhanced with a wide range of social activities and community-based learning.

Through our hub, older students partake in work experience, pursue formal qualifications or might even organise a football tournament with other local schools and colleges.

Rated 'Outstanding' for education, and 'Outstanding' for care under the new Ofsted criteria,

we are always pushing for excellence for our students, thinking creatively to adapt to their needs and aspirations.

As one of only a few schools with our own therapeutic team, your child will develop not only academically but foster strong social and communication skills so they can thrive alongside their peers.

Placements are funded by your local authority.

National Autistic Society

"We support the students and design the curriculum with our eyes on the rest of life: we want to prepare our students for the skills needed for skilled employment."

Cathy Riggs, Deputy Principal

Moor House School & College

Mill Lane, Hurst Green, Oxted,
Surrey RH8 9AQ
Tel: 01883 712271
Email:
information@moorhouseschool.co.uk
Website: www.moorhouseschool.co.uk
Principal: Mrs H A Middleton

School type:
Coeducational Day & Residential
Age range of pupils: 7–19
No. of pupils enrolled as at 01/01/2019: 150
Fees per annum as at 01/01/2019:
On request

Our vision is of a society where speech and language disabilities do not prevent a young person from achieving his or her learning and communication potential, building an independent life and contributing positively to society.

Moor House is a Non-Maintained Special School and College, a registered charity and a world class centre of excellence, consistently rated outstanding by Ofsted. It provides specialist education, therapy and residential care for children and young people with speech and language needs, increasingly referred to as Developmental Language Disorder (DLD).

We provide a nurturing environment where experienced teams care for the educational, emotional and developmental needs of each student, preparing them for a safe, happy and fulfilling life. Moor House provides integrated teaching, therapy and residential care services for students with DLD.

Each student is surrounded by a multi-disciplinary team, supporting their learning and emotional well- being with intensive speech and language therapy, specialist literacy intervention, occupational therapy, physiotherapy and psychotherapy. Students receive one-to-one and small group teaching and bespoke therapy, and have access to a range of activities to develop new skills and build friendships.

This enables students to reach their highest educational and communication potential, and also to develop much higher levels of independent living skills, self-expression, and self-esteem.

Learning
Students are taught in small groups by teachers with experience working with children with language difficulties. Adapted language and specialist teaching strategies are used so that students can understand and develop the language that they need for learning.

Speech and language therapists (SLTs) work closely with teachers to support each child's difficulties and strengths. Teachers plan and deliver lessons collaboratively with SLTs to help students develop curriculum language.

Curriculum and Progress (School)
An adapted National Curriculum is taught and tailored to the students' strengths while helping them with areas of difficulty, and there is a particular emphasis on English, literacy, life skills and social skills.

We deliver exceptional outcomes for DLD children, helping our students to make outstanding academic progress, narrowing the gap significantly between themselves and their mainstream peers. Students take qualifications that match with their skills and level of development. We offer GCSEs in English Language, English Literature, Mathematics, Science, ICT, History, Fine Art and Ceramics. We also offer Functional Skills qualifications in English and Maths, vocational qualifications such as Home Cooking Skills at Levels 1 and 2, the AQA Unit Award Scheme in Science, and Entry Level qualifications in subjects such as English, Maths, ICT, DT and Music.

College (Sixth Form) Curriculum

Our objective is to support students to gain vocational qualifications, make confident and appropriate life choices and to be prepared for the next stage of their adult life. Specialist staff support students to access local partner college courses in Art and Design, Child Care, Media Studies, Floristry, Construction, Catering, Sport, Performing Arts and Animal Management, from Foundation and Level 1 in Year 12 to Level 4 at the end of Year 14.

We provide specialist support to achieve additional qualifications in Maths and English and develop important skills for life and employment, through individual study programmes and after college support.

Speech and Language Therapy

SLTs work throughout the day with students, individually, in groups, as well as in the classroom where lessons such as English are jointly planned and delivered.

Each therapist has a small caseload of children and gets to know their abilities and personalities. The intensive therapy programme may focus on learning skills, developing strategies to communicate, and support the student to understand their own strengths and difficulties. We teach skills for talking in everyday situations, language for lessons, social skills, friendship skills and independence.

We have developed specialist evidence based methods such as Electropalatography (EPG), Shape Coding by Susan Ebbels® and signing with grammatical markers.

Occupational Therapy

Occupational Therapists (OTs) work on life skills to help students develop their independence in areas such as handwriting, touch typing, doing up a tie or shoe laces, travel or cooking skills. Strategies are provided to develop sensory processing in lessons to manage and improve attention control.

We have a dedicated Team of OTs and a fully equipped OT suite which includes sensory integration equipment. The therapists communicate regularly with parents about their child's progress.

Residential Care

Our residential community provides single room facilities within our beautiful Village; three newly built student houses, located around a communal square for relaxing after school.

The students frequently describe their house as a 'home from home' and their wellbeing is assured by their key workers, who look after students' emotional welfare and provide a range of therapeutic strategies after school in a happy, stimulating and caring environment.

Our Residential Care continues to be rated "Outstanding" by Ofsted who noted: 'Children and young people thrive in this residential setting … (they) blossom in their confidence and self-esteem. Those who have had very poor school experiences and, in some cases, have refused school, look forward to their return to the provision after the weekend. Children and young people who stay in the residential setting feel safe and secure. There is an excellent approach to supporting children and young people towards independence'.

Moor House Research and Training

Our pioneering institute for training and research into DLD informs our therapeutic practice and teaching methods. Our therapists engage in cutting edge research in all areas of speech and language, working with Universities and sharing knowledge with other professionals through journals and presentations. Moor House is deservedly highly regarded by academics and specialists in the field. For information on our research, please see www.moorhouse.surrey.sch.uk/research. For information on our training, please see www.moorhouse.surrey.sch.uk/courses-and-conferences.

Moor House also provides a range of outreach, information and training services in all aspects of speech and language disabilities for parents and the wider community.

Thames Valley School

NAS Thames Valley School
Conwy Close, Tilehurst, Reading, Berkshire RG30 4BZ
T: 0118 9424 750 | E: thames.valley@nas.org.uk
www.thamesvalleyschool.org.uk

Principal: Jo Galloway

School type: mixed free school with day placements for children and young people on the autism spectrum

Catchment area: Reading, Berkshire and neighbouring local authorities
Age range: 5-16
Capacity: 50
Established: 2013

Thames Valley School is a high-achieving specialist school for children and young people on the autism spectrum. Our school has been purpose-built for us, meaning we could design it to be perfectly suitable for our students. We have calming pods where children can relax or read, independent rooms attached to every classroom, outdoor play areas for all ages and a state-of-the-art innovation hub, opening up opportunities for pupils to take on digital projects such as coding, social media and cyber security.

We have high expectations of our pupils, and through delivering the National Curriculum at all key stages, we expect the majority of our students to attain at least the same levels as their mainstream school peers. At age 16 our pupils take national qualifications, and our aim is for most to achieve a wide range of GCSE's at A to C or equivalent vocational qualifications.

Small classes, committed and experienced specialist teachers and a wonderful learning environment all contribute to making our school an exceptional place to be. We follow the principles of the National Autistic Society's **MyProgress®** strategy to give your child an education specific to them, so they can flourish.

Placements are funded by your local authority.

"The school has been the making of my son, he loves coming to school!"
Parent

Church Lawton School

NAS Church Lawton School, Cherry Tree Avenue, Church Lawton, Stoke-on-Trent, Staffordshire ST7 3EL
T: 01270 877 601 | E: church.lawton@nas.org.uk
www.churchlawtonschool.org.uk

Principal: Paul Scales

School type: mixed free school with day placements for children and young people on the autism spectrum

Catchment area: Cheshire East and surrounding authorities, including Cheshire West, Stoke-on-Trent and Staffordshire

Age range: 4-19
Capacity: 60
Established: 2015

Church Lawton School is the National Autistic Society's second free school providing tailored care for local autistic students. We opened in 2015 and offer a highly specialised learning environment to our pupils on our brand new, purpose-built site.

With large open classrooms and an average class size of six, our pupils have the space and attention they need to reach their full potential.

Combined with well-resourced classrooms our building is equipped for academic excellence, and so we aim for our pupils to perform well in different exam pathways including Entry Level, GCSEs, ASDAN, A Levels and more. We have recently received an Ofsted rating of good with outstanding features.

We follow the principles of **MyProgress®**, the National Autistic Society's overall strategy for working with children on the autism spectrum. Systematic and thorough, we work with you and your child to create the best education for them.

We equip pupils with the skills and knowledge to support them as they move into further study and adult life. They get to know their community and, as they move through the school, have the opportunity to take part in work experience or study in local colleges and universities. Above all we are dedicated to making sure every one of our pupils is given the tools they need to thrive.

Placements are funded by your local authority.

National Autistic Society

"I have never come across a school that is as kind, caring and understanding about its pupils."
A visiting parent

Ofsted
Good Provider

Cruckton Hall

(Founded 1981)

Cruckton, Shrewsbury, Shropshire SY5 8PR
Tel: 01743 860206
Fax: 01743 860941
Email: admissions@kisimul.co.uk
Website: www.cruckton.com
Head Teacher: Robert Arrowsmith

School type:
Co-educational Independent Special
School and Children's Home
Age range of pupils: 8–19
No. of pupils enrolled as at 01/01/2019: 80
Fees per annum as at 01/01/2019:
On application

Cruckton Hall School's mission is to continually strive for excellence in the care and education of its children and young people. The school provides a homely and safe environment for children and young people who have learning difficulties and/or autism and display behaviours that challenge.

The hall is a listed building surrounded by ten acres of gardens that include woods, playing fields and play areas.

The site is located within a friendly rural community, in beautiful countryside, four miles from the market town of Shropshire. The Welsh marches provide a stunning backdrop and a rich source of options for our regular trips and adventures. The town of Shrewsbury offers excellent amenities for the school and is now linked to the motorway network of the West Midlands, greatly improving access.

The school offers day and residential education, alongside care and leisure programmes, for up to 52 weeks of the year. The school is registered with the Department for Education and Ofsted for pupils aged 8 to 19 years.

Residential and therapy staff work closely together to enable all children and young people to progress in their personal development and learning. The 24-hour approach incorporates a wide range of activities to enrich the learning

experiences of all pupils, helping them to learn to communicate and cooperate more effectively with others. In turn, this enables them to grow in confidence, self-esteem and independence.

The highly structured school curriculum aims to address the very specific needs of our children and young people by providing every opportunity for them to enjoy their education and develop their skills, knowledge and understanding.

The curriculum incorporates aspects of the National Curriculum and an accreditation based learning model for older pupils. An integrated therapeutic approach including; psychology, speech and language, music therapy and occupational therapy is available through the school.

Classes are small and matched to learning profiles, alongside the dynamics of peers. A high staffing ratio reflects the complex needs of learners.

All pupils at the school have an Individual Pupil Care Plan that sets out their educational and therapeutic needs in addition to care, behavioural or medical information.

A key priority for the school is to develop our children and young people's communication skills. Where appropriate, we teach the alternative and augmentative systems of Makaton signing and the Picture Exchange Communication System (PECS), alongside vocalisations and speech.

The structure that provides success for the children and young people in the classroom environment is replicated in the residential area. The children and young people have a range of recreational activities provided for them, which reflect their needs and encourage their interests. The links between pupils' individual targets are shared across the 24- hour approach, both in the home and school.

It is accepted that many young people come to Cruckton Hall School exhibiting challenging behaviour. The structural consistency of various approaches, combined with a consistent nurturing environment, has a proven track record of reducing both the intensity and frequency of these behaviours over time.

Cruckton Hall School works closely with the parents, carers and professionals from its placing authorities to ensure the highest possible standards of care and education. Kisimul School is committed to the view that all people are entitled to equality of opportunity regardless of ability, disability, sex, age, status, religion, belief, nationality, ethnic origins or sexual orientation.

Entry to the school is by assessment. The multi-disciplinary team of professionals will carry out a baseline assessment on each pupil within the first twelve weeks of admission.

For further information, including exciting job opportunities within Cruckton Hall School, please visit our website at www.cruckton.com or contact us at the address above.

Queen Alexandra College (QAC)
A National College for People with Disabilities

(Founded 1847)
Court Oak Road, Harborne, Birmingham,
West Midlands B17 9TG
Tel: 0121 428 5050
Fax: 0121 428 5048
Email: info@qac.ac.uk

Website: www.qac.ac.uk
Principal: Bev Jessop
School type:
Coeducational Day & Residential
Age range of pupils: 16+
No. of pupils enrolled as at 01/01/2019: 260

QAC is a national residential College that supports a diverse range of student abilities and needs.

The College has been at its current location since 1903 and offers an innovative, holistic approach to learning and support. We welcome students who come to our College from all over the country – as well as many who are local to us.

We offer support and guidance for students with visual impairment, autistic spectrum conditions, those with moderate to severe learning difficulties, students with physical disabilities and those with other needs.

Ultimately, we have a great mix of students which adds to the wonderful atmosphere here in College. Class sizes are small and support levels high.

At QAC your learning is planned around your individual needs, interests and ambitions. Our curriculum covers a wide range of programmes including entry level courses (Preparation for Life) and a range of vocational qualifications to level 3. We have a dedicated Employment Pathways curriculum including LEAP (Learning, Employment and Progression) programmes. A supported internship study programme could also be followed, which involves spending the majority of time with an employer in a real job role.

The College has a team of specialists on site who are able to support students, including Speech and Language Therapists, a Visual Impairment Training Officer, Educational and Clinical Psychologists, Counsellors, Mentors, a Braille Tutor, Occupational Therapy and Sensory Support, a Dyslexia Tutor, Healthcare Professionals including a Physiotherapist, Rehabilitation and Travel Trainers and a Personal and Sexual Health Education (PSHE) Lead.

Enrichment programmes enhance the curriculum and help to develop self-esteem, confidence and independence. Our residential provision develops essential skills for personal development such as independent living and social skills.

Facilities include new buildings with the latest technology, a fitness centre, state-of-the-art sports hall, sports field, sensory room, onsite travel training area, library and student centre.

Fullerton House School

Autism | Learning Disabilities | Complex Needs

(Founded 1990)

Tickill Square, Denaby, Doncaster, South Yorkshire DN12 4AR

Tel: 01709 861663
Email: enquiries@hesleygroup.co.uk
Website: www.fullertonhouseschool.co.uk
General Manager:
Heidi Dugdale-Dawkes
Appointed: 2017
Registered Manager: Deborah Smith

Head of Education: Michael Walsh
School type: Independent Specialist Residential School
Age range of pupils: 8–19
Fees per annum as at 01/01/2019:
Available on request

A specialist residential school offering flexible education and care, principally as a 52-week service with limited capacity for day placements, for young people aged 8-19, all of whom have complex needs including behaviour that may challenge and a learning disability, often in association with autism.

Fullerton House School is situated in the heart of the village of Denaby Main, near Doncaster. Its central location provides easy access by road, rail or air. Our mission is to enhance the lives of the young people entrusted to us by focusing on their specific needs, capabilities and aspirations.

Education: Each person has a carefully designed Individual Learning Plan based on their EHCP as well as their specific needs in line with the National Curriculum, which supports their positive progress in a range of areas.

Extended learning: During evenings, weekends and school holidays a wide range of extra-curricular activities are on offer to ensure that people are fully engaged with stimulating and meaningful experiences both on and off-site.

Professional services: A dedicated on-site team including carers, teachers, tutors, communication, behaviour and occupational therapy , psychology and other specialists ensure that people have ready access to the services they require.

High-quality accommodation: Single person and small group occupancy of high-quality accommodation is provided at Fullerton House School. Each person has their own bedroom, the majority of which have en-suite bathrooms. We also have a range of on-site facilities to complement and enrich the lives of those who come to live and learn with us.

Keeping in contact: We understand that while we may offer a very positive option for the person, we may not be on your doorstep. Keeping in touch with loved ones is essential. Everyone has a plan to support optimum contact with family/carers and friends whether this be by phone, letter, email or Skype.

Robert Ogden School

NAS Robert Ogden School
Clayton Lane, Thurnscoe, South Yorkshire S63 0BG
T: 01709 874 443 | F: 01709 807 701
E: robert.ogden@nas.org.uk | www.robertogdenschool.org.uk

Principal: Lorraine Dormand

School type: mixed independent school with day, weekly term-time and 52-week residential placements for children and young people on the autism spectrum

Catchment area: national
Age range: 5-19
Capacity: 127
Established: 1976

One of the largest schools in the UK for autistic children and young people, Robert Ogden School offers an environment where students can feel safe, supported and encouraged to achieve beyond their expectations. Following the principles of **MyProgress®**, the National Autistic Society's strategy for working with your child, we create a tailor-made experience for each student so they reach their full potential.

We are autism experts, with a specialist team dedicated to providing the highest quality care and education to our students. We have two Inclusive Learning Hubs run by a highly skilled group of staff who ensure pupils with particularly complex needs, requiring a non-directive approach, get the individualised curriculum and attention they need to thrive alongside their peers.

With autism-friendly buildings and facilities, your child will comfortably settle into school life. We even have a pottery room, several sensory and soft play rooms, a purpose-built primary unit and a teaching flat for independent living skills. Our students have every opportunity to develop the skills they will need for adult life, which is why we have a student-run café and shop, an award-winning fudge making enterprise project and a partnership with local charity shops. We give our students the help they need to make the best of their strengths and build upon them.

Placements are funded by your local authority.

"You have achieved what many others could not... I am so grateful for Robert Ogden, no wonder so many parents are fighting for a place, it truly is a magnificent school with magnificent staff."

Sarah, parent

National Autistic Society

Ofsted Good Provider

Specialist Colleges

Autism | Learning Disabilities | Complex Needs

(Founded 2013)

Fullerton House College

Tickhill Square, Denaby, Doncaster,

South Yorkshire DN12 4AR

Tel: 01709 861663

Wilsic Hall College

Wadworth, Doncaster,

South Yorkshire, DN11 9AG

Tel: 01302 856382

Email: enquiries@hesleygroup.co.uk

Website: www.hesleygroup.co.uk

General Manager:

Heidi Dugdale-Dawkes

Appointed: 2017

School type: Independent Specialist Residential College

Age range of pupils: 18–25

Fullerton House College Capacity: 12

Wilsic Hall College Capacity: 8

Fees per annum as at 01/01/2019:

On request

Specialist residential colleges offering flexible education care and support for up to 52 weeks per year for young people aged 18-25, who have complex needs including behaviour that may challenge and a learning disability, often in association with autism.

At Wilsic Hall College, everyone lives within a beautiful rural setting with ready community access and at Fullerton House College in the heart of the community, in an urban setting with many local facilities including a sports centre, restaurants and shops.

Mission

We have 2 pathways available for the young people attending college.

Formal Education Pathway with a focus on gaining educational qualifications, skills and experience to move on to employment opportunity and further independence in their lives.

Next Steps Pathway for young people who have completed their formal educational route and are now wishing to build vocational and independence skills for life style experience and development-including social enterprise work.

Both pathways offer accreditation in the skills and qualifications the young people achieve, but the journeys are varied and personalised to the young persons needs and outcomes at this significant life stage.

Education: Everybody has a highly personalised programme of learning, equipping them with skills they will need for adult life.

Extended learning: During evenings, weekends and college holidays a wide range of extra-curricular activities are on offer to ensure people are fully engaged with stimulating experiences both on and off site providing further, meaningful learning opportunities.

Professional services: A dedicated multi-disciplinary therapeutic team including college tutors, college support workers, consultant clinical psychologist, consultant psychiatrist, applied behaviour analysts, speech and language therapists, occupational therapists, registered manager, care and support staff work together to support each individual's progress.

High quality accommodation: College accommodation includes individualised bedrooms, quality living spaces that promote independence and progressive skills development assisted by the appropriate use of specialist/adaptive technology. We also have a range of on-site and off-site facilities that offer progressive learning opportunities for young people with a range of needs and wishes.

Keeping in contact: We work to develop relationships between staff and families that are strong, positive and mutually respectful. People are supported to be in contact with their friends and family; we welcome visits to the colleges at any time. Everyone has a plan that will include the best means for them to maintain this contact whether by 'phone, letter, email or Skype.

Wilsic Hall School

Hesley Group

Autism | Learning Disabilities | Complex Needs

(Founded 1996)
Wadworth, Doncaster,
South Yorkshire DN11 9AG

Tel: 01302 856382
Email: enquiries@hesleygroup.co.uk
Website: www.wilsichallschool.co.uk
Head: Geoff Turner
Appointed: 2008
School type:
Independent Specialist Residential School

Age range of pupils: 11–19
Capacity as at 01/01/2019: 32
Fees per annum as at 01/01/2019:
Available on request

A specialist residential school offering flexible education and care, principally as a 52-week service with limited capacity for day placements, for young people aged 11-19, all of whom have complex needs including behaviour that may challenge and a learning disability, often in association with autism.

Wilsic Hall School is situated in its own 14-acre site approximately five miles south of Doncaster. Its central location provides easy access by road, rail or air. Our mission is to enhance the lives of the people entrusted to us by focusing on their specific needs, capabilities and aspirations.

Education: Each person has a carefully designed Individual Education Plan based on their specific needs in line with the National Curriculum, which supports their positive progress in a range of areas.

Extended learning: During evenings, weekends and school holidays a wide range of extra-curricular activities are on offer to ensure that people are fully engaged with stimulating and meaningful experiences both on and off-site.

Professional services: A dedicated team including carers, teachers, tutors, behaviour, communication and occupational therapy, psychology and other specialists ensure that each person has ready access to the services they require.

High-quality accommodation: Single person and small group occupancy of high-quality accommodation is provided at Wilsic Hall School. Each person has their own bedroom, the majority of which have en-suite bathrooms. We also have a range of on-site facilities to complement and enrich the lives of those who come to live and learn with us.

Keeping in contact: We understand that while we may offer a very positive option for the person, we may not be on your doorstep. Keeping in touch with loved ones is essential. Everyone has a plan to support optimum contact with family/carers and friends whether this be by phone, letter, email or Skype.

Daldorch House School

NAS Daldorch House School
Sorn Road, Catrine, East Ayrshire, Scotland KA5 6NA
T: 01290 551 666 | F: 01290 553 399
E: daldorch@nas.org.uk | www.daldorchhouseschool.org.uk

Principal: Bernadette Casey

School type: mixed independent school with day, weekly, termly and 52-week residential placements for children and young people on the autism spectrum

Catchment area: national
Age range: 8-21
Capacity: 28 residential
Established: 1998

At Daldorch House School we work compassionately with each of our pupils, while challenging them to achieve to the best of their ability. Our 11 acre site is in a beautiful rural setting, while being only an hour from the bustle of Glasgow city centre.

Our classrooms are designed to suit the needs of all our pupils, and each lesson is arranged according to those learning in it.

Developing communication, social and life skills is at the core of our 24-hour curriculum at Daldorch, and we enrich each pupil's learning by capitalising on their interests and expanding their understanding of the world.

We also have a satellite school in East Kilbride, offering a year-round residential provision for families living in the South Lanarkshire local authority area, meaning your child can live and learn close to home in an area they know well.

Our curriculum is relevant, engaging and designed to develop each child's independence as they mature, our focus on lifelong learning strengthening as they approach adult life. With a blended approach to learning through The National Autistic Society's **MyProgress®** strategy, your child will have an education at Daldorch that is entirely personalised to them.

Placements are funded by your local authority.

National Autistic Society

"Young people have positive and trusting relationships with staff across the school."
Education Scotland

Beechwood College

(Founded 2004)

Hayes Road, Sully,
Vale of Glamorgan CF64 5SE
Tel: 029 2053 2210
Fax: 029 2053 1774
Email:
enquiries@beechwoodcollege.co.uk
Website: www.beechwoodcollege.co.uk

Director of Education: Angela Kent
School type:
Coeducational Residential & Day
Age range of pupils: 16–25
No. of pupils enrolled as at 01/01/2019: 44
Fees per annum as at 01/01/2019:
On application

Opened in 2004, Beechwood College is a specialist day and residential service for young adults between the ages of 16 and 25 with a formal diagnosis of Autistic Spectrum Condition or Asperger's Syndrome.

Based upon the principles of TEACCH, PECS and Makaton, the College's goal is to provide opportunities and experiences for each individual, regardless of ability, to prepare them for later life. The integrated approach to learning has qualified lecturers, residential and clinical teams partnering together so that each student's personalised education programme is developed and reinforced consistently in a 24-hour learning environment which can lead to formal accreditation.

It is a tribute to the hard work of our students and the efforts of the Beechwood College team that students enjoy success in a wide area of skills. In the year 2018 83% of students achieved BTEC and ASDAN qualifications. Students also participate and complete Duke of Edinburgh Bronze and Silver Scheme Awards and Enterprise Projects aimed at building confidence, team working and community living skills.

Beechwood College is situated in Sully South Wales, adjoining green fields and overlooking the Bristol Channel. Yet the shops and social facilities of Barry are only a few minutes drive away.

Beechwood College is part of the South Wales-based Ludlow Street Healthcare Group. Employing more than 1100 staff including extensive clinical teams, Ludlow Street Healthcare is a provider of tailored care solutions for adults over the age of 16 who have a range of complex mental health, personality disorder and physical health needs.

Schools and colleges specialising in emotional, behavioural and/or social difficulties (EBSD)

Essex Fresh Start Independent School (EFS)

Essex Fresh Start
Independent School

(Founded 2007)
1 Wellesley Road, Clacton, Essex CO15 3PP
Tel: 01255 225204
Email: referrals@tces.org.uk
Website: www.tces.org.uk

Head Teacher: Cheryl Rutter
Appointed: 2007
Schools' Proprietor: Thomas Keaney
School type: Coeducational Day
Age range of pupils: 7–19 years

Essex Fresh Start (EFS) is a TCES Group school, providing LA funded day-school education for pupils aged 7-19 years whose Social, Emotional or Mental Health (SEMH) needs or Autism Spectrum Condition (ASC), plus complex co-morbid needs has made it difficult for them to achieve success in a mainstream school. Pupils often have undiagnosed speech, language and communication needs, sensory or learning difficulties, which can create barriers to learning that are addressed before the pupil can settle into education.

Our integrated approach to education, health and care, takes each pupil on an individual journey that encourages a love of learning. We provide a well-structured routine in a safe, calm and happy environment which promotes tolerance and respect throughout our school community. We nurture ambition and work with each child to provide them with the life skills, accreditation and certification needed to achieve future careers.

Pupils are taught in groups of up to six to ensure each individual receives an intensive level of support, with a Teacher and TA as minimum. TCES Group's Inclusion Model is embedded at EFS, delivered by the Inclusion Manager and Pastoral Care Co-ordinator: tutor support, key work, group process, nurture groups and leadership skills are part of the core offer.

The school delivers TCES Group's 5 Part Curriculum, which includes access to support from the Clinical and Therapy Team on an as-needs basis. Individualised therapy programmes are delivered by our in-house team and access to Clinical Psychology and a Paediatrician at Consultant level can be arranged for pupils whose needs require further investigation.

Pupils attending EFS often need highly personalised learning programmes and can remain for Post-16 programmes of study, specialising in developing independence, preparation for adult life and life after school.

We nurture each child's ambitions by accrediting them with as many achievements as possible to help them make positive choices for their future careers. As a result, 80% of our leavers happily go straight into work, education or training.

A parallel service to our schools, TCES Group's Create Service offers therapeutic education, delivered through a case co-ordination model, to pupils who present (or are at) significant risk to themselves or others, and who cannot be educated in a school setting.

To find out more about the school and its facilities please come and visit us! In the first instance please contact us on referrals@tces.org.uk or 020 8543 7878.

East London Independent School (ELIS)

East London
Independent School

Welfare Road, Stratford Marsh,
London E15 4HT
Tel: 020 8555 6737
Email: referrals@tces.org.uk
Website: www.tces.org.uk

Head Teacher: Adele Stedman
Schools' Proprietor: Thomas Keaney
School type: Coeducational Day
Age range of pupils: 7–19 years

East London Independent School (ELIS) is a TCES Group school, providing LA funded day-school education for pupils aged 7-19 years whose Social, Emotional or Mental Health (SEMH) needs or Autism Spectrum Condition (ASC), plus complex co-morbid needs has made it difficult for them to achieve success in a mainstream school. Pupils often have undiagnosed speech, language and communication needs, sensory or learning difficulties, which can create barriers to learning that are addressed before the pupil can settle into education.

ELIS is housed in a newly developed state-of-the-art school building, which boasts a specially designed low-arousal, autism friendly environment that suits all pupils regardless of their needs. Uniquely, the school successfully teaches ASC and SEMH pupils together.

Our integrated approach to education, health and care, takes each pupil on an individual journey that encourages a love of learning. We provide a well-structured routine in a safe, calm and happy environment that promotes tolerance and respect throughout our school community. We nurture ambition and work with each child to provide them with the life skills, accreditation and certification needed to achieve future careers.

Pupils are taught in groups of up to six to ensure each individual receives an intensive level of support, with a Teacher and TA as minimum. TCES Group's Inclusion Model is embedded at ELIS, delivered by the Inclusion Manager and Pastoral Care Co-ordinator: tutor support, key work, group process, nurture groups and leadership skills are part of the core offer.

The school delivers TCES Group's 5 Part Curriculum, which includes access to support from the Clinical and Therapy Team on an as-needs basis. Individualised therapy programmes are delivered by our in-house team and access to Clinical Psychology and a Paediatrician at Consultant level can be arranged for pupils whose needs require further investigation.

Pupils attending ELIS often need highly personalised learning programmes and can remain for Post-16 programmes of study, specialising in developing independence, preparation for adult life and life after school.

A parallel service to our schools, TCES Group's Create Service offers therapeutic education, delivered through a case co-ordination model, to pupils who present (or are at) significant risk to themselves or others, and who cannot be educated in a school setting.

To find out more about the school and its facilities please come and visit us! In the first instance please contact us on referrals@tces.org.uk or 020 8543 7878.

North West London Independent School (NWLIS)

North West London
Independent School

(Founded 2008)

85 Old Oak Common Lane, Acton,
London W3 7DD

Tel: 020 8749 5403

Email: referrals@tces.org.uk

Website: www.tces.org.uk

Head Teacher: Katrina Medley

Schools' Proprietor: Thomas Keaney

School type: Coeducational Day

Age range of pupils: 7–19 years

TCES Group's North West London Independent School (NWLIS) provides LA funded day-school education for pupils aged 7-19 years whose Social, Emotional or Mental Health (SEMH) needs or Autism Spectrum Condition (ASC), plus complex co-morbid needs has made it difficult for them to achieve success in a mainstream school. Pupils often have undiagnosed speech, language and communication needs, sensory or learning difficulties, which can create barriers to learning that

are addressed before the pupil can settle into education.

Our integrated approach to education, health and care, described by Ofsted as innovative and unique, takes each pupil on an individual journey that encourages a love of learning. We provide a well-structured routine in a safe, calm and happy environment which promotes tolerance and respect throughout our school community. We nurture ambition and work with each child to provide

them with the life skills, accreditation and certification needed to achieve successful future careers.

Pupils are taught in groups of up to six to ensure each individual receives an intensive level of support, with a Teacher and TA as minimum. TCES Group's Inclusion Model is embedded at NWLIS, delivered by the Inclusion Manager and Pastoral Care Co-Ordinator: tutor support, key work, group process, nurture groups and leadership skills are part of the core offer.

The school delivers TCES Group's 5 Part Curriculum, which includes access to support from the Clinical and Therapy Team on an as-needs basis. Individualised therapy programmes are delivered by our in-house team and access to Clinical Psychology and a Paediatrician at Consultant level can be arranged for pupils whose needs require further investigation. *"Pupils rapidly develop their social skills and resilience to manage their emotions through the school's unique therapeutic approach."* Ofsted 2017

Pupils attending NWLIS often need highly personalised learning programmes and can remain for Post-16 programmes of study, specialising in developing independence, preparation for adult life and life after school.

A parallel service to our schools, TCES Group's Create Service offers therapeutic education, delivered through a case co-ordination model, to pupils who present (or are at) significant risk to themselves or others, and who cannot be educated in a school setting.

To find out more about the school and its facilities please come and visit us! In the first instance please contact us on referrals@tces.org.uk or 020 8543 7878.

Early Intervention Works

Therapeutic Care and Education for Younger Children

www.appletreetreatmentcentre.co.uk

Over 20 years' experience specialising in therapeutic care and education for girls and boys 6 to 12 years old with emotional, health, social and associated learning difficulties, who have suffered: Trauma, Neglect, Physical, Emotional, Sexual abuse.

Therapy in Action - Not Therapy in a Vacuum

Qualified, Experienced Psychologists and Therapists provide individual therapy for our children, clinical input for each childs' programme, clinical consultation and training for our care, teaching and support teams.

Therapeutic Relationships, Structured 24 hour Programme Our therapeutically informed teams are skilled at helping our children form healthy attachments, build emotional resilience and confidence, increasing their self-esteem, helping them acquire the skills needed to succeed at home, in life and in school.

Stability and Felt Security are Key to our Children's Success Once a child is placed with us we will not exclude them, they will only experience planned moves forward. This stability and security helps them develop meaningful relationships, build self esteem and develop resilience.

Successful reintegration to families

After an average of just 2 years and 6 months with us at least 90% of our leavers year after year are able to leave residential care/special school provision and return to families or foster families and day schools. The remaining 10% of our leavers continued in residential care to facilitate increased and appropriate contact with their families.

We work alongside adoptive, foster and birth families

All children engage in individual therapy, most continue throughout their stay with us

Close to 100% attendance in education with no unauthorized absence

Appletree Treatment Centre has three children's homes

Appletree for up to 12 children

Fell House for up to 8 children

Willow Bank for up to 5 children

We provide high quality therapeutic care and education. We help children who are vulnerable and require a nurturing environment.

Appletree and Fell House each have their own school on site, Willow Bank children attend Appletree school

tel 015395 60253 - Natland, Kendal Cumbria LA9 7QS - **email clair.davies@appletreetc.co.uk**

Everyone within Appletree Treatment Centre has a responsibility for, and is committed to, safeguarding and promoting the welfare of children and young people and for ensuring that they are protected from harm.

Philpots Manor School

(Founded 1959)

West Hoathly, East Grinstead,
West Sussex RH19 4PR
Tel: 01342 810268
Email: info@philpotsmanorschool.co.uk
Website: www.philpotsmanorschool.co.uk
Education Co-ordinator:
Mr Darin Nobes BA (Hons), PGCE, NPQH

School type: Coeducational Boarding
Age range of pupils: 7–19
No. of pupils enrolled as at 01/01/2019: 43
Fees per annum as at 01/01/2019:
On application

Founded in 1959 and set in the heart of the Sussex countryside, Philpots Manor School is an independent residential special needs school. Along with primary and secondary schools we also have a 6th form and training centre offering 36 weeks of academic and social education to children and young adults from 7 to 19 years of age.

Our children and young people come from a range of social backgrounds and will have identified social, emotional, behavioural and mental health needs and social communication difficulties.

Students who do particularly well at Philpots Manor are Students who:
- Are highly anxious
- Are sensitive to their environment
- Benefit from a low stimulus environment
- Are creative

- Are emotionally sensitive
- Struggle with social interactions
- Love being outdoors
- Enjoy the space and freedom to be

Classes contain a maximum of eight students with one class teacher and at least one teaching assistant. We have six welfare units where students spend their free time. We have five units offering weekly boarding and one unit that solely houses day students. Our residential units can accommodate up to five boarding students with additional space for day students to access at the breaks during the school day. We also offer more flexible boarding arrangements for students who do not wish to board full time.

We currently offer accredited courses in GCSEs, BTECs and Functional Skills with students being entered at a time that is

appropriate for each. GCSEs are offered in seven subjects with BTECS in Cookery and ICT. As well as formal academic qualifications we also offer horse riding, pottery, gardening, weaving, art and Forest School.

As our students progress through the school, we begin a programme of work experience placements and college courses at a number of local colleges. Our aim is for our students to leave us going into full time education college courses, employment or apprenticeships.

We offer a wide range of therapies including speech and language, occupational therapy, drama therapy and creative arts therapy.

For further information, please visit our website.

West Heath School

WEST HEATH
REBUILDING LIVES THROUGH EDUCATION

(Founded 1998)

Ashgrove Road, Sevenoaks, Kent TN13 1SR

Tel: 01732 460553

Fax: 01732 456734

Email: admissions@westheathschool.com

Website: www.westheathschool.com

Principal: Mr James Nunns

Appointed: September 2016

School type:

Coeducational Day & Boarding

Age range of pupils: 10–20

No. of pupils enrolled as at 01/01/2019: 135

Fees per annum as at 01/01/2019:

Day: £52,500

Residential supplement: From £35,500

(Higher Needs plus fee are extra)

Who we are

West Heath is an Ofsted Outstanding and award-winning charity set up specifically to support vulnerable children for whom maintained SEN and mainstream schools were unable to meet needs. The school designation of Social, Emotional and Mental Heath only goes a short way to describing the complexity of need of our students. We have up to 130 places, 29 of which are residential, therapeutic centre and training facilities, all based on our 32 acre site in Sevenoaks, Kent.

Who we support

Students referred to us will have seen their mainstream provision break down, some having worked their way through a number of specialist providers unable to meet need or effectively engage with the young person. Others may have come from the Health sector, having been resident in a mental health provision. The SEN diagnosis of our student group is varied, many have a diagnosis of an Austism Spectrum Condition; all our students face challenges with their social communication and interaction with the social world in which they live.

How we support

Our focus is on education, both in terms of academic and personal development. Barriers to learning and the challenges our students face are met rather than avoided, with strategies put in place to support ongoing development. We have a range of therapies on site, working directly with students to meet needs identified from professionals. Therapy is embedded into our curriculum, with Speech and Language and Self Science lessons forming part of the weekly timetable. We have created a number of different learning environments and approaches to education to enable students to successfully access provision and to make learning possible.

What can you study?

We follow the National Curriculum and have a range of options in Key Stage 4. Our facilities are extensive including a professional catering kitchen, sports facilities including tennis courts and swimming pool, expressive arts, including a studio and textiles room. We also offer options including Duke of Edinburgh, animal-based studies and Princes Trust. Study is not limited to the subjects we offer on site, students work toward studying at college with support before finally making the transition to independent study.

The environment

Our school has a number of study environments. All our class sizes are small, with a maximum of six per class in Key Stage 3 and eight in Key Stage 4. Students whom are unable to meet the challenges of a general school structure and require a higher level of support and will be based within our Therapeutic Centre, some of our students are unable to keep themselves safe and therefore will study with our offsite team until they are able to meet the challenges of their daily lives.

After West Heath

We are pleased to say that the majority of our learners have positive and successful outcomes. These may include returning to study in a mainstream environment, gaining full time employment or simply being better placed to meet the personal challenges that had previously been barriers to their becoming active members of society.

The Roaches School

The Roaches School

- Children Aged from 7 to 16
- Trained to support social, emotional and behavioural difficulties
- Based on two sites;
- Lower School - Roach End Farm, nestling in the Peak District
- Upper School - Satis House, located in Biddulph to support boys and girls with complex social difficulties.

Therapeutic Centre

- 24 hour therapeutic placement
- Staff are trained to meet young people's therapeutic needs.
- A member of the Community of Communities
- Young People's needs are identified and guided by qualified Psychotherapists
- Individual key workers are allocated to ensure that your child's needs are being addressed.

Testimonial

"My son has been attending the Roaches School for four years. During this time he has been in full time education where previously he had been excluded from two mainstream schools. His self esteem and confidence were very low and he had attempted suicide at 7 years old and often stated he wished he was dead. Since attending The Roaches his confidence has excelled, his behaviour has improved dramatically and he is much happier within himself. This wouldn't have happened without the Roaches staff who give regular feedback, and offer outstanding support to my son and to us as a family. I would recommend the Roaches School to any family who have a child who requires a lot of extra support with their education and their social/emotional needs and general wellbeing."

The Roaches School has been graded as "Outstanding" by Ofsted since Oct 2010.

Schools and colleges specialising in learning difficulties (including dyslexia/SPLD)

Fairfield Farm College

Fairfield Farm College

(Founded 1976)

43 High Street, Dilton Marsh, Wiltshire
BA13 4DL
Tel: 01373 823028
Email: admissions@ffc.ac.uk
Website: www.ffc.ac.uk
CEO/Principal: Dr Tina Pagett

School type:
Coeducational Day & Residential
Age range of pupils: 16–26
No. of pupils enrolled as at 01/01/2019: 105
Fees per annum as at 01/01/2019:
On application

Set in the village of Dilton Marsh in rural Wiltshire, Fairfield Farm College is a Specialist College for students with SEND. The 26-acre farm site hosts a variety of day, residential and flexible respite breaks and was rated 'Good' by OFSTED and CQC in our last inspections.

Fairfield Farm College provides students with a safe and stimulating learning environment, where they can gain essential skills to support their transition to adulthood. Study programmes are undertaken from the age of 16. Flexible residential programmes are delivered in one of our houses, a few minutes stroll from the College.

The College boasts a variety of well-resourced teaching and vocational learning areas, where students can work in real life environments. On the premises there is a Café, Farm Shop, Post Office, Conference Venue, commercial kitchen, reception area as well as a Café and Animal Park on the outskirts of Trowbridge.

Students follow an externally accredited employability programme, developing skills in Enterprise, Farming, Animal Management, Horse Studies and Horticulture. All students study English, Maths, IT, Sports and Independence Skills through the I-Curriculum. The commercial areas provide work-based learning in our cafés, catering kitchens, retail and customer services areas, as well as external work experiences through our local partnerships with employers.

We pride ourselves on our Advice and Guidance to support transition to adulthood. This is readily available from our Careers Lead, Job Coaches and through our partnerships.

Whilst at the College, students can enjoy their own common room with leisure and IT facilities, a multi-use games area, gym, a variety of extracurricular activities and events as well as our popular Youth Club and Holiday Workshops. We host a variety of student events throughout the year such as the Summer Ball, culminating in a Graduation Ceremony for our leavers.

The College is a Registered Charity and forms part of Fairfield Farm Trust.

I CAN'S Dawn House School

helps children communicate
(Founded 1974)

Helmsley Road, Rainworth, Mansfield, Nottinghamshire NG21 0DQ
Tel: 01623 795361
Fax: 01623 491173
Email: enquiries@dawnhouse-ican.notts.sch.uk
Website: www.dawnhouseschool.org.uk

Principal: Jenny McConnell
School type: Coeducational Day & Residential
Age range of pupils: 5–19
No. of pupils enrolled as at 01/01/2019: 66
Fees per annum as at 01/01/2019: On request

I CAN's Dawn House School is an Outstanding specialist speech, language and communication school for children and young people aged 5-19 years. We are committed to the highest quality education, therapy and care for pupils with a primary need of complex speech and language communication needs (SLCN) and/or Asperger's Syndrome.

At Dawn House School the young people receive the specialist intensive support they need. We cater for many conditions which are commonly associated with communication needs.

Children's individual needs are assessed prior to entry and are met through a holistic, integrated, multidisciplinary approach to the curriculum. For young people who need more specific focused work to develop their speech and language skills, individual or small group sessions are timetabled during the school day.

Children and young people with more complex needs are offered a bespoke, quieter area of school (Chimes) where they receive enhanced support.

Our Occupational Therapy team deliver more focused, intensive work where necessary. Sensory Integration is an integral part of every child's school day and in the residential setting.

Our well-being team, including a child and adolescent psychotherapist, support all young people and their families throughout their time at Dawn House School.

Residential Care at Dawn House School aims to ensure the emotional and physical well-being of our boarding pupils through an extended curriculum. The school can provide opportunities for non-residential young people to benefit from extended days, after-school clubs and overnight stays.

Dawn House has maintained an Outstanding rating from Ofsted when last inspected in February 2018.

Our specialist 6th Form provision is based on the school site and works in close partnership with local schools, colleges and workplaces.

Dawn House School is part of I CAN, the children's communication charity (www.ican.org.uk).

Kisimul School

(Founded 1977)

The Old Vicarage, 61 High Street,
Swinderby, Lincoln, Lincolnshire LN6 9LU
Tel: 01522 868279
Email: admissions@kisimul.co.uk
Website: www.kisimul.co.uk
Director of Education:
Ms Emma Sanderson

School type: Coeducational
Independent Residential Special School
Age range of pupils: 8–19
No. of pupils enrolled as at 01/01/2019: 60
Fees per annum as at 01/01/2019:
On application

Kisimul School is one of the UK's leading independent special schools, offering a homely and safe environment for children and young people who have severe learning difficulties and autism and display behaviours that challenge.

Kisimul School offers day and residential education, alongside care and leisure programmes for up to 52 weeks of the year. The school is registered with the Department for Education and Ofsted for pupils aged 8 to 19 years.

The name Kisimul, pronounced 'kishmul', was taken from Kisimul Castle, which overlooks one of the safest harbours in the British Isles. Like its namesake, Kisimul School offers a safe haven, providing care and protection for its pupils, whilst preparing them for the journey ahead into adulthood.

The original Kisimul School was founded in 1977, in a comfortable Georgian house (known today as the Old Vicarage) set in four acres within the small Lincolnshire village of Swinderby. Facilities at the Old Vicarage include an indoor heated swimming pool, large playground, soft play areas with ball pool and multi-sensory rooms for relaxation and stimulation.

In 2003, the school expanded to an additional site, Acacia Hall, offering the same standard of exceptional care and education, adapted and utilised in a way to reflect the older age group. Acacia Hall offers riding stables, an adventure playground, collection of small farm animals and an area dedicated to horticulture.

Kisimul School opened an additional school, Woodstock House, in Long Ditton, Surrey in April 2008. Again, Woodstock House offers the same quality of care and education for pupils aged 8 to 19 years. Kisimul School has developed this site to

be a mirror image of its existing school operations, using the same teaching methods and ethos.

Kisimul School's mission is to continuously strive for excellence in the care and education of its pupils, with a vision to have the best assisted living environment. The school provides a caring, consistent, safe and supportive environment in which its young people can flourish and develop their skills, in order to fully realise their potential.

Residential and school staff work closely together to enable the pupils to progress in their personal development and learning. The 24-hour approach to the curriculum incorporates a wide range of activities that enrich the learning experiences of all pupils, helping them to learn to communicate and cooperate more effectively with others. In turn, this enables them to grow in confidence, self-esteem and independence.

The highly structured school curriculum aims to address the very specific needs of our pupils, by providing every opportunity for them to enjoy their education and develop their skills, knowledge and understanding.

Classes are small and matched to learning profiles, alongside the dynamics of peers. A high staffing ratio reflects the complex needs of learners.

The curriculum incorporates aspects

of the National Curriculum and an accreditation based vocational learning model for older pupils. An integrated therapeutic approach including; psychology, speech and language, music therapy and occupational therapy is part of the core provision of the school.

A key priority for Kisimul is to develop our children and young people's communication skills. Since many are pre-verbal, we teach the alternative and augmentative systems of Makaton signing and the Picture Exchange Communication System (PECS), alongside vocalisations and speech.

External accreditation is gained through a wide variety of ASDAN 'Towards Independence' programmes and the Duke of Edinburgh's Award Scheme.

Kisimul School works closely with the parents, carers and professionals from its placing authorities to ensure the highest possible standards of care and education. Kisimul School is committed to the view that all people are entitled to equality of opportunity regardless of ability, disability, sex, age, status, religion, belief, nationality, ethnic origins or sexual orientation.

For further information, including exciting job opportunities within Kisimul School, please visit our website at www.kisimul.co.uk or contact us at the address above.

Kisimul School – Woodstock House

(Founded 1977)

Woodstock Lane North, Long Ditton,
Surbiton, Surrey KT6 5HN
Tel: 020 8335 2570
Fax: 020 8335 2571
Email: admissions@kisimul.co.uk
Website: www.kisimul.co.uk

Director of Education:
Ms Emma Sanderson
School type: Coeducational
Independent Residential Special School
Age range of pupils: 8–19
No. of pupils enrolled as at 01/01/2019: 40
Fees per annum as at 01/01/2019:
On application

Kisimul School is one of the UK's leading independent special schools, offering a homely and safe environment for children and young people who have severe learning difficulties and autism and display behaviours that challenge.

Kisimul School offers day and residential education, alongside care and leisure programmes for up to 52 weeks of the year. The school is registered with the Department for Education and Ofsted for pupils aged 8 to 19 years.

The name Kisimul, pronounced 'kishmul', was taken from Kisimul Castle, which overlooks one of the safest harbours in the British Isles. Like its namesake, Kisimul School offers a safe haven, providing care and protection for its pupils, whilst preparing them for the journey ahead into adulthood.

The original Kisimul School was founded in 1977, in a comfortable Georgian house (known today as the Old Vicarage) set in four acres within the small Lincolnshire village of Swinderby. Facilities at the Old Vicarage include an indoor heated swimming pool, large playground, soft play areas with ball pool and multi-sensory rooms for relaxation and stimulation.

In 2003, the school expanded to an additional site, Acacia Hall, offering the same standard of exceptional care and education, adapted and utilised in a way to reflect the older age group. Acacia Hall offers riding stables, an adventure playground, collection of small farm animals and an area dedicated to horticulture.

Woodstock House received its first pupils in April 2008, and again offers the same quality of care and education for pupils aged 8 to 19 years. Kisimul School developed this site to be a mirror image

of its existing school operations, using the same teaching methods and ethos. Woodstock House is situated within eight acres of tranquil countryside, offering space to develop in a safe and secure environment. Woodstock House is within easy access from the M25 via the A3.

Kisimul School's mission is to continuously strive for excellence in the care and education of its pupils, with a vision to have the best assisted living environment. The school provides a caring, consistent, safe and supportive environment in which its young people can flourish and develop their skills, in order to fully realise their potential.

Residential and school staff work closely together to enable the pupils to progress in their personal development and learning. The 24-hour approach to the curriculum incorporates a wide range of activities that enrich the learning experiences of all pupils, helping them to learn to communicate and cooperate more effectively with others. In turn, this enables them to grow in confidence, self-esteem and independence.

The highly structured school curriculum aims to address the very specific needs of our pupils, by providing every opportunity for them to enjoy their education and develop their skills, knowledge and understanding.

Classes are small and matched to learning profiles, alongside the dynamics of peers. A high staffing ratio reflects the complex needs of learners.

The curriculum incorporates aspects of the National Curriculum and an accreditation based vocational learning model for older pupils. An integrated therapeutic approach including; psychology, speech and language, music

therapy and occupational therapy is part of the core provision of the school.

A key priority for Kisimul is to develop our children and young people's communication skills. Since many are pre- verbal, we teach the alternative and augmentative systems of Makaton signing and the Picture Exchange Communication System (PECS), alongside vocalisations and speech.

External accreditation is gained through a wide variety of ASDAN 'Towards Independence' programmes and the Duke of Edinburgh's Award Scheme.

Kisimul School works closely with the parents, carers and professionals from its placing authorities to ensure the highest possible standards of care and education. Kisimul School is committed to the view that all people are entitled to equality of opportunity regardless of ability, disability, sex, age, status, religion, belief, nationality, ethnic origins or sexual orientation.

For further information, including exciting job opportunities within Kisimul School, please visit our website at www. kisimul.co.uk or contact us at the address above.

I CAN's Meath School

helps children communicate

(Founded 1982)

Brox Road, Ottershaw, Surrey KT16 0LF
Tel: 01932 872302
Fax: 01932 875180
Email: meath@meath-ican.org.uk
Website: www.meathschool.org.uk
Headteacher:
Rob Walton B.Ed (Hons) Primary

Appointed: September 2018
School type:
Coeducational Day & Residential
No. of pupils enrolled as at 01/01/2019: 60
Fees per annum as at 01/01/2019:
On request

I CAN's Meath School is a residential (weekly) and day school providing children aged 4-11 years with severe speech and language disorders, including high functioning ASD. Meath School is a unique proactive specialised learning community. The school and care settings have been recognised by Ofsted as continuously 'outstanding' since 2008 and are on the Ofsted Outstanding Providers list. Children with associated difficulties may also benefit from the provision. These include attention control, fine and gross motor coordination problems, mild visual and/or hearing impairments, medical needs and social interaction problems.

Learning and achieving

All pupils are taught within a dynamic broad, balanced and relevant curriculum, based on the National Primary Curriculum (2014) but highly differentiated. Classes are primarily based on pupils' language comprehension levels, also taking account of curriculum attainments, learning and social needs. Class groups are between eight and twelve pupils, across year groups and Key Stages. Each class has a core team of teacher, speech and language therapist and at least one learning support assistant. The speech and language therapy team and occupational therapist department are a critical and integral part of the pupils' education.

Partnership with parents

Meath School staff collaborate closely with parents, sharing successes and helping with any concerns or difficulties at home. The Family Support Worker offers proactive assistance and liaises closely with social care.

The School

Meath School is housed in fine Victorian buildings and the site includes a teaching block, gym, music, art and cookery rooms, ICT suite, small swimming pool, school field, activity play areas and a woodland park with bike track.

Meath School is part of I CAN, the children's communication charity (www.ican.org.uk), and is an integral part of the I CAN Centre in Surrey. The Centre offers holistic multi-disciplinary independent two-day specialist assessment services, training and outreach programmes.

More House School

Tel: 01252 792303
Fax: 01252 797601
Email:
schooloffice@morehouseschool.co.uk
Website: www.morehouseschool.co.uk
Headmaster:
Jonathan Hetherington BA(Hons),
MSc(ed), QTS

(Founded 1939)
Moons Hill, Frensham, Farnham,
Surrey GU10 3AP

School type: Boys' Boarding & Day
Age range of boys: 8–18
No. of pupils enrolled as at 01/01/2019: 470
Fees per term as at 01/01/2019:
Day: £4,524 – £6,341
Weekly Boarding: £8,046 – £9,112
Full Boarding: £8,803 – £9,869

Founded in 1939, More House School is an independent day and boarding school with more than 470 boys on roll, making it the largest specialist school of its type in the country. Many boys travel long distances to attend the school, which is currently used for placements by 30 local authorities.

We are dedicated to helping boys with a range of learning difficulties and styles, who require a small, supportive learning environment in which to flourish.

Our aim is to help each boy who joins us, achieve, in the widest possible sense, more than he, or his parents, ever expected. This is accomplished by knowing a great deal about each student – his strengths as well as his difficulties. For his strengths, he must first be helped to identify them and, eventually, change them into a marketable form. His difficulties will not be static. We are mindful that we must be alert to changes caused by a student's own development, those of society and by the curriculum and make sure that each of our students is equipped to meet them.

The Learning Development Centre (LDC) is a purpose-built area, housed centrally in the school, where all therapy is delivered by fully qualified therapists and specialist tutors. Almost all boys in the school attend lessons weekly for between 2 and 8 half hour sessions, with support continuing through GCSE and A level year where necessary. Attendance in the LDC forms part of each boy's timetable, removing any need to miss lessons.

The work of the Learning Development Centre is fully integrated into school life, with many staff being form tutors and mentors. The pooling of shared expertise within the inclusive staff body of the school – highly qualified Speech and Language Therapists, Occupational Therapists, Literacy Therapists, Numeracy Therapists, Cognitive Behavioural Therapist, Adolescent Psychotherapeutic Counsellor, as well as classroom subject-specialist teachers experienced in supporting pupils with a broad range of learning difficulties.

Our recent Ofsted inspection graded us Outstanding across all areas, and we also look forward to celebrating our 80th anniversary this year. More House School is a transformative experience for the students who attend and also their families, our students' journey's will vary hugely from that of their mainstream peer group, but the end result will be the same. Academic success and a platform with which to move on to the next stage of their lives.

St Joseph's Specialist Trust

(Founded 1950)

Amlets Lane, Cranleigh, Surrey GU6 7DH
Tel: 01483 272449
Email: admissions@
st-josephscranleigh.surrey.sch.uk
Website:
www.st-josephscranleigh.surrey.sch.uk
Principal: Mrs Annie Sutton

Appointed: April 2016
School type:
Coeducational Day & Residential
Age range of pupils: 5–19
No. of pupils enrolled as at 01/01/2019: 65
Fees per annum as at 01/01/2019:
Day: £57,905 *Full Boarding:* £83,898

St Joseph's Specialist Trust is recognised by Ofsted as an "Outstanding" well established day school and Children's Home providing care over 52 weeks of the year for children and young people with special needs from ages 5 to 19 years.

Currently with 73% of students on the Autistic Spectrum we also specialise in a range of complex needs including Speech & Language difficulties, severe learning difficulties, social communication disorders and challenging behaviours. Autism Accredited by the National Autistic Society, St Joseph's is a proven solution for both families and Local Authorities seeking the next step for education, care and therapy.

With Specialisms in Communication Interaction and the Creative Arts, we offer tailor made teaching and learning styles, environment, therapies, and professional standards to meet all the needs of ASD students through personalised learning programmes based on an integrated curriculum, functional communication, visual structure and positive behaviour management. These programmes incorporate a number of methods recognised for working with ASD students: TEACHH, Intensive Interaction, PECS, Social Stories and Makaton signing and symbols. By focusing on learning and behavioural needs, as well as personal preferences, enabling a truly bespoke and personalised approach is taken to ensure success. Information is carefully gathered from a wide range of sources including: the Education Health Care Plan; the diagnosis; developmental history; educational records and assessments; medical records; parents, care staff and observations.

The school is situated close to Cranleigh Village, which retains a great sense of 'community' with a range of amenities including a Leisure Centre, library, shops, cafes, Arts Centre, churches, sports and social clubs. With good transport links to both Horsham and Guildford where more leisure and social facilities including cinemas, theatre and indoor bowling can be found. The school is an active member of the local community and all students are encouraged to take an active part in community life, to maximise their potential and engage with local people.

Strong leadership, teaching, care and therapeutic intervention combine to deliver positive outcomes to meet high expectation and aspirations of both students and families. A calming environment takes into account a wide variety of complex sensory issues and uses a variety of techniques – photographs, symbols and visual clues – children feel comfortable in their surroundings and cope easily with daily routines.

We specifically adapt the curriculum to meet each child's individual needs and focus on the development of personal social and communication along with independent living skills, especially for those aged 16+ years.

By maintaining routines within a structured environment and promoting functional communication we enable students to stay motivated, maximise their potential and work towards positive learning outcomes, whilst seeing a reduction in both anxiety and challenging behaviours.

Therapies

We have our own dedicated team of integrated therapists who work within both class and residential settings to enhance and complement the education and care of all students. Our Director of Therapies co-ordinates and leads a department which includes Speech and Language, Occupational Therapy, Music, Arts, Equine and Drama.

We believe communication underpins successful learning, self-esteem, positive behaviour and opportunities for life. All students are assessed and a therapy programme devised based on their individual needs. To ensure learning is transferred to real life situations, our therapists accompany our children and young people into the community on a regular basis to access local facilities and activities.

Residential Options

Registered as a Children's Home, we provide care, education and therapies for up to 52 weeks a year. We can offer a variety of residential options to meet the needs of Local Authorities, students and families, ranging from weekly boarding to 52 week placements.

We offer an environment where each student is supported and able to develop the skills needed to maximise personal independence. Each residential house is staffed on an individual basis and well equipped to provide a homely atmosphere. Our last Ofsted Inspection rated the Children's home as "Good". By maintaining a waking day curriculum we believe our students benefit greatly from a consistency of approach.

Fully integrated into our community we ensure all our students' skills are transferred and managed in realistic settings and reflects their levels of need. A Speech and Language therapist also regularly visits all the residential groups to ensure consistency across the waking day.

Supported Living

We also provide Supported Living for young people aged 19+. Springvale in Cranleigh and Long Barn in Beare Green offer accommodation for adults with learning difficulties where each young person has their own tenancy and is supported by a tailored individual support package reflecting their own lifestyle choices and activities.

The Loddon School

(Founded 1988)
Wildmoor Lane, Sherfield-on-Loddon, Hook, Hampshire RG27 0JD

Tel: 01256 884600
Fax: 01256 882929
Email: info@loddonschool.co.uk
Website: www.loddonschool.co.uk
Principal: Dr Gill Barrett PhD, MEd, BA(Hons), NPQH, PCGE
Appointed: September 2015

School type: Coeducational Residential Special School and Children's Home
Age range of pupils: 8–19
No. of pupils enrolled as at 01/01/2019: 30
Boys: 26 **Girls:** 4
No. of boarders: 30
Fees per annum as at 01/01/2019:
On request

The Loddon School is a residential special school for children aged 8-19 years with profound autistic spectrum disorders, associated challenging behaviours and severe learning difficulties.

Set in extensive rural grounds, in Sherfield on Loddon, Hampshire. The Loddon School provides a homely,

caring environment for children and young people to learn and thrive in. The Loddon School educates those in their care through a homeschool type model surrounded by a highly integrated multidisciplinary team for 52 weeks a year. All children live in small family groups with their own staff who are responsible for their

care and support programme and their social development.

The Loddon School is a leading pioneer in the world of autistic education. Designing its own outstanding methodology and behavioural approaches (PROACT-SCIPr-UK®) which is used nationally and internationally in both schools and adult care provision. The school operates a truly unique curriculum (PLLUSS®) delivered throughout the waking day incorporating a personalized sensory diet maintaining high levels of engagement with children who have previously failed to thrive in their educational settings.

What makes The Loddon School outstanding?

- Children, most of whom have struggled in other residential special schools, make exceptional progress. They engage with their learning, find new ways to communicate other than through challenging behaviour, grow in confidence and self-esteem. Consequently, they are very well prepared for life beyond school.
- Pupils' personal development is exemplary. Highly knowledgeable, multidisciplinary teams make life-changing differences for pupils.
- Safeguarding practice is outstanding. The protection of children is embedded in practice across the entire team.
- Senior managers show exceptional leadership. They are inspirational, confident and ambitious. Monitoring is excellent.
- Staff have exemplary insight into the abilities of individual pupils. Assessment is outstanding, including the analysis of pupils' behaviours. There is nothing that leaders and staff do not think about or provide for pupils.

Kingston Maurward College

KINGSTON MAURWARD COLLEGE

Dorchester, Dorset DT2 8PY
Tel: 01305 215000
Fax: 01305 215001
Email: fulltimecourses@kmc.ac.uk
Website: www.kmc.ac.uk
Principal: Luke Rake

Appointed: August 2016
School type: Coeducational Day
No. of pupils enrolled as at 01/01/2019: 53
Fees per annum as at 01/01/2019:
On request

Set within the stunning English country estate of Kingston Maurward College in the heart of rural Dorset, our Foundation Studies department boasts a range of study programmes for learners with special educational needs and disabilities. These combine multidisciplinary specialist teaching with Social Enterprise participation. Students will study a variety of vocational subjects including animal care, agriculture, horticulture and conservation as well as employability and personal development, English and mathematics.

The diverse student experience, combining inter-departmental teaching with student participation in the Peakhill Social Enterprise glasshouse, allows learners to gain a wide variety of transferable, practical skills. This promotes progression towards long-term aspirations of employment and community participation and provides learners with opportunities to make choices about their own future.

Our provision not only equips learners with a diverse set of skills to improve their employability prospects, but provides learners with individualised support and essential life skills coaching. This affords learners with a clear sense of direction, autonomy and motivation and awards them a greater sense of self-worth and wellbeing.

Sharing resources with other departments in the College including a working dairy farm, Animal Park and formal Victorian gardens provides learners on study programmes with the opportunity to work with our SEND learners. This has proven to be a great success in terms of raising awareness of learning disabilities and difficulties and promotes inclusive teaching and learning across the entire College estate.

Our provision aims to equip students with the academic, personal and social skills needed to enable them to fully participate in college and community life and prepare them for adulthood.

In addition, there are no fees up until the age of 19, unless students have an Education Health & Care Plan in which case there are no fees up until the age of 25.

Entry requirements are a love for all things outdoors!

Overley Hall School

(Founded 1979)
Overley, Wellington, Telford, West
Midlands TF6 5HE
Tel: 01952 740262
Fax: 01952 740875

Email: info@overleyhall.com
Website: www.overleyhall.com
Headteacher: Mrs Beverley Doran
Appointed: September 2013
School type: Coeducational Residential

Age range of pupils: 8–19
No. of pupils enrolled as at 01/01/2019: 21
Boys: 20 **Girls:** 1
No. of boarders: 21

Overley Hall School is an independent, residential special school and Children's Home, providing therapeutic education and care to children and young adults aged from eight to 19 years who have a wide range of complex needs including autism and severe learning disabilities. The school is committed to offering each child a wide range of good quality experiences; this occurs through partnerships with parents/carers, teachers and therapists in the delivery of a waking day curriculum by a dedicated team.

Our therapy team is comprised of a Speech and Language Therapist, Occupational Therapist, Clinical Psycologist, Learning Coordinator and Therapy Assistants.

The school and residential home is set in a quiet, rural location which provides a calm and nurturing learning and living environment for young people in our care. Our school building, alongside the residential house, stands in 13 acres of lawn, walled kitchen garden and woodland.

Other facilities within the campus and grounds include a lifeskills room, indoor sensory hydropool, soft play space, art and craft workshops, sensory lodge, cinema room, farm shop, recreational and relaxation areas.

Our registered 'Forest School' operates within the woodland areas, and is led by qualified practitioners from Overley Hall School; this offers pupils opportunities for multi-sensory outdoor learning and recreation experiences throughout the seasons.

Overley Hall School also offers day placements for young people who reside locally.

Fullerton House School

Autism | Learning Disabilities | Complex Needs

(Founded 1990)
Tickill Square, Denaby, Doncaster,
South Yorkshire DN12 4AR

Tel: 01709 861663
Email: enquiries@hesleygroup.co.uk
Website: www.fullertonhouseschool.co.uk
General Manager:
Heidi Dugdale-Dawkes
Appointed: 2017
Registered Manager: Deborah Smith

Head of Education: Michael Walsh
School type: Independent Specialist
Residential School
Age range of pupils: 8–19
Fees per annum as at 01/01/2019:
Available on request

A specialist residential school offering flexible education and care, principally as a 52-week service with limited capacity for day placements, for young people aged 8-19, all of whom have complex needs including behaviour that may challenge and a learning disability, often in association with autism.

Fullerton House School is situated in the heart of the village of Denaby Main, near Doncaster. Its central location provides easy access by road, rail or air. Our mission is to enhance the lives of the young people entrusted to us by focusing on their specific needs, capabilities and aspirations.

Education: Each person has a carefully designed Individual Learning Plan based on their EHCP as well as their specific needs in line with the National Curriculum, which supports their positive progress in a range of areas.

Extended learning: During evenings, weekends and school holidays a wide range of extra-curricular activities are on offer to ensure that people are fully engaged with stimulating and meaningful experiences both on and off-site.

Professional services: A dedicated on-site team including carers, teachers, tutors, communication, behaviour and occupational therapy , psychology and other specialists ensure that people have ready access to the services they require.

High-quality accommodation: Single person and small group occupancy of high-quality accommodation is provided at Fullerton House School. Each person has their own bedroom, the majority of which have en-suite bathrooms. We also have a range of on-site facilities to complement and enrich the lives of those who come to live and learn with us.

Keeping in contact: We understand that while we may offer a very positive option for the person, we may not be on your doorstep. Keeping in touch with loved ones is essential. Everyone has a plan to support optimum contact with family/carers and friends whether this be by phone, letter, email or Skype.

Specialist Colleges

Hesley Group

Autism | Learning Disabilities | Complex Needs

(Founded 2013)

Fullerton House College
Tickhill Square, Denaby, Doncaster,
South Yorkshire DN12 4AR
Tel: 01709 861663

Wilsic Hall College
Wadworth, Doncaster,
South Yorkshire, DN11 9AG
Tel: 01302 856382
Email: enquiries@hesleygroup.co.uk
Website: www.hesleygroup.co.uk
General Manager:
Heidi Dugdale-Dawkes
Appointed: 2017

School type: Independent Specialist Residential College
Age range of pupils: 18–25
Fullerton House College Capacity: 12
Wilsic Hall College Capacity: 8
Fees per annum as at 01/01/2019:
On request

Specialist residential colleges offering flexible education care and support for up to 52 weeks per year for young people aged 18-25, who have complex needs including behaviour that may challenge and a learning disability, often in association with autism.

At Wilsic Hall College, everyone lives within a beautiful rural setting with ready community access and at Fullerton House College in the heart of the community, in an urban setting with many local facilities including a sports centre, restaurants and shops.

Mission

We have 2 pathways available for the young people attending college.

Formal Education Pathway with a focus on gaining educational qualifications, skills and experience to move on to employment opportunity and further independence in their lives.

Next Steps Pathway for young people who have completed their formal educational route and are now wishing to build vocational and independence skills for life style experience and development-including social enterprise work.

Both pathways offer accreditation in the skills and qualifications the young people achieve, but the journeys are varied and personalised to the young persons needs and outcomes at this significant life stage.

Education: Everybody has a highly personalised programme of learning, equipping them with skills they will need for adult life.

Extended learning: During evenings, weekends and college holidays a wide range of extra-curricular activities are on offer to ensure people are fully engaged

with stimulating experiences both on and off site providing further, meaningful learning opportunities.

Professional services: A dedicated multi-disciplinary therapeutic team including college tutors, college support workers, consultant clinical psychologist, consultant psychiatrist, applied behaviour analysts, speech and language therapists, occupational therapists, registered manager, care and support staff work together to support each individual's progress.

High quality accommodation: College accommodation includes individualised bedrooms, quality living spaces that promote independence and progressive

skills development assisted by the appropriate use of specialist/adaptive technology. We also have a range of on-site and off-site facilities that offer progressive learning opportunities for young people with a range of needs and wishes.

Keeping in contact: We work to develop relationships between staff and families that are strong, positive and mutually respectful. People are supported to be in contact with their friends and family; we welcome visits to the colleges at any time. Everyone has a plan that will include the best means for them to maintain this contact whether by 'phone, letter, email or Skype.

Wilsic Hall School

Autism | Learning Disabilities | Complex Needs

(Founded 1996)
Wadworth, Doncaster,
South Yorkshire DN11 9AG

Tel: 01302 856382
Email: enquiries@hesleygroup.co.uk
Website: www.wilsichallschool.co.uk
Head: Geoff Turner
Appointed: 2008
School type:
Independent Specialist Residential School

Age range of pupils: 11–19
Capacity as at 01/01/2019: 32
Fees per annum as at 01/01/2019:
Available on request

A specialist residential school offering flexible education and care, principally as a 52-week service with limited capacity for day placements, for young people aged 11-19, all of whom have complex needs including behaviour that may challenge and a learning disability, often in association with autism.

Wilsic Hall School is situated in its own 14-acre site approximately five miles south of Doncaster. Its central location provides easy access by road, rail or air. Our mission is to enhance the lives of the people entrusted to us by focusing on their specific needs, capabilities and aspirations.

Education: Each person has a carefully designed Individual Education Plan based on their specific needs in line with the National Curriculum, which supports their positive progress in a range of areas.

Extended learning: During evenings, weekends and school holidays a wide range of extra-curricular activities are on offer to ensure that people are fully engaged with stimulating and meaningful experiences both on and off-site.

Professional services: A dedicated team including carers, teachers, tutors, behaviour, communication and occupational therapy, psychology and other specialists ensure that each person has ready access to the services they require.

High-quality accommodation: Single person and small group occupancy of high-quality accommodation is provided at Wilsic Hall School. Each person has their own bedroom, the majority of which have en-suite bathrooms. We also have a range of on-site facilities to complement and enrich the lives of those who come to live and learn with us.

Keeping in contact: We understand that while we may offer a very positive option for the person, we may not be on your doorstep. Keeping in touch with loved ones is essential. Everyone has a plan to support optimum contact with family/carers and friends whether this be by phone, letter, email or Skype.

Schools and colleges specialising in sensory or physical impairment

National Star College

National Star
Realising the aspirations
of people with disabilities

Ullenwood Manor Road, Ullenwood,
Cheltenham, Gloucestershire GL53 9QU
Tel: 01242 527631
Email: admissions@nationalstar.org
Website: www.nationalstar.org

Principal: Pauline Bayliss-Jones
School type:
Coeducational Day & Residential
Age range of pupils: 16–25
No. of pupils enrolled as at 01/01/2019: 242

Young people with complex disabilities and learning difficulties are at the heart of everything we do – that's why we were named Specialist Provider of the Year at the TES Awards 2019. Judges said: *'National Star are swimming against the tide by sticking to what they do best – and doing it better than the rest.'*

We work with more than 70 different local authorities and support students with a range of needs.

Personalised learning

We offer programmes of learning that are tailored to meet the needs of individual students, preparing them to live more independently and learn new skills. Our commitment to excellence was recognised as Ofsted 'Outstanding' in 2018. For some students learning to make choices and work with others will be what matters, whilst others may wish to develop work skills in real, practical environments.

Learning opportunities are highly flexible and tailored to meet the needs of individual students; this is why 95% of National Star leavers achieved their primary learning goals in 2017-2018. We're proud that last year 44% of National Star leavers progressed to live outside the family home.

Our locations

With campuses in South Wales, Hereford-shire and Gloucestershire we support day and residential students to achieve their aspirations. Our facilities include an aquatic therapy pool, sensory suites, dance studio, theatre, sports facilities, swimming pool and adapted gym.

Our accommodation

We have a number of residences on our main Ullenwood campus and at the heart of local communities in Cheltenham and Gloucester. Each residence offers a different experience. Some have large communal living spaces and kitchens ideal for shared living. Others have flats to prepare students for living on their own or with friends.

The Care Quality Commission rated our residential accommodation at Ullenwood and Elizabeth House in Gloucester as 'Outstanding' in all areas.

Life after college

From day one we work with students to put together a plan for life after college. We offer a range of work-based programmes to ensure the best long-term job outcomes. Recent alumni have gained jobs in financial services, hospitality and the creative arts.

The Pace Centre

Specialist education and therapy
for children with motor disorders

(Founded 1990)

Coventon Road, Aylesbury,
Buckinghamshire HP19 9JL
Tel: 01296 392739
Fax: 01296 334836
Email: info@thepacecentre.org
Website: www.thepacecentre.org

Head Teacher: Mrs Claire Smart
Appointed: September 2016
School type: Independent Special School
Age range of pupils: 3–16
Fees per annum as at 01/01/2019:
Available on request

Pace is a family centred school that specialises in educating children with Cerebral Palsy and related disorders. Pace provides an innovative education tailored to the child or young person's individual abilities that is centred around pertinent and personalised academic and functional goals. Due to the complex nature of many Pace children and young people, Pace also has an onsite nursing team.

Our unique Pace approach brings together input from paediatric occupational therapists, physiotherapists, speech and language therapists, conductive educationalists and teachers. This breadth of expertise means the "whole child" remains at the centre of their education. At Pace we believe in every child's ability to achieve and progress, and it is our job to ensure that the children and young people at Pace have the right skills to do just that.

A bespoke curriculum is developed for each individual, at a 'just right level' to ensure they are challenged and make progress functionally and academically. The Pace Integrated Curriculum is broad, deep and rich, and the range of methodology in the Pace toolkit for delivery adds real value to the individual learning experience. This is evident in the children's progress both academically and in relation to social, physical, communication, and functional independence skills.

Pace School is a positive and nurturing environment that empowers pupils to demonstrate knowledge, access and engage in their education, however they communicate. We celebrate success with the children, their class and with you. We use recognised achievement as a powerful motivational tool, further empowering the individual learner in their personal journey towards achieving their goals.

Early Years Foundation Stage

We offer an Early Years Foundation Stage (EYFS) provision for children aged 2-5 where early therapeutic intervention is combined with the EYFS Curriculum, to provide a unique approach for EYFS children with sensory motor challenges. Focusing on the development of fundamental skills the children need to access and engage with their education in this critical early window of development.

Primary School

Our school groups cater for a range of both physical and cognitive abilities from very complex challenges relating to their sensory motor challenges, to children who have mild to moderate physical difficulties. Pace caters for children and young people with a full range of learning abilities, ranging from a pre-formal level for those with learning difficulties to those individuals who are accessing the curriculum at or near an age appropriate level.

Secondary School

In Key Stages three and four, the integrated curriculum focus shifts to prioritise functional and life skills to help prepare these young people for their future lives as adults in the community. Regular opportunities to develop and apply their problem solving and academic skills are offered throughout the week, for example through purposeful trips to the supermarket followed by cooking activities, which have been carefully planned to work on gross/fine motor and mathematical skills.

When asked in a recent survey, 100% of Pace parents who took part reported that they would recommend Pace to other parents. One said *"Yes – wholeheartedly, without question. Without a doubt. We love you all. G loves you all and feels safe & happy at school. We feel G is pushed to his full potential and encouraged to achieve above and beyond."*

If you would like to organise a tour of Pace Primary or Secondary or would like to speak to one our team, please call 01269 392739 or visit thepacecentre.org/pace-school.

RNIB College Loughborough

RNIB

College
Loughborough

(Founded 1989)
Radmoor Road, Loughborough,
Leicestershire LE11 3BS
Tel: 01509 611077
Fax: 01509 232013
Email: enquiries@rnibcollege.ac.uk

Website: www.rnibcollege.ac.uk
Principal: June Murray
School type: Coeducational College and
residence
Age range of pupils: 16–65
No. of pupils enrolled as at 01/01/2019: 108

We are a friendly residential college supporting young people and adults with vision impairment and additional disabilities to achieve their goals. Our programmes are designed to develop independence skills for involvement in community life.

Education and skills

Choose us for your Further Education and you'll learn practical skills and gain work experience within our enterprises – our Café, eBay business, Media Hub, Arts Centre, Shop and Office. You could also choose a course at our partner mainstream college located next door.

If you are a young adult wanting to gain the skills and confidence to progress into independent or supported living, you may want to apply for a package of regular overnight stays or short breaks. Join us on a Supported Internship, a work-related programme. On an Internship you will spend time with an employer alongside developing your literacy, numeracy and employability skills.

Also on offer is Flexible Futures, our daytime activities programme. You could spend time in each of our different enterprises, providing a vital role in these real businesses and being part of college life. You could also go out and enjoy the local community.

Accommodation

Our Stan Bell Centre offers modern, purpose built, safe accommodation. Learners are encouraged to be as independent as possible; however we recognise that some people will always need a little more support.

Needs we support

- Vision impairment
- Learning difficulties and disabilities
- Autistic Spectrum Conditions
- Physical disabilities
- Communication difficulties
- Mild hearing problems
- Additional healthcare needs, such as epilepsy
- Additional emotional and behavioural difficulties

Wider services

RNIB offers a wide range of other services for children, young people, their families and the professionals who work with them. Find out more at www.rnib.org.uk/children

Visit us!

The best way to find out more about our college is to come and have a look round. Call us today to arrange your visit!

RNIB Sunshine House School

R N I B

Sunshine
House School

33 Dene Road, Northwood, Middlesex
HA6 2DD
Tel: 01923 822538
Fax: 01923 826227
Email: sunshinehouse@rnib.org.uk

Website: www.rnib.org.uk/sunshinehouse
Head: Jackie Seaman and Mark Fuel
School type: Coeducational
Age range of pupils: 2–14

At RNIB Sunshine House School we offer specialist support to blind and partially sighted children with significant learning difficulties and disabilities and their families.

With a range of specialist indoor and outdoor facilities, we provide a safe and supportive environment for children to meet their full potential.

We're part of a family of five local special schools with The Eden Academy, working together to offer your child access to an enhanced range of expertise, activities and resources.

Education and Curriculum
Everyone at Sunshine House is treated as an individual with their own specific needs and learning goals. Working together with parents and specialists we ensure that achievements go beyond the classroom into everyday life.

Our specialist school educates children and young people from two to 14 years who have a range of physical, learning and sensory needs. Children follow an individually tailored curriculum supporting their special education needs. Most children are working between P levels 1 and 8. Each class has no more than eight children with a minimum support ratio of two adults for every three children.

Therapies and Healthcare
Our team of in-house therapists combine their work with a child's learning, making therapies a part of everyday school life. We also have a paediatric community nurse who ensures that all health needs are met.

Family services
You can get to know other parents and children and have fun through our thriving family services. Activities include after-school and holiday clubs, family events, sibling support groups, networking and advice for parents.

Needs we support
- Vision impairment
- Multi-sensory impairment and deafblindness
- Significant learning difficulties and disabilities
- Physical disabilities
- Communication difficulties
- Additional medical and health needs, including long-term ventilation or life-threatening or life-limiting conditions

Wider services
RNIB offers a wide range of other services for children, young people, their families and the professionals who work with them. Find out more at www.rnib.org.uk/children
Visit us!
The best way to find out more about our school is to come and have a look round. Call us today to arrange your visit!

Chailey Heritage School

(Founded 1903)

Haywards Heath Road, North Chailey, Lewes, East Sussex BN8 4EF
Tel: 01825 724444
Fax: 01825 723773
Email: office@chf.org.uk
Website: www.chf.org.uk
Charity Chief Executive: Helen Hewitt
Headteacher: Simon Yates

Director of Social Care: Denise Banks
School type:
Coeducational Boarding & Day
Age range of pupils: 3–19
No. of pupils enrolled as at 01/01/2019: 95
Fees per annum as at 01/01/2019:
Please contact the school for details

Chailey Heritage School, part of Chailey Heritage Foundation, is a non-maintained special school for children and young people aged 3-19 with complex physical disabilities and health needs. Chailey Heritage School was judged to be 'Outstanding' by Ofsted in October 2014 for a third consecutive time. Chailey Heritage Residential is a registered children's home and offers flexible care packages from short breaks to 52 weeks of the year.

Meeting Children's Health and Therapy Needs

Chailey Heritage School has a unique on-site partnership with Chailey Clinical Services, part of Sussex Community NHS Foundation Trust. The pupils' health and therapy needs are met by a highly skilled team that includes Paediatric Medical Consultants and Doctors, Therapists, residential Nursing team and Rehabilitation Engineers, as well as our expert teachers.

Purposeful Learning

Chailey Heritage School has developed its own curriculum driven by the individual learner's needs, skills and desired outcomes. It is meaningful to each child and their family as it covers all aspects of their development and it weighs up the input that is needed specifically for them.

Support for Parents and Families at Every Step

We work with parents and families at each point of their Chailey Heritage Foundation journey by providing support at difficult times whilst also celebrating achievements together.

Chailey Heritage Residential

Chailey Heritage Residential is a nationally recognised, registered children's home for 3 to 19 year olds with complex physical disabilities and health needs. We offer flexible residential provision ranging from short breaks to 52 weeks a year.

Find Out More

We would be delighted to show you around our site. Please get in touch to arrange a visit.

Chailey Heritage School and Chailey Heritage Residential are part of Chailey Heritage Foundation, registered charity number 1075837, registered in England as a charitable company limited by guarantee No. 3769775

The Children's Trust School
Non-Maintained Special School

The
Children's Trust
School

(Founded 1985)

Tadworth Court, Tadworth,
Surrey KT20 5RU
Tel: 01737 365810
Fax: 01737 365819
Email: school@thechildrenstrust.org.uk
Website: www.thechildrenstrust.org.uk/
the-childrens-trust-school

Head Teacher: Samantha Newton
School type:
Day and Residential to 52 weeks
Age range of pupils: 2–19
No. of pupils enrolled as at 01/01/2019: 44
Fees per annum as at 01/01/2019:
On application

At The Children's Trust School our aim is to provide high quality education and expertise to meet each pupil's individual special educational needs and to celebrate all achievements in a happy, secure environment.

As a non-maintained special school for 2-19 year olds, we pride ourselves on seeing the 'whole' child and delivering education, health and care for children and young people with complex needs in an integrated and holistic approach.

Through day and residential placements (of up to 52 weeks) we focus on personalised planning supporting pupils to improve and develop understanding of the world around them and their functional skills.

We have a skilled team of teachers, classroom and care support staff and nursing and medical staff. We also have an extensive team of therapists, ranging from occupational, physio and speech and language to play, leisure and music therapists. We also offer education, care and therapy to children from the age of three. Our early years pupils are offered age-appropriate education and activities based on our specially-developed curriculum. Taddies is a weekly run parent and child group for children aged 0-5 years old who have additional needs.

Our curriculum focuses on communication, language and literacy, fine and gross motor physical skills, environmental control technology, social, emotional and personal wellbeing and cognitive development.

We provide stimulating educational opportunities, supported by unparalleled expertise delivering significant outcomes for our pupils.

Treloar School

(Founded 1908)

Holybourne, Alton, Hampshire GU34 4GL
Tel: 01420 547400
Email: admissions@treloar.org.uk
Website: www.treloar.org.uk
Principal: Martin Ingram
School type:
Coeducational Boarding & Day

Religious Denomination: Non-denominational
Age range of pupils: 2–19
No. of pupils enrolled as at 01/01/2019: 81
Boys: 40 **Girls:** 41 **Sixth Form:** 21
No. of boarders: 37
Fees per annum as at 01/01/2019:
As per assessment

Treloar Nursery and School provide outstanding education, care, therapy and independence training to children and young people from 2 to 19 years of age with complex physical disabilities. Provision is both day and residential and students come from across the UK. Our educational and residential School provision were rated Outstanding by Ofsted in 2018 and 2019 respectively. Our College, based on the same site, offers continued education and care up to the age of 25 and was similarly rated Outstanding by Ofsted in 2017. At Treloar's we prepare students for life after they leave and equip them with the confidence, the independence skills and, where applicable, qualifications they require.

Students have access to an on-site health centre, occupational as well as speech and language and physio therapists. There are also visual impairment and assistive technology specialists plus dieticians and counsellors on-site. Therapy is integrated into the school day to maximise opportunities for learning. Our transition team work with each student from assessment through to their expected destination to help them reach their goals and aspirations.

Entry Requirement

Admission is considered on the basis of each student's needs following discussion and assessment with education, medical, therapy and care staff. Each student's programme is constructed to ensure we meet their individual needs. Part-time placements, limited time placements and respite for day students are all available.

Life on Campus

Treloar's is situated in beautiful East Hampshire on the edge of Alton with a good road and rail network. We ensure a varied range of extra-curricular activities including sports, art, drama, clubs and visits off-site utilising our own specialist fleet of vehicles. On-site facilities include a swimming pool, all weather sports facilities, a hydrotherapy pool, a Rebound Therapy room and a social club.

Treloar Trust is a registered charity which supports Treloar School and College (Charity No 1092857).

New College Worcester
A residential college for blind and partially sighted children and young people aged 11-19

(Founded 1866)

Whittington Road, Worcester,
Worcestershire WR5 2JX
Tel: 01905 763933
Email: office@ncw.co.uk
Website: www.ncw.co.uk

Principal: Miss Nicki Ross
School type:
Coeducational Residential Special
Age range of pupils: 11–19
No. of pupils enrolled as at 01/01/2019: 80

New College Worcester

New College Worcester is a national residential school for young people aged 11 to 19, who are blind or vision impaired. We are delighted to be working with the Kidderminster Harriers – the students have loved visiting the ground, meeting the players and finding out more. We are looking forward to getting more involved with the club over the coming months!

About NCW

Every student has a tailored programme, carefully planned and delivered to meet their individual needs in three key areas; academic achievement, independent living skills and involvement in extracurricular activities at the College and in the community. The National curriculum timetable is interspersed with additional curriculum lessons in mobility, Braille, access technology and independent living skills.

The opportunities provided to students in these three areas of provision play a crucial role in the development of confidence and self-esteem and preparation for life beyond our College.

Learner Outcomes

At NCW we are working towards eight key learner outcomes which will underpin an individual's successful transition into further education, work and becoming an independent and fulfilled member of their community.

These eight learner outcomes are:
* Independence and negotiation skills
* Life after college
* Meeting others
* Participation
* Getting Around
* Learning to Access
* Use of equipment
* Self care

Having links to organisations like the Kidderminster Harriers helps NCW students work towards many of these goals.

"I'm really happy and I have lots of friends...what I'm going through at the moment is just brilliant" Max, Current Year 12 student

St John's Catholic School for the Deaf

St John's
Catholic School for the Deaf
Boston Spa, Yorkshire

(Founded 1870)
Church Street, Boston Spa, Wetherby,
West Yorkshire LS23 6DF

Tel: 01937 842144
Fax: 01937 541471
Email: info@stjohns.org.uk
Website: www.stjohns.org.uk
Headteacher:
Mrs A Bradbury BA(Hons), MSc, NPQH

School type:
Coeducational Boarding & Day
Age range of pupils: 4–19
Fees per annum as at 01/01/2019:
On application

Special needs catered for

St John's Catholic School is a centre of excellence for sensory and communication needs for pupils aged 4-19. It is a school where spoken language is used, and where every young person communicates equally and successfully with others. We encourage and nurture ambition, self-esteem and confidence in all pupils.

The school offers a broad and balanced curriculum offering the opportunity to take GCSEs, entry level qualifications and a wide range of vocational courses. There is a specialist unit for pupils with very complex needs, including multi-

sensory impairment and autism. Older pupils attend the well-established sixth form, where courses are hosted in local FE colleges and pupils are supported by qualified and experienced learning mentors. We accept day and weekly boarding pupils, and welcome pupils of all faiths and denominations.

Specialist facilities

All pupils are taught by teachers with additional qualifications in deafness or multi-sensory impairments. The school classrooms are acoustically treated and benefit from Soundfield technology. There is a resident audiologist and health and medical needs are coordinated

by the school nurse and supported by a programme of personal, social and health education. There are strong links with the local child and adolescent mental health team who specialise in working with deaf young people.

We have a team of highly specialised speech and language therapists who deliver both individual and group therapy sessions to all pupils. The therapists work with staff across the whole school and maintain close contact with parents, so everyone is clear how to maximise pupils' progress.

Primary

Teaching is tailored to pupils' individual needs by specialist teachers and a broad and imaginative curriculum inspires creative and enthusiastic learners. Indoor and outdoor zones provide a vibrant learning environment, and there are sensory and soft play rooms for sensory integration. Primary pupils enjoy regular integration and social opportunities at neighbouring schools and take part in an extensive programme of enrichment activities.

Secondary

There is a high level of personalisation in the curriculum for secondary pupils – more than sixteen subjects can be studied at different levels, from entry level to GCSEs and their equivalent. The development of literacy and numeracy is a key priority, and this is achieved through intensive specialist teaching in small classes. As well as traditional academic subjects, our curriculum provides a strong focus on creative and practical subjects that develop social communication and other essential skills for future adult life.

Sixth form

The sixth form offers our students the opportunity to study a wide range of

academic and vocational courses linked to two local colleges. Students have full time support from learning mentors who are all trained to support the communication needs of deaf people. Linking with mainstream colleges helps students build wider friendship groups and offers new social opportunities.

The sixth form residential setting provides a full life-skills programme which is accessible for young people with a range of additional needs such as visual impairments. By the end of their time at St John's, students have well-developed independence skills for adult life.

Multi-sensory impairment

There is a small specialist unit for pupils who have more complex needs, including multi-sensory impairment (MSI) and autism. These young people are supported by expert staff, and learning concentrates on presenting meaningful experiences that avoid sensory overload. Communication systems are built around the child's preferences, including PECs (Picture Exchange Communication system), Makaton, hand over hand signing and computer aided systems.

Boarding facilities

The residential areas are homely and welcoming. Young people who board live in small family units and are looked after by an experienced and knowledgeable

staff team, who help them to form positive relationships and develop negotiation and co-operation skills. There is a full programme of leisure activities, and children have the opportunity to participate in local clubs and sports societies. The school offers weekly or flexi-boarding, and all students go home every weekend. In 2018 our residential care was rated as 'Outstanding' by Ofsted.

Home school links

Very close links with families are maintained, with regular updates on progress and achievements. Parents are welcome to visit the school, and are kept up to date with activities by the half termly newsletter.

General environment

The school is within walking distance of the elegant and vibrant Georgian village of Boston Spa, where there are shops, cafés and parks. The extensive buildings are well-equipped and include a gym with specialist fitness equipment, a purpose built theatre and sound recording room, a fully stocked library, an IT suite and a number of sensory rooms. The grounds are perfect for sports and leisure activities, with marked pitches and a newly-developed sensory garden.

The Royal Blind School

ROYAL BLIND
THE ROYAL BLIND SCHOOL

(Founded 1835)

43 Canaan Lane, Edinburgh, EH10 4SG

Tel: 0131 446 3120

Fax: 0131 447 9266

Email: office@royalblindschool.org.uk

Website: www.royalblind.org/education

Head Teacher: Elaine Brackenridge (BEd)

School type: Coeducational, National Grant Aided Special School

Age range of pupils: 5–19

Fees per annum as at 01/01/2019:

Available on request

The Royal Blind School is run by Scotland's largest vision impairment charity, Royal Blind, and is regulated by Education Scotland and the Care Inspectorate. We are a grant-aided special school supported by the Scottish Government. The school, situated in Morningside, Edinburgh, is Scotland's only residential school specialising in the care and education of children and young people with vision impairment, including those with complex needs.

Places are paid for through fees from local authorities or privately. We offer 52-week residential or term-time boarding, as well as nightly and weekly boarding. Our residential houses are fully accessible and designed to be a home from home. We enrol pupils from P1 to S6 and in addition, there is a free pre-school playgroup held

on Friday mornings during term-time.

The Royal Blind School has a high ratio of staff to pupils and we offer a full curriculum of subjects. Each child follows an individualised education programme underpinned by the Curriculum for Excellence and Getting it Right for Every Child (GIRFEC). We deliver a broad general education and offer qualifications and accreditation by the Scottish Qualifications Authority (SQA), Junior Awards Scheme Scotland, Personal Achievement Awards and ASDAN in the senior phase.

Our approach is inclusive and pupil-centred, providing many opportunities for experience and achievement. We strive to make learning fun, challenging and self-affirming.

We deliver independent living skills, building self-confidence and self-esteem by providing a greater awareness of the wider environment through mobility and orientation to ensure that all pupils become as independent as possible.

Pupils in fourth, fifth and sixth year have the opportunity to take part in work experience. Some pupils are involved in a Coffee Shop Enterprise Project. This activity gives young people the opportunity to develop a valuable range of life skills such as social interaction, handling money, planning, shopping and baking.

Outreach Support

We also provide an education outreach service offering support, training, resources and advice to staff in mainstream schools who are working with blind and partially sighted pupils through our Learning Hub, www.royalblind.org/learninghub.

For more information please visit our website www.royalblind.org/education or telephone 0131 446 3120, or email office@ royalblindschool.org.uk. *Scottish Charity No. SC 017167.*

Directory

Schools and colleges specialising in social interaction difficulties (Autism, ASC & ASP)

Abbreviations

ACLD	Autism, Communication and Associated Learning Difficulties
ADD	Attention Deficit Disorder
ADHD	Attention Deficit and Hyperactive Disorder (Hyperkinetic Disorder)
ASC	Autistic Spectrum Conditions
ASP	Asperger Syndrome
AUT	Autism
BESD	Behavioural, Emotional and Social Difficulties
CCD	Complex Communication Difficulties
CLD	Complex Learning Difficulties
CP	Cerebral Palsy
D	Deaf
DEL	Delicate
DYS	Dyslexia
DYSP	Dyspraxia
EBD	Emotional and Behavioural Difficulties
EBSD	Emotional, Behavioural and/ or Social Difficulties
EPI	Epilepsy
GLD	General Learning Difficulties
HA	High Ability
HI	Hearing Impairment
HS	Hospital School
LD	Learning Difficulties
MLD	Moderate Learning Difficulties
MSI	Multi-sensory Impairment
OCD	Obsessive Compulsive Disorder
PD	Physical Difficulties
PH	Physical Impairment
Phe	Partially Hearing
PMLD	Profound and Multiple Learning Difficulties
PNI	Physical Neurological Impairment
PRU	Pupil Referral Unit
SCD	Social and Communication Difficulties
SCLD	Severe and Complex Learning Difficulties
SEMH	Social, Emotional & Mental Health Difficulties
SEBN	Social, Emotional and Behavioural Needs
SLD	Severe Learning Difficulties
SLI	Specific Language Impairment
SPLD	Specific Learning Difficulties
SP&LD	Speech and Language Difficulties
SLCN	Speech Language & Communication Needs
VIS	Visually Impaired

Key to Symbols

Type of school:

- Boys' school
- Girls' school
- International school

School offers:

- (A) A levels
- Residential
- (16+) Entrance at 16+
- Vocational qualifications
- Learning support

- (✓) This is a DfE approved independent or non-maintained school under section 41 of the Children and Families Act 2014 or section 342 of the 1996 Education Act

Please note: Unless otherwise indicated, all schools are coeducational day schools. Single-sex and boarding schools will be indicated by the relevant icon.

England – Central & West

Bath & North-East Somerset

Rookery Radstock
Wells Road, Radstock, Bath, Bath & North-East Somerset BA3 3RS
Tel: 01761 438611
Age range: 18–25
No. of pupils: 27
Special needs catered for: ASC, ASP
16 🏛

Bristol

Aurora Hedgeway School
Rookery Lane, Pilning, Bristol BS35 4JN
Tel: 01454 632532
Age range: 7–19
Special needs catered for: ASC, ASP, AUT, LD, SCD
🏛 16

Buckinghamshire

Cambian Bletchley Park School
Whaddon Way, Bletchley, Milton Keynes, Buckinghamshire MK3 7EB
Tel: 01908 048380
Age range: 7–19
No. of pupils: 60
Special needs catered for: ASC, ASP, AUT, BESD, EBD, SCD
16

Gloucestershire

The Peak Academy
Drake Lane, Dursley, Gloucestershire GL11 5HD
Tel: 01453 542130
Age range: 11–16
Special needs catered for: SEMH

Oxfordshire

LVS OXFORD
For further details see p. 68
Spring Hill Road, Begbroke, Oxfordshire OX5 1RX
Tel: 01865 595170
Email: enquiries@lvs-oxford.org.uk
Website: www.lvs-oxford.org.uk
Head Teacher: Mrs Louisa Allison-Bergin
Age range: 11–19
No. of pupils: 68
Special needs catered for: ASC, ASP, AUT
16

SWALCLIFFE PARK SCHOOL
For further details see p. 66
Swalcliffe, Banbury, Oxfordshire OX15 5EP
Tel: 01295 780302
Email: rpiner@swalcliffepark.co.uk
Website: www.swalcliffepark.co.uk
Principal: Mr Rob Piner
Age range: B10–19
No. of pupils: 55
Special needs catered for: ADHD, ASC, BESD, DYS, DYSP, MLD, SP&LD
👦 🏛 16 ✔

West Berkshire

PRIOR'S COURT SCHOOL
For further details see p. 64
Hermitage, Thatcham, West Berkshire RG18 9NU
Tel: 01635 247202/245914
Email: mail@priorscourt.org.uk
Website: www.priorscourt.org.uk
Director of Education and Learning: Sue Piper
Age range: 5–19
No. of pupils: 65 VIth22
Special needs catered for: ASC, AUT, CLD, EPI, MLD, SCLD
🏛 ✔

Wiltshire

Farleigh Further Education College Swindon
Fairview House, 43 Bath Road, Old Town, Swindon, Wiltshire SN1 4AS
Tel: 01793 719500
Age range: 16–25
No. of pupils: 63
Special needs catered for: ASP, LD
16 🏛

Stratford Lodge
4 Park Lane, Castle Road, Salisbury, Wiltshire SP1 3NP
Tel: 01722 421504
Age range: 16–19
No. of pupils: 9
Special needs catered for: ADHD, ASC, ASP
🏛 16

East

Cambridgeshire

Gretton School
Manor Farm Road, Girton, Cambridge, Cambridgeshire CB3 0RX
Tel: 01223 277438
Age range: 5–19
No. of pupils: 100 VIth12
Special needs catered for: ASC, ASP, AUT
Ⓐ 🏛 16 ✔

On Track Education Centre, Wisbech
Enterprise House, Old Field Lane, Wisbech, Cambridgeshire PE13 2RJ
Tel: 01945 580898
Age range: 11–19
No. of pupils: 32
Special needs catered for: ASC, MLD, SCLD, SEMH, SPLD
16

Park House
Wisbech Road, Thorney, Peterborough, Cambridgeshire PE6 0SA
Tel: 01733 271187
Age range: 4–16
Special needs catered for: AUT
✔

The Beeches Independent School
218 Dogsthorpe Road, Peterborough, Cambridgeshire PE1 3PB
Tel: 01733 344448
Age range: G10–18
Special needs catered for: AUT
16

Essex

NAS ANDERSON SCHOOL
For further details see p. 69
Luxborough Lane, Chigwell, Essex IG7 5AB
Email: theandersonschool@nas.org.uk
Website: www.autism.org.uk/andersonschool
Principal: Gary Simm
Age range: 11–19
No. of pupils: 78
Special needs catered for: ASC, ASP, AUT
🏛 16

The Yellow House School
1 Alderford Street, Sible Hedingham, Halstead, Essex CO9 3HX
Tel: 01787 462504
Age range: 13–17
No. of pupils: 11
Special needs catered for: ADHD, ASP, EBD
✔

Hertfordshire

NAS RADLETT LODGE SCHOOL
For further details see p. 70
Harper Lane, Radlett, Hertfordshire WD7 9HW
Tel: 01923 854922
Email: radlett.lodge@nas.org.uk
Website: www.autism.org.uk/radlettlodge
Principal: Jeremy Keeble
Age range: 4–19
No. of pupils: 55
Special needs catered for: ASC, ASP, AUT
🏛 16 ✔

Norfolk

Acorn Park School
Andrew's Furlong, Mill
Road, Banham, Norwich,
Norfolk NR16 2HU
Tel: 01953 888 656
Age range: 6–19
Special needs catered for:
ASC, AUT, SCD
🏛 16

Aurora Eccles School
Quidenham, Norwich,
Norfolk NR16 2NZ
Tel: 01953 887217
Age range: 5–19
Special needs catered for: ASC,
ASP, AUT, DYS, LD, MLD, SCD
🏛 16

East Midlands

Derbyshire

High Grange School
Hospital Lane, Mickleover,
Derby, Derbyshire DE3 0DR
Tel: 01332 412777
Age range: 8–19
Special needs catered for:
ADHD, ASC, ASP, AUT
Ⓐ 16 ✔

Leicestershire

Dovetree School
Ferness Road, Hinckley,
Leicestershire LE10 0TB
Tel: 01455 243918
Age range: 8–18
Special needs catered for:
ADHD, ASC, ASP, SEMH
16

Sketchley School and Forest House
Manor Way, Sketchley, Burbage,
Leicestershire LE10 3HT
Tel: 01455 890 023
Age range: 8–19
No. of pupils: 30
Special needs catered for:
ASC, ASP, AUT
16 ✔

Lincolnshire

Doulton House School
Main Street, Anwick, Sleaford,
Lincolnshire NG34 9SJ
Tel: 01526 831055
Age range: 11–18
No. of pupils: 8
Fees: Day £60,000
Special needs catered for: BESD
16

South Park Enterprise College
Newdown Court, Newdown
Road, South Park Industrial Estate,
Scunthorpe, Lincolnshire DN17 2TX
Tel: 01724 291509
Age range: 11–16
No. of pupils: 70
Special needs catered for:
ADHD, DYS, DYSP

Northamptonshire

Cambian Potterspury Lodge School
Towcester, Northamptonshire
NN12 7LL
Tel: 01908 542912
Age range: B8–18
No. of pupils: 70
Special needs catered for: ASC,
ASP, AUT, CLD, DYS, DYSP, SCD
🚹 🏛 16

Hill Farm College
c/o The Manor House,
Squires Hill, Rothwell,
Northamptonshire NN14 6BQ
Tel: 01536 711111
Age range: 14–19
No. of pupils: 12
Special needs catered for:
ADHD, ASC, ASP
🏛 16

On Track Education Centre, Northampton
Unit 6 Quarry Park Close, Moulton
Park Industrial Estate, Northampton,
Northamptonshire NN3 6QB
Tel: 01604 645934
Age range: 11–19
No. of pupils: 32
Special needs catered for:
ASC, MLD, SCLD, SEMH, SPLD
16

Rutland

Wilds Lodge School
Stamford Road, Empingham,
Rutland LE15 8QQ
Tel: 01780 767254
Age range: 5–18
Special needs catered for:
ASC, MLD, SEMH
16

Greater London

Kent

Baston House School
Baston Road, Hayes,
Bromley, Kent BR2 7AB
Tel: 020 8462 1010
Age range: 5–19 years
Special needs catered for:
ASC, AUT, LD, MLD
16

London
North London

Ambitious College
Pears Campus, The College
of Haringey, Enfield and North
East London, Tottenham Green
Centre, Clyde Road, South
Tottenham, London N15 4RX
Tel: 020 3870 8775
Special needs catered for:
ASC, ASP, AUT, CLD

Middlesex

Hillingdon Manor School
The Manor, Harlington Road,
Hillingdon, Middlesex UB8 3HD
Tel: 01895 813679
Age range: 3–19 years
Special needs catered for:
ASC, AUT, LD, MLD
16

NAS SYBIL ELGAR SCHOOL
For further details see p. 71
Havelock Road, Southall,
Middlesex UB2 4NY
Tel: 020 8813 9168
Email: sybil.elgar@nas.org.uk
Website:
www.autism.org.uk/sybilelgar
Principal: Chloe Phillips
Age range: 4–22
No. of pupils: 90
Special needs catered for:
ASC, ASP, AUT
🏛 16 ✔

Surrey

**Link Secondary
Day School**
82-86 Croydon Road, Beddington,
Croydon, Surrey CR0 4PD
Tel: 020 8688 7691
Age range: 11–19
No. of pupils: 48 VIth9
Special needs catered for:
ASC, ASP, SP&LD, SLI
(✔)

London

North London

Kestrel House School
104 Crouch Hill, London N8 9EA
Tel: 020 8348 8500
Age range: 5–16
Special needs catered for:
ASC, ASP, AUT

The Holmewood School
88 Woodside Park Road,
London N12 8SH
Tel: 020 8920 0660
Age range: 7–19
Special needs catered for:
ASC, ASP, AUT, SP&LD
(IB) (16+) (✔)

TreeHouse School
Woodside Avenue, London N10 3JA
Tel: 020 8815 5424
Age range: 3–19
No. of pupils: 67
Special needs catered for:
ASC, AUT
(16+) (✔)

South-East London

**NAS VANGUARD
SCHOOL**
For further details see p. 72
Lollard Street, Kennington,
Lambeth, London SE11 6UJ
Website:
www.vanguardschool.org.uk
Executive Principal: Jo Galloway
Age range: 11–19
No. of pupils: 78
Special needs catered for:
ASC, ASP, AUT
(16+)

Riverston School
63-69 Eltham Road, Lee
Green, London SE12 8UF
Tel: 020 8318 4327
Age range: 9 months–19 years
No. of pupils: 215
Special needs catered for:
ASC, ASP, AUT, LD
(🌐) (£) (✎)

South-West London

Park House School
48 North Side, Wandsworth
Common, London SW18 2SL
Tel: 020 3031 9700
Age range: 4–13
Special needs catered for:
ASC, ASP, AUT, SCD
(✔)

Priory Lodge School
Priory Lane, London SW15 5JJ
Tel: 020 8392 4410
Age range: 5–19
No. of pupils: 40
Special needs catered for:
ADHD, ASC, ASP, AUT, LD
(16+) (✔)

**The Chelsea Group
of Children**
The Hall, Waynflete Street,
London SW18 3QG
Tel: 020 8946 8330
Age range: 4–11
Special needs catered for: ADHD,
ASP, AUT, LD, MLD, SP&LD, SPLD
(✔)

Tram House School
520 Garratt Lane, London SW17 0NY
Tel: +44 (0)20 3031 9707
Age range: 14–19
Special needs catered for:
ASC, ASP, AUT

Middlesex

**Options West London
Community College**
The Courtyard Campus, Church
Rd, Hayes, Middlesex UB3 2UH
Tel: 01895 619700
Age range: 16+
Special needs catered for:
ASC, ASP, AUT
(16+)

North-East

Durham

Aycliffe School
Cedar Drive, Newton
Aycliffe, Durham DL5 6UN
Tel: 01325 328 090
Age range: 3–9
Special needs catered for:
ASC, ASP, AUT

Hurworth House School
Westfield Drive, Hurworth,
Darlington, Durham DL2 2AD
Tel: 01325 729 080
Age range: 7–19
No. of pupils: 30
Special needs catered for:
AUT, BESD, EBD
(16+)

Northumberland

**Buzz Learning
Independent
Special School**
8 Esther Court, Wansbeck Business
Park, Rotary Parkway, Ashington,
Northumberland NE63 8AP
Tel: 01670 852244
Age range: 13–16
No. of pupils: 25
Special needs catered for: ASC,
ASP, AUT, MLD, SCD, SLD, SPLD
(16+)

Tyne & Wear

Ashbrooke School
Ashbrooke Road, Sunderland,
Tyne & Wear SR2 7JA
Tel: 0191 6075610
Age range: 5–19
Special needs catered for:
ADHD, ASC, ASP, AUT, SEMH

ESPA College
6-7 The Cloisters, Ashbrooke,
Sunderland, Tyne & Wear SR2 7BD
Tel: 0191 510 2600
Age range: 16–25
No. of pupils: 100
Special needs catered for:
ASC, ASP, AUT
(♿)

Thornhill Park School
24 Thornhill Park, Ashbrooke,
Sunderland, Tyne & Wear SR2 7LA
Tel: 0191 565 3965
Age range: 4–19
No. of pupils: 74
Fees: Day £33,752–£45,806
FB £117,433–£204,986
Special needs catered for:
ASC, ASP, AUT
(♿) (16+)

North-West

Cheshire

Inscape House School
Together Trust Campus,
Schools Hill, Cheadle,
Stockport, Cheshire SK8 1JE
Tel: 0161 283 4750
Age range: 5–19
Special needs catered for:
ASC, ASP, AUT, CLD
🔞 ✓

Royal College Manchester
Seashell Trust, Stanley Road,
Cheadle, Cheshire SK8 6RQ
Tel: 01616 100100
Age range: 19–25
No. of pupils: 70
Special needs catered for:
ASC, D, MSI, PD, PMLD, VIS
♿

Royal School Manchester
Seashell Trust, Stanley Road,
Cheadle, Cheshire SK8 6RQ
Tel: 01616 100100
Age range: 2–19
No. of pupils: 45
Special needs catered for:
ASC, D, HI, MSI, PMLD
🔞

Cumbria

Lindeth College
Wigton Road, Carlisle,
Cumbria CA2 6LB
Tel: 01228 822649
Age range: 16–25
No. of pupils: 30
Special needs catered for:
MLD, SLD
🔞 ♿

Greater Manchester

Fairfield House School
59 Warburton Lane, Partington,
Manchester, Greater
Manchester M31 4NL
Tel: 0161 7762827
Age range: 8–19
Special needs catered for: ASC
🔞 ✓

Great Howarth School
Rochdale, Greater
Manchester OL12 9HJ
Tel: 01706 631 804
Age range: 7–18
Special needs catered for: ASC,
ASP, AUT, BESD, EBD, SEMH

Lancashire

Aurora Brambles East School
The Woodlands, Holly Tree Close,
Darwen, Lancashire BB3 2NG
Tel: 01254 706 600
Age range: B10–19
Special needs catered for: ADHD,
ASC, ASP, AUT, DYS, MLD, SEMH
♂ 🔞

Bracken School
1 Harbour Lane, Warton,
Preston, Lancashire PR4 1YA
Tel: 01772 631531
Age range: G11–16
No. of pupils: 5
Special needs catered for:
ADHD, DYS, MLD
♂

Oliver House School
Hallgate, Astley Village,
Chorley, Lancashire PR7 1XA
Tel: 01257 220 011
Age range: 6–19
No. of pupils: 28
Special needs catered for:
ASC, ASP, AUT, LD
♿ 🔞 ✓

Red Rose School
28-30 North Promenade,
St Annes on Sea, Lytham St
Annes, Lancashire FY8 2NQ
Tel: 01253 720570
Age range: 5–16
Special needs catered for:
ASC, DEL, SPLD
✓

Rossendale School
Bamford Road, Ramsbottom,
Bury, Lancashire BL0 0RT
Tel: 01706 822779
Age range: 8–18
Special needs catered for:
ADD, ADHD, ASC, ASP, AUT,
BESD, CLD, DYS, DYSP, EBD, EPI,
HA, SCD, SEMH, SLD, SPLD
Ⓐ ♿ ✓

Trax Academy
1 Stuart Road, Bredbury,
Stockport, Lancashire SK6 2SR
Tel: 0161 483 1505
Age range: 11–18
No. of pupils: 30
Special needs catered for:
ADHD, EBD
🔞 ✓

Westmorland School
Weldbank Lane, Chorley,
Lancashire PR7 3NQ
Tel: 01257 278899
Age range: 5–11
Special needs catered for:
ADHD, ASC, ASP, AUT, BESD,
MLD, SEMH, SP&LD, SPLD
✓

Merseyside

Arden College
40 Derby Road, Southport,
Merseyside PR9 0TZ
Tel: 01704 534 433
Age range: 16–25
No. of pupils: 53
Special needs catered for: ASC, LD
🔞 ♿

Lakeside School
Naylors Road, Huyton, Liverpool,
Merseyside L27 2YA
Tel: 0151 4877211
Age range: 5–13
Special needs catered for: ADD,
ADHD, ASC, ASP, AUT, BESD, CLD,
DEL, DYS, DYSP, EPI, HA, HI, LD,
PH, SCD, SEMH, SP&LD, SPLD, SLI, VIS
✓

Peterhouse School for Pupils with Autism & Asperger's Syndrome
Preston New Road, Southport,
Merseyside PR9 8PA
Tel: 01704 506682
Age range: 5–19
No. of pupils: 47 VIth23
Fees: Day £38,190
WB £90,896 FB £120,045
Special needs catered for:
ASC, ASP, AUT
♿ 🔞 ✓

WEST KIRBY SCHOOL AND COLLEGE
For further details see p. 73
Meols Drive, West Kirby, Wirral,
Merseyside CH48 5DH
Tel: 0151 632 3201
Website: www.wkrs.co.uk
Head of Day School: Mr
Pete Smith
Age range: 5–19
No. of pupils: 87
Special needs catered for:
ADHD, ASC, ASP, AUT,
BESD, SCD, SEMH, SLI
♿ ✓

South-East

Berkshire

Heathermount School
Devenish Road, Ascot,
Berkshire SL5 9PG
Tel: 01344 875101
Age range: 5–19
No. of pupils: 25
Special needs catered for:
ASC, ASP, AUT
🔞 ✓

NAS THAMES VALLEY SCHOOL
For further details see p. 78
Conwy Close, Tilehurst,
Reading, Berkshire RG30 4BZ
Tel: 0118 9424 750
Email: thames.valley@nas.org.uk
Website: www.autism.org.uk/
thamesvalley
Principal: Jo Galloway
Age range: 5–16
No. of pupils: 50
Special needs catered for:
ASC, ASP, AUT

East Sussex

Rookery Hove
22-24 Sackville Gardens,
Hove, East Sussex BN3 4GH
Tel: 01273 202 520
Age range: 18–35
No. of pupils: 13
Special needs catered for:
ASC, ASP
🔞 ♿

Step by Step School for Autistic Children
Neylands Farm, Grinstead Lane,
Sharpethorne, East Sussex RH19 4HP
Tel: 01342 811852
Age range: 4–11
No. of pupils: 12
Special needs catered for: AUT
✓

Hampshire

Grateley House School
Pond Lane, Grateley, Andover,
Hampshire SP11 8TA
Tel: 01264 889751
Age range: 9–19
No. of pupils: 42
Special needs catered for:
ASC, ASP, AUT, DYS, DYSP
🏛 16+ ✔

Hill House School
Rope Hill, Boldre, Lymington,
Hampshire SO41 8NE
Tel: 01590 672147
Age range: 11–19
No. of pupils: 31
Special needs catered for:
ASC, AUT
🏛 16+ ✔

Southlands School
Vicars Hill, Boldre, Lymington,
Hampshire SO41 5QB
Tel: 01590 675350
Age range: B7–19
No. of pupils: 54
Special needs catered for:
ASC, ASP, DYS, DYSP
🧍 🏛 16+ ✔

Tadley Court School
Tadley Common Road, Tadley,
Basingstoke, Hampshire RG26 3TB
Tel: 0118 981 7720
Age range: 5–19
No. of pupils: 67
Special needs catered for:
ASC, ASP, AUT
🏛 16+ ✔

Kent

Blue Skies School
126 Maidstone Road,
Chatham, Kent ME4 6DQ
Tel: 01634 357770
Age range: 11–19
No. of pupils: 17
Special needs catered for:
ASC, ASP, AUT
16+ ✔

Clannad Education Centre
Crown Lane, Bromley, Kent BR2 9PW
Special needs catered for: SEMH

NAS HELEN ALLISON SCHOOL
For further details see p. 75
Longfield Road, Meopham,
Kent DA13 0EW
Tel: 01474 814878
Email: helen.allison@nas.org.uk
Website:
www.autism.org.uk/helenallison
Principal: Kim McConnell
Age range: 5–19
No. of pupils: 77
Special needs catered for:
ASC, ASP, AUT
🏛 16+ ✔

The Quest School
The Hop Farm, Maidstone
Road, Paddock Wood,
Tonbridge, Kent TN12 6PY
Tel: 01732 522700
Age range: 4–14
No. of pupils: 8
Special needs catered for: AUT, EBD
✔

Surrey

Aurora Redehall School
Redehall Road, Smallfield,
Nr. Horley, Surrey RH6 9QA
Tel: 01342 778650
Age range: 6–16
Special needs catered for:
ASC, ASP, AUT, SCD

Brookways School
660 London Road, North
Cheam, Surrey SM3 9BZ
Tel: 0208 641 9191
Age range: 7–16
Special needs catered for: ASC

Eagle House School (Mitcham)
224 London Road, Mitcham,
Surrey CR4 3HD
Tel: 020 8687 7050
Age range: 4–11
Special needs catered for:
ASC, ASP, AUT, MLD, SCD, SLD
✔

Eagle House School (Sutton)
95 Brighton Road, Sutton,
Surrey SM2 5SJ
Tel: 020 8661 1419
Age range: 11–19
Special needs catered for: AUT
16+ ✔

Jigsaw CABAS® School
Building 20, Dunsfold Park, Stovolds
Hill, Cranleigh, Surrey GU6 8TB
Tel: 01483 273874
Age range: 4–19
No. of pupils: VIth17
Fees: Day £49,900–£52,732
Special needs catered for:
ASC, AUT
16+ ✔

MOOR HOUSE SCHOOL & COLLEGE
For further details see p. 76
Mill Lane, Hurst Green,
Oxted, Surrey RH8 9AQ
Tel: 01883 712271
Email: information@
moorhouseschool.co.uk
Website:
www.moorhouseschool.co.uk
Principal: Mrs H A Middleton
Age range: 7–19
No. of pupils: 150
Special needs catered for: ASP,
DYS, DYSP, SCD, SLD, SP&LD, SLI
Ⓐ 🏛 ✔

Papillon House School
Pebble Close, Tadworth,
Surrey KT20 7PA
Tel: 01372 363663
Age range: 4–16
Fees: Day £45,000
Special needs catered for:
ASC, AUT
✔

Unsted Park School and Sixth Form
Munstead Heath Road,
Godalming, Surrey GU7 1UW
Tel: 01483 892 061
Age range: 7–19
No. of pupils: 55
Special needs catered for:
ASC, ASP, AUT
🏛 16+ ✔

West Sussex

LVS HASSOCKS
For further details see p. 74
London Road, Sayers Common,
Hassocks, West Sussex BN6 9HT
Tel: 01273 832901
Email: info@lvs-hassocks.org.uk
Website:
www.lvs-hassocks.org.uk
Head Teacher: Ms Jen Weeks
Age range: 11–19
No. of pupils: 48
Special needs catered for:
ASC, ASP, AUT
16+

Slindon College
Slindon House, Slindon, Arundel,
West Sussex BN18 0RH
Tel: 01243 814320
Age range: B8–18 years
No. of pupils: 80 VIth17
Fees: Day £21,795 FB £32,280
Special needs catered for:
ADHD, ASC, AUT, DYS, DYSP
🧍 🧑 Ⓐ 🏛 £ ✎

South-West

Cornwall

Three Bridges Education Centre
East Hill, Blackwater, Truro,
Cornwall TR4 8EG
Tel: 01872 561010
Age range: 11–19
No. of pupils: 8
Special needs catered for:
ASC, ASP, AUT
16+ ✔

Devon

Acorn School
Little Oak, Knowstone, South
Molton, Devon EX36 4SA
Tel: 01271 859720
Age range: 11–16
Special needs catered for:
BESD, EBD, SEMH

Devon Education and Children's Services
Bere Alston, Yelverton,
Devon PL20 7EX
Tel: 01822 840379
Age range: 7–19
No. of pupils: 63
Special needs catered for:
ADHD, ASC, ASP, AUT, BESD, CLD,
EBD, GLD, MLD, SCD, SCLD
🏛 16+ ✔

Dorset

Cambian Wing College
126 Richmond Park Road,
Bournemouth, Dorset BH8 8TH
Tel: 01202 635630
Age range: B16–25
No. of pupils: 46
Special needs catered for:
ASC, ASP
🧍 🏛 16+

Portfield School
Parley Lane, Christchurch,
Dorset BH23 6BP
Tel: 01202 573808
Age range: 3–19
No. of pupils: 68
Special needs catered for:
ASC, AUT
16+ ✓

Purbeck View School
Northbrook Road, Swanage,
Dorset BH19 1PR
Tel: 01929 422760
Age range: 7–19
No. of pupils: 57
Special needs catered for:
ASC, AUT
16+

Somerset

3 Dimensions
Chardleigh House, Chardleigh
Green, Wadeford, Chard,
Somerset TA20 3AJ
Tel: 01460 68055
Age range: 7–25
No. of pupils: 16
Special needs catered for:
ADHD, AUT, LD, SEMH
16+ ✓

The Forum School
Shillingstone, Blandford
Forum, Dorset DT11 0QS
Tel: 01258 860295
Age range: 7–19
No. of pupils: 68
Special needs catered for:
ASC, AUT, LD
16+

Farleigh College Mells
Newbury, Nr Mells, Frome,
Somerset BA11 3RG
Tel: 01373 814980
Age range: 11–19
No. of pupils: 52
Special needs catered for: ADD,
ADHD, ASC, ASP, AUT, DYS, DYSP
16+ ✓

Farleigh Further Education College Frome
North Parade, Frome,
Somerset BA11 2AB
Tel: 01373 475470
Age range: 16–19
No. of pupils: 87
Special needs catered for: ASP, LD
16+

North Hill House School
Fromefield, Frome,
Somerset BA11 2HB
Tel: 01373 466 222
Age range: B6–19
No. of pupils: 62
Special needs catered for:
ADD, ADHD, ASC, ASP, AUT
16+ ✓

Park House
277 Cheddon Road, Taunton,
Somerset TA2 7AX
Age range: 9–19
No. of pupils: 14
Special needs catered for: SEMH
16+

West Midlands

Shropshire

CRUCKTON HALL
For further details see p. 80
Cruckton, Shrewsbury,
Shropshire SY5 8PR
Tel: 01743 860206
Email: admissions@kisimul.co.uk
Website: www.cruckton.com
Head Teacher: Robert
Arrowsmith
Age range: 8–19
No. of pupils: 80
Special needs catered for:
ADD, ADHD, ASP, AUT, BESD,
DYS, EBD, PMLD, SEMH, SPLD
A 16+ ✓

Options Higford
Higford Hall, Higford, Shifnal,
Shropshire TF11 9ET
Tel: 01952 630600
Age range: 8–19 years
Special needs catered for: ASC,
AUT, CLD, LD, MLD, SCLD
16+

Staffordshire

Aurora Hanley School
Cambrian Way, off Eaves Lane,
Bucknall, Staffordshire ST2 8PQ
Tel: 01782 973 737
Age range: 6–19
Special needs catered for:
ASC, ASP, AUT, LD, SCD
16+

NAS CHURCH LAWTON SCHOOL
For further details see p. 79
Cherry Tree Avenue, Church
Lawton, Stoke-on-Trent,
Staffordshire ST7 3EL
Tel: 01270 877601
Email: church.lawton@
nas.org.uk
Website: www.autism.org.uk/
churchlawton
Principal: Paul Scales
Age range: 4–19
No. of pupils: 60
Special needs catered for:
ASC, AUT
16+

Options Trent Acres
Alrewas Road, Kings Bromley,
Staffordshire DE13 7HR
Tel: 01543 473772
Age range: 8–18 years
Special needs catered for: ASC,
ASP, AUT, CLD, LD, MLD, SCLD
16+

Priory Highfields
9 & 11 Highfields Road, Chasetown,
Burntwood, Staffordshire WS7 4QR
Tel: 01543 672 173
Age range: 18–25
No. of pupils: 10
Special needs catered for: ASC
16+

Rugeley School
Blithbury Road, Blithbury, Rugeley,
Staffordshire WS15 3JQ
Tel: 01889 504 400
Age range: 5–19
No. of pupils: 48
Special needs catered for:
ASC, ASP, AUT, MLD, SLD
16+ ✓

Strathmore College
Unit 7 Imex Centre, Technology
Park, Stoke-on-Trent,
Staffordshire ST4 8LJ
Tel: 01782 647380
Age range: 16–25
No. of pupils: 37
Special needs catered for: ASC,
ASP, BESD, CLD, GLD, LD, MLD, SLD
16+

Warwickshire

Avon Park School
St John's Avenue, Rugby,
Warwickshire CV22 5HR
Tel: 01788 524448
Age range: 5–16
Special needs catered for: ADD,
ADHD, ASC, ASP, AUT, BESD, CLD,
DYSP, LD, SCD, SEMH, SP&LD

West Midlands

Arc Oakbridge School
Buckingham Street, Birmingham,
West Midlands B19 3HU
Tel: 01212 225201
Age range: 7–16
Special needs catered for: ASC

QUEEN ALEXANDRA COLLEGE (QAC)
For further details see p. 82
Court Oak Road,
Harborne, Birmingham,
West Midlands B17 9TG
Tel: 0121 428 5050
Email: info@qac.ac.uk
Website: www.qac.ac.uk
Principal: Bev Jessop
Age range: 16+
No. of pupils: 260
Special needs catered for:
ADD, ADHD, ASC, ASP, AUT,
BESD, CLD, CP, D, DYS, DYSP,
EBD, EPI, GLD, HA, HI, LD, MLD,
MSI, PD, Phe, PH, PNI, SCD,
SCLD, SLD, SP&LD, SPLD, SLI, VIS
16+

The Island Project School
Diddington Hall, Diddington Lane,
Meriden, West Midlands CV7 7HQ
Tel: 01675 442588
Age range: 6–19
Special needs catered for:
ASC, AUT
✓

Worcestershire

Cambian New Elizabethan School
Quarry Bank, Hartlebury,
Kidderminster,
Worcestershire DY11 7TE
Tel: 01299 250258
Age range: 7–19
No. of pupils: 45
Special needs catered for: ASC,
ASP, AUT, CLD, SCD, SEMH
£ 16+

Yorkshire & Humberside

Lincolnshire

Options Barton
Barrow Road, Barton-upon-Humber, Lincolnshire DN18 6DA
Tel: 01652 631280
Age range: 8–19 years
Special needs catered for:
ASC, AUT, LD, MLD

North Lincolnshire

Demeter House School
Bigby Street, Brigg, North Lincolnshire DN20 8EF
Tel: 01652 654251
Age range: B5–14
No. of pupils: 5
Special needs catered for:
ADD, EBD

South Yorkshire

Abbeywood School
Rother Way, Bramley, Rotherham, South Yorkshire S66 8QN
Tel: 01709 916900
Age range: 10–18
Special needs catered for:
ADHD, ASC, ASP, SEMH

FULLERTON HOUSE COLLEGE
For further details see p. 85
Tickhill Square, Denaby, Doncaster, South Yorkshire DN12 4AR
Tel: 01709 861663
Email: enquiries@hesleygroup.co.uk
Website: www.hesleygroup.co.uk
General Manager: Heidi Dugdale-Dawkes
Age range: 18–25
No. of pupils: 12
Special needs catered for:
ASC, ASP, AUT, CLD, DYS, DYSP, GLD, LD, MLD, SCLD, SLD, SPLD

FULLERTON HOUSE SCHOOL
For further details see p. 83
Tickill Square, Denaby, Doncaster, South Yorkshire DN12 4AR
Tel: 01709 861663
Email: enquiries@hesleygroup.co.uk
Website: www.fullertonhouseschool.co.uk
General Manager: Heidi Dugdale-Dawkes
Age range: 8–19
Special needs catered for:
ASC, ASP, AUT, CLD, DYS, DYSP, GLD, LD, MLD, SCLD, SLD, SPLD

NAS ROBERT OGDEN SCHOOL
For further details see p. 84
Clayton Lane, Thurnscoe, Rotherham, South Yorkshire S63 0BG
Tel: 01709 874443
Email: robert.ogden@nas.org.uk
Website: www.autism.org.uk/robertogden
Principal: Lorraine Dormand
Age range: 5–19
No. of pupils: 127
Special needs catered for:
ASC, ASP, AUT

North Bridge Enterprise College
Marshgate, Elwis Street, Doncaster, South Yorkshire DN5 8AF
Tel: 01302 343935
Age range: 14–16
No. of pupils: 50
Special needs catered for:
BESD, SEMH

WILSIC HALL COLLEGE
For further details see p. 85
Wadworth, Doncaster, South Yorkshire DN11 9AG
Tel: 01302 856382
Age range: 18–25
No. of pupils: 8
Special needs catered for:
ASC, ASP, AUT, CLD, DYS, DYSP, GLD, LD, MLD, SCLD, SLD, SPLD

WILSIC HALL SCHOOL
For further details see p. 86
Wadworth, Doncaster, South Yorkshire DN11 9AG
Tel: 01302 856382
Email: enquiries@hesleygroup.co.uk
Website: www.wilsichallschool.co.uk
Head: Geoff Turner
Age range: 11–19
No. of pupils: 32
Special needs catered for:
ASC, ASP, AUT, CLD, DYS, DYSP, GLD, LD, MLD, SCLD, SLD, SPLD

West Yorkshire

Fountain House School
Leeds, West Yorkshire
Special needs catered for: SEMH

Hall Cliffe Primary School
Wrenthorpe Lane, Wrenthorpe, Wakefield, West Yorkshire WF2 0QB
Tel: 01924 614 490
Age range: 5–13
Special needs catered for:
ADHD, ASC, SCLD, SEMH

Scotland

Aberdeenshire

Troup House School
Gamrie, Banff, Aberdeenshire AB45 3JN
Tel: 01261 851 584
Age range: 8–16+
No. of pupils: 12
Special needs catered for:
AUT, BESD

East Ayrshire

NAS DALDORCH HOUSE SCHOOL
For further details see p. 87
Sorn Road, Catrine, East Ayrshire KA5 6NA
Tel: 01290 551666
Email: daldorch@nas.org.uk
Website: www.autism.org.uk/daldorch
Principal: Bernadette Casey
Age range: 8–21
Special needs catered for:
ASC, ASP, AUT

South Lanarkshire

NAS Daldorch Satellite School
St Leonards, East Kilbride, South Lanarkshire G74
Tel: 01355 246242
Age range: 5–19
No. of pupils: 5
Special needs catered for:
ASC, ASP, AUT

Wales

Caerphilly

Mynydd Haf School
Ty Ysgol, Newport Road,
Trethomas, Caerphilly CF83 8BY
Tel: 07967 404804
Age range: 11–17
No. of pupils: 24
Special needs catered for:
BESD, SEMH
16+

Carmarthenshire

Coleg Elidyr
Rhandirmwyn, Llandovery,
Carmarthenshire SA20 0NL
Tel: 01550 760400
Age range: 18–25
No. of pupils: 43
Special needs catered for:
ADD, ADHD, ASC, ASP, AUT,
BESD, CLD, DEL, DYSP, EBD, EPI,
GLD, LD, MLD, Phe, SCD, SLD
16+

Flintshire

Options Kinsale
Kinsale Hall, Llanerch-y-Mor,
Holywell, Flintshire CH8 9DX
Tel: 01745 562500
Age range: 8–19 years
Special needs catered for: ASC,
AUT, CLD, LD, MLD, SCLD
16+

Torfaen

Priory College South Wales
Coleg Gwent, Pontypool
Campus, Blaendare Road,
Pontypool, Torfaen NP4 5YE
Tel: 01495 762 609
Age range: 16–25
No. of pupils: 11
Special needs catered for:
ASC, ASP, LD
16+

Vale of Glamorgan

BEECHWOOD COLLEGE
For further details see p. 88
Hayes Road, Sully, Vale of
Glamorgan CF64 5SE
Tel: 029 2053 2210
Email: enquiries@
beechwoodcollege.co.uk
Website:
www.beechwoodcollege.co.uk
Director of
Education: Angela Kent
Age range: 16–25
No. of pupils: 44
Special needs catered for:
ASC, ASP, SLD
16+ 16+

Wrexham

Priory College North Wales
Ty Dewi Sant, Rhosddu
Road, Wrexham LL11 0ZX
Tel: 01978 340580
Age range: 16–25
No. of pupils: 5
Special needs catered for:
ASC, ASP, LD
16+

Schools and colleges specialising in emotional, behavioural and/or social difficulties (EBSD)

Abbreviations

ACLD	Autism, Communication and Associated Learning Difficulties
ADD	Attention Deficit Disorder
ADHD	Attention Deficit and Hyperactive Disorder (Hyperkinetic Disorder)
ASC	Autistic Spectrum Conditions
ASP	Asperger Syndrome
AUT	Autism
BESD	Behavioural, Emotional and Social Difficulties
CCD	Complex Communication Difficulties
CLD	Complex Learning Difficulties
CP	Cerebral Palsy
D	Deaf
DEL	Delicate
DYS	Dyslexia
DYSP	Dyspraxia
EBD	Emotional and Behavioural Difficulties
EBSD	Emotional, Behavioural and/or Social Difficulties
EPI	Epilepsy
GLD	General Learning Difficulties
HA	High Ability
HI	Hearing Impairment
HS	Hospital School
LD	Learning Difficulties
MLD	Moderate Learning Difficulties
MSI	Multi-sensory Impairment
OCD	Obsessive Compulsive Disorder
PD	Physical Difficulties
PH	Physical Impairment
Phe	Partially Hearing
PMLD	Profound and Multiple Learning Difficulties
PNI	Physical Neurological Impairment
PRU	Pupil Referral Unit
SCD	Social and Communication Difficulties
SCLD	Severe and Complex Learning Difficulties
SEBD	Severe Emotional and Behavioural Disorders
SEBN	Social, Emotional and Behavioural Needs
SLD	Severe Learning Difficulties
SLI	Specific Language Impairment
SPLD	Specific Learning Difficulties
SP&LD	Speech and Language Difficulties
SLCN	Speech Language & Communication Needs
VIS	Visually Impaired

Key to Symbols

Type of school:

(symbol)	Boys' school
(symbol)	Girls' school
(symbol)	International school

School offers:

(A)	A levels
(symbol)	Residential
(16+)	Entrance at 16+
(symbol)	Vocational qualifications
(symbol)	Learning support
(✓)	This is a DfE approved independent or non-maintained school under section 41 of the Children and Families Act 2014 or section 342 of the 1996 Education Act

Please note: Unless otherwise indicated, all schools are coeducational day schools. Single-sex and boarding schools will be indicated by the relevant icon.

England – Central & West

Buckinghamshire

Benjamin College
4 Wren Path, Fairford Leys,
Aylesbury, Buckinghamshire
HP19 7AR
Tel: 01296 483584
Age range: 12–18
Special needs catered for: BESD
(16) (✓)

Gloucestershire

Cotswold Chine School
Box, Stroud, Gloucestershire
GL6 9AG
Tel: 01453 837550
Age range: 9–19
No. of pupils: 48
Special needs catered for:
ADD, ADHD, ASP, AUT, DYS,
DYSP, EBD, EPI, MLD, SP&LD
(🌐) (🏛) (✓)

Oxfordshire

Action for Children Parklands Campus
Chardleigh House, Near Appleton,
Abingdon, Oxfordshire OX13 5QB
Tel: 01865 390436
Age range: 11–19
No. of pupils: 7 VIth2
Fees: Day £50,000 FB £192,000
Special needs catered for: ADD,
ADHD, ASC, ASP, AUT, BESD,
EBD, LD, MLD, SEMH, SPLD
(🏛) (16) (✓)

Chilworth House School
Thame Road, Wheatley, Oxford,
Oxfordshire OX33 1JP
Tel: 01844 339077
Age range: 5–11
Special needs catered for:
ADHD, ASC, ASP, AUT, BESD,
EBD, MLD, SCD, SEMH, SLD
(16) (✓)

Chilworth House Upper School
Grooms Farm, Thame Road,
Wheatley, Oxfordshire OX33 1JP
Tel: 01844 337720
Age range: 11–18
Special needs catered for: ADD,
ADHD, ASC, ASP, AUT, BESD,
DEL, GLD, HI, LD, MLD, Phe, SCD,
SCLD, SEMH, SP&LD, SPLD
(✓)

Hillcrest Park School
Southcombe, Chipping Norton,
Oxford, Oxfordshire OX7 5QH
Tel: 01608 644621
Age range: 7–18 years
No. of pupils: 28
Special needs catered for:
ADD, ADHD, ASC, AUT,
BESD, EBD, SCD, SEMH
(🏛) (16)

Mulberry Bush School
Standlake, Witney,
Oxfordshire OX29 7RW
Tel: 01865 300202
Age range: 5–12
No. of pupils: 36
Special needs catered for: EBD
(🏛) (✓)

West Berkshire

Hillcrest New Barn School
The Long Barn, Welford, Newbury,
West Berkshire RG20 8HZ
Tel: 01488 505145
Age range: 6–16 years
No. of pupils: 20
Special needs catered for: ADD,
ADHD, BESD, EBD, SCD, SEMH
(16)

Wiltshire

The Spires
School Lane, Salisbury,
Wiltshire SP1 3YA
Age range: 8–18
No. of pupils: 22
Special needs catered for:
ASC, BESD, MLD
(16)

East

Cambridgeshire

Begdale House School
Begdale Road, Elm, Wisbech,
Cambridgeshire PE14 0AZ
Tel: 01945 860055
Age range: 12–15
No. of pupils: 7
Special needs catered for:
LD, SEMH

Cambian Home Tree School
172 March Road, Friday Bridge,
Wisbech, Cambridgeshire PE14 0LP
Tel: 01945 660988
Age range: 12–18
No. of pupils: 25
Special needs catered for:
BESD, EBD, SEMH
(✓)

Cambian Wisbech School
The Old Sessions House, 32
Somers Road, Wisbech,
Cambridgeshire PE13 1JF
Tel: 01945 427276
Age range: 7–17
No. of pupils: 40
Special needs catered for:
BESD, EBD, SEMH
(16) (✓)

Chartwell House School
Goodens Lane, Newton, Wisbech,
Cambridgeshire PE13 5HQ
Tel: 01945 870793
No. of pupils: 8
Fees: FB £67,600
Special needs catered for: DYS, EBD
(👤) (🏛) (✓)

The Old School House
March Road, Friday Bridge,
Wisbech, Cambridgeshire PE14 0HA
Tel: 01945 861114
Age range: B7–13
Special needs catered for: EBD
(👤) (🏛) (✓)

Essex

ESSEX FRESH START INDEPENDENT SCHOOL (EFS)
For further details see p. 90
1 Wellesley Road, Clacton,
Essex CO15 3PP
Tel: 01255 225204
Email: referrals@tces.org.uk
Website: www.tces.org.uk
Head Teacher: Cheryl Rutter
Age range: 7–19 years
Special needs catered for: ASC,
AUT, BESD, EBD, SEMH, SP&LD
(16) (✓)

Hopewell School
Harmony House, Baden Powell
Close, Dagenham, Essex RM9 6XN
Tel: 020 8593 6610
Age range: 5–18
Special needs catered for:
EBD, MLD, SEMH
(16) (✓)

Jacques Hall
Harwich Road, Bradfield,
Manningtree, Essex CO11 2XW
Tel: 01255 870311
Age range: 11–18
No. of pupils: 21
Special needs catered for:
ADHD, BESD, EBD, MLD, SEMH
(🏛) (16)

The Ryes College & Community
New Road, Aldham,
Colchester, Essex CO6 3PN
Tel: 01787 372 611
Age range: 7–24
Special needs catered for:
ADD, ADHD, ASC, ASP, AUT,
BESD, EBD, SCD, SEMH
(🏛) (16) (✓)

Norfolk

Avocet House
The Old Vicarage, School Lane,
Heckingham, Norfolk NR14 6QP
Tel: 01508 549320
Age range: B8–16
No. of pupils: 8
Special needs catered for:
EBD, SEMH, SPLD
(👤) (🏛) (✓)

Future Education
168b Motum Road, Norwich,
Norfolk NR5 8EG
Tel: 01603 250505
Age range: 14–16
Special needs catered for: BESD
(•)

Sheridan School
Thetford Road, Northwold,
Thetford, Norfolk IP26 5LQ
Tel: 01366 726 040
Age range: 8–17
No. of pupils: 40
Special needs catered for:
ASC, ASP, BESD, SPLD
(🏛) (16) (✓)

Suffolk

Bramfield House School
Walpole Road, Bramfield,
Halesworth, Suffolk IP19 9AB
Tel: 01986 784 235
Age range: B7–16
Special needs catered for:
SCD, SEMH
(symbols)

On Track Education Centre, Mildenhall
82e & 82F Fred Dannatt Road,
Mildenhall, Suffolk IP28 7RD
Tel: 01638 715555
Age range: 11–19
No. of pupils: 32
Special needs catered for:
ASC, MLD, SCLD, SEMH, SPLD
(16) (✔)

East Midlands

Derbyshire

Eastwood Grange School
Milken Lane, Ashover, Chesterfield,
Derbyshire S45 0BA
Tel: 01246 590255
Age range: B9–16+
No. of pupils: 34
Special needs catered for: BESD
(symbols) (✔)

Longdon Park School
Park Hill, Hilton Road, Egginton,
Derbyshire DE65 6GU
Tel: 01283 733 195
Age range: 7–18
Special needs catered for:
ASC, ASP, AUT
(16)

The Linnet Independent Learning Centre
107 Mount Pleasant Road,
Castle Gresley, Swadlincote,
Derbyshire DE11 9JE
Tel: 01283 213989
Age range: 5–16
No. of pupils: 13
Fees: Day £74,250
Special needs catered for: ADD,
ADHD, ASC, ASP, BESD, CLD,
DEL, DYS, DYSP, EBD, GLD, LD,
MLD, SCD, SEMH, SP&LD, SPLD
(✔)

The Meadows
Beech Lane, Dove Holes,
Derbyshire SK17 8DJ
Tel: 01298 814000
Age range: 11–16
Special needs catered for: EBD
(✔)

Leicestershire

Gryphon School
Quorn Hall, Meynell Road,
Quorn, Leicestershire LE12 8BQ
Tel: 01509 414 338
Age range: 11–17
Special needs catered for: EBD
(✔)

Lewis Charlton Learning Centre
North Street, Ashby-De-La-
Zouch, Leicestershire LE65 1HU
Tel: 01530 560775
Age range: 11–16
No. of pupils: 20
Special needs catered for: EBD
(symbols) (✔)

Meadow View Farm School
c/o Brookland Farm House, Kirby
Road, Barwell, Leicestershire LE9 8FT
Tel: 01455 840 825
Age range: 6–11
Special needs catered for:
ASC, BESD, SCD
(✔)

Oakwood School
20 Main Street, Glenfield,
Leicester, Leicestershire LE3 8DG
Tel: 0116 2876218
Age range: 8–18
No. of pupils: 18
Special needs catered for: EBD
(✔)

Trinity College
Moor Lane, Loughborough,
Leicestershire LE11 1BA
Tel: 01509 218906
Age range: 9–16
Special needs catered for:
EBD, MLD, SEMH

Lincolnshire

Broughton House
Brant Broughton,
Lincolnshire LN5 0SL
Special needs catered for:
ASC, AUT
(symbol)

Northamptonshire

Belview Lodge
124b Midland Road,
Wellingborough,
Northamptonshire NN8 1NF
Tel: 01933 441877
Age range: 11–17
No. of pupils: 4
Special needs catered for: BESD
(✔)

Cambian Northampton School
67a Queens Park Parade,
Kingsthorpe, Northampton,
Northamptonshire NN2 6LR
Tel: 01604 719711
Age range: 11–18
No. of pupils: 24
Special needs catered for:
BESD, EBD, LD, SEMH
(16)

Thornby Hall School
Thornby Hall, Thornby,
Northampton,
Northamptonshire NN6 8SW
Tel: 01604 740001
Age range: 12–18
No. of pupils: 20
Fees: FB £106,177
Special needs catered for: EBD
(symbols) (16) (✔)

Nottinghamshire

Freyburg School
The Poppies, Greenmile
Lane, Babworth,
Nottinghamshire DN22 8JW
Tel: 01777 709061
Age range: B11–16
Special needs catered for: BESD
(✔)

Hope House School
Barnby Road, Newark,
Nottinghamshire NG24 3NE
Tel: 01636 700 380
Age range: 4–19
No. of pupils: 3
Fees: Day £135,000–£155,000
FB £160,000–£180,000
Special needs catered for:
ADD, ADHD, ASC, ASP, AUT,
BESD, DEL, EBD, SCD, SEMH
(16) (✔)

Westbourne School
Huthwaite Road, Sutton-in-Ashfield,
Nottinghamshire NG17 2EL
Tel: 01204 558038
Age range: 11–18
Special needs catered for:
ASC, ASP, AUT, SEMH
(16)

Wings School, Nottinghamshire
Kirklington Hall, Kirklington, Newark,
Nottinghamshire NG22 8NB
Tel: 01636 817430
Age range: 9–17
Special needs catered for:
ADHD, ASC, SEMH
(symbols) (16) (✔)

Rutland

The Grange Therapeutic School
15-17 Somerby Road,
Knossington, Rutland LE15 8LY
Tel: 01664 454 264
Age range: 7–18
Special needs catered for:
ASC, ASP, AUT, SEMH
(symbols) (16)

Greater London

Essex

Barnardos
Tanners Lane, Barkingside,
Ilford, Essex IG6 1QG
Tel: 020 8550 8822
Special needs catered for: AUT,
EBD, MLD, PMLD, SLD, SP&LD, SPLD

Middlesex

Unity School
62 The Ride, Hounslow,
Middlesex TW8 9LA
Age range: 11–16
No. of pupils: 4
Special needs catered for: EBD

Surrey

Cressey College
Croydon, Surrey CR0 6XJ
Tel: 0208 655 2798
Age range: 11–17
Special needs catered for:
BESD, EBD, SCD

Kingsdown Secondary School
112 Orchard Road, Sanderstead,
Croydon, Surrey CR2 9LQ
Tel: 020 8657 1200
Age range: 11–16
No. of pupils: 12
Special needs catered for:
ASC, ASP, EBD, SPLD

London

East London

EAST LONDON INDEPENDENT SCHOOL (ELIS)
For further details see p. 91
Welfare Road, Stratford
Marsh, London E15 4HT
Tel: 020 8555 6737
Email: referrals@tces.org.uk
Website: www.tces.org.uk
Head Teacher: Adele Stedman
Age range: 7–19 years
Special needs catered for:
ASC, AUT, BESD, EBD, SEMH

Leaways School London
Theydon Road, Clapton,
London E5 9NZ
Tel: 020 8815 4030
Age range: 7–17
Special needs catered for:
ADHD, ASC, SEMH

North-West London

Gloucester House
The Tavistock Children's Day
Unit, 33 Daleham Gardens,
London NW3 5BU
Tel: 0207 794 3353
Age range: B5–12
Special needs catered for: BESD

South-East London

Cavendish School
58 Hawkstone Road, Southwark
Park, London SE16 2PA
Tel: 020 7394 0088
Age range: 11–16
No. of pupils: 42
Special needs catered for: EBD

Octavia House School, Vauxhall
Vauxhall Primary School, Vauxhall
Street, London SE11 5LG
Tel: 02036 514396 (Option:1)
Age range: 5–14
No. of pupils: 65
Special needs catered for: ADD,
ADHD, BESD, EBD, SCD, SEMH

Octavia House School, Walworth
Larcom House, Larcom
Street, London SE17 1RT
Tel: 02036 514396 (Option:2)
Special needs catered for: ADD,
ADHD, BESD, EBD, SCD, SEMH

West London

Insights School & Skills Academy
3-5 Alexandria Road,
Ealing, London W13 0NP
Tel: 020 8840 9099
Age range: 7–18
No. of pupils: 62
Special needs catered for: ADD,
ADHD, ASC, ASP, BESD, DYS,
EBD, GLD, MLD, SCD, SPLD

NORTH WEST LONDON INDEPENDENT SCHOOL (NWLIS)
For further details see p. 92
85 Old Oak Common Lane,
Acton, London W3 7DD
Tel: 020 8749 5403
Email: referrals@tces.org.uk
Website: www.tces.org.uk
Head Teacher: Katrina Medley
Age range: 7–19 years
Special needs catered for: ASC,
AUT, BESD, EBD, SEMH, SP&LD

North-East

Durham

Highcroft School
The Green, Cockfield, Bishop
Auckland, Durham DL13 5AG
Tel: 01388 710753
Age range: 11–18
No. of pupils: 12
Special needs catered for: BESD

Priory Pines House
Middleton St George,
Darlington, Durham DL2 1TS
Tel: 01325 331177
Age range: 7–16
No. of pupils: 16
Special needs catered for: EBD

Thornbeck College
Cedar Drive, Newton
Aycliffe, Durham DL5 6UN
Tel: 01325 328 088
Age range: 16–25
Special needs catered for:
ASC, ASP, AUT

Hartlepool

Cambian Hartlepool School
Unit E, Sovereign Park, Brenda
Road, Hartlepool TS25 1NN
Tel: 01429 224965
Age range: 11–17
No. of pupils: 18
Special needs catered for:
EBD, LD, SEMH

Northumberland

Cambois House School
Cambois, Blyth,
Northumberland NE24 1SF
Tel: 01670 857689
Age range: 11–16
No. of pupils: 8
Special needs catered for:
BESD, EBD

Tyne & Wear

Talbot House School
Hexham Road, Walbottle,
Newcastle upon Tyne,
Tyne & Wear NE15 8HW
Tel: 0191 229 0111
Age range: 7–18
No. of pupils: 40
Special needs catered for: ADD,
ADHD, ASC, BESD, EBD, MLD

North-West

Cheshire

Halton School
31-33 Main Street, Halton Village, Runcorn, Cheshire WA7 2AN
Tel: 01928 589810
Age range: 7–18
No. of pupils: 28
Special needs catered for: EBD
(16) (✓)

High Peak School
Mudhurst Lane, Higher Disley, Stockport, Cheshire SK12 2AP
Tel: 01663 721731
Age range: 7–18
Special needs catered for: ADHD, ASC, MLD, SEMH
(🏠) (16)

Hope Corner Academy
70 Clifton Road, Runcorn, Cheshire WA7 4TD
Tel: 01928 580860
Age range: 14–16
Special needs catered for: ASC, BESD, MLD

Cumbria

APPLETREE SCHOOL
For further details see p. 93
Natland, Kendal, Cumbria LA9 7QS
Tel: 01539 560253
Email: clair.davies@appletreeschool.co.uk
Website: www.appletreetreatmentcentre.co.uk
Age range: 6–12
Special needs catered for: ADD, ADHD, BESD, DEL, DYS, DYSP, EBD, GLD, HA, LD, MLD, SCD, SEMH
(🏠) (✓)

Cambian Whinfell School
110 Windermere Road, Kendal, Cumbria LA9 5EZ
Tel: 01539 723322
Age range: B11–19
No. of pupils: 14
Special needs catered for: ASC, ASP, AUT, DYS, DYSP, MLD
(🏃) (🏠) (16) (✓)

Eden Grove School
Bolton, Appleby, Cumbria CA16 6AJ
Tel: 01768 361346
Age range: 8–19
No. of pupils: 65
Special needs catered for: ADHD, ASP, AUT, BESD, CP, DYS, EBD, EPI, MLD, PH, SP&LD
(🏠) (16) (✓)

Eden Park Academy
119 Warwick Road, Carlisle, Cumbria CA1 1JZ
Tel: 01228 537 609
Age range: 11–16
No. of pupils: 6
Special needs catered for: EBD

Fell House School
Grange Fell Road, Grange-Over-Sands, Cumbria LA11 6AS
Tel: 01539 535926
Age range: 7–12
No. of pupils: 8
Special needs catered for: EBD
(🏠) (✓)

Kirby Moor School
Longtown Road, Brampton, Cumbria CA8 2AB
Tel: 016977 42598
Age range: B7–18
Special needs catered for: ADHD, ASC, AUT, BESD, EBD, SEMH
(🏃) (🏠) (16) (✓)

Oversands School
Witherslack, Grange-Over-Sands, Cumbria LA11 6SD
Tel: 01539 552397
Age range: 8–19
Special needs catered for: ADHD, ASC, ASP, AUT, BESD, EBD, MLD, SEMH, SPLD
(🏃) (🏠) (✓)

Underley Garden
Kirkby Lonsdale, Carnforth, Cumbria LA6 2DZ
Tel: 01524 271 569
Age range: 5–19
Special needs catered for: ASC, ASP, AUT, LD
(🏠) (16) (✓)

Wings School, Cumbria
Whassett, Milnthorpe, Cumbria LA7 7DN
Tel: 01539 562006
Age range: 9–17
Special needs catered for: ADHD, ASC, SEMH
(🏠) (16)

Greater Manchester

Acorns School
19b Hibbert Lane, Marple, Stockport, Greater Manchester SK6 7NN
Tel: 01614 495820
Age range: 5–17
No. of pupils: 40
Special needs catered for: EBD
(✓)

Ashcroft School
Together Trust Campus, Schools Hill, Cheadle, Greater Manchester SK8 1JE
Tel: 0161 283 4832
Age range: 8–18
Special needs catered for: ADHD, ASC, BESD, EBD, SEMH
(✓)

Cambian Chesham House School
Chesham House, Thrush Drive, Bury, Greater Manchester BL9 6JD
Tel: 01617 637072
Age range: 10–18
No. of pupils: 20
Special needs catered for: BESD, EBD, LD, SEMH
(✓)

Cambian Tyldesley School
Shuttle Street, Tyldesley, Leigh, Greater Manchester M29 8BS
Tel: 01942 877660
Age range: 11–19
No. of pupils: 34
Special needs catered for: ADHD, ASC, AUT, EBD, SEMH, SLD
(✓)

Lime Meadows
73 Taunton Road, Ashton-Under-Lyne, Greater Manchester OL7 9DU
Tel: 0161 3399412
Age range: B14–19
No. of pupils: 5
Special needs catered for: EBD
(🏃) (🏠) (16) (✓)

Nugent House School
Carr Mill Road, Billinge, Wigan, Greater Manchester WN5 7TT
Tel: 01744 892551
Age range: B7–19
No. of pupils: 65
Fees: Day £63,036–£84,048
Special needs catered for: EBD
(🏃) (🏠) (16) (✓)

Reddish Hall School
Denstone Road, Reddish, Stockport, Greater Manchester SK5 6UY
Tel: 0161 442 1197
Age range: 5–18
Special needs catered for: ADHD, ASP, DYS, DYSP, MLD, SPLD
(16)

St. John Vianney School
Rye Bank Road, Firswood, Stretford, Greater Manchester M16 0EX
Tel: 0161 881 7843
Age range: 4–19
No. of pupils: 80
Fees: Day £7,155
Special needs catered for: MLD
(16) (✓)

Lancashire

Aurora Brambles School
159 Longmeanygate, Midge Hill, Leyland, Lancashire PR26 7TB
Tel: 01772 454 826
Age range: B9–16
Special needs catered for: ASC, ASP, AUT, DYS, EBD, MLD, SEMH
(🏃)

Aurora Keyes Barn School
Station Road, Salwick, Preston, Lancashire PR4 0YH
Tel: 01772 673 672
Age range: 5–12
Special needs catered for: SEMH
(✓)

Belmont School
Haslingden Road, Rawtenstall, Rossendale, Lancashire BB4 6RX
Tel: 01706 221 043
Age range: B5–18
Special needs catered for: SEMH
(🏃) (16) (✓)

Cambian Red Rose School
Meadow Lane, Bamber Bridge, Preston, Lancashire PR5 8LN
Tel: 01772 281140
Age range: 5–17
No. of pupils: 30
Special needs catered for: ADHD, BESD, EBD, SEMH
(✓)

Cedar House School
Bentham, Lancaster,
Lancashire LA2 7DD
Tel: 015242 61149
Age range: 7–18
Special needs catered for:
ADD, ADHD, ASC, ASP, BESD,
DYSP, EBD, EPI, GLD, LD, MLD,
SCD, SEMH, SP&LD, SPLD

Crookhey Hall School
Crookhey Hall, Garstang
Road, Cockerham, Lancaster,
Lancashire LA2 0HA
Tel: 01524 792 618
Age range: B10–17
Special needs catered for: SEMH

Cumberland School
Church Road, Bamber Bridge,
Preston, Lancashire PR5 6EP
Tel: 01772 284435
Age range: 11–18
Special needs catered for: ADHD,
ASC, ASP, BESD, MLD, SEMH, SP&LD

Elland House School
Unit 7, Roman Road, Royton,
Lancashire OL2 5PJ
Tel: 0161 6283600
Age range: 11–16
Special needs catered for: BESD

Learn 4 Life
Quarry Bank Community Centre,
364 Ormskirk Road, Tanhouse,
Skelmersdale, Lancashire WN8 9AL
Tel: 01695 768960
Age range: 11–16
No. of pupils: 4
Special needs catered for:
ADD, ADHD, ASC, ASP, AUT,
BESD, DYS, EBD, GLD, SCD

Moorlands View School
Manchester Road, Dunnockshaw,
Burnley, Lancashire BB11 5PQ
Tel: 01282 431144
Age range: 7–17
No. of pupils: 24
Special needs catered for: EBD

Oakfield House School
Station Road, Salwick, Preston,
Lancashire PR4 0YH
Tel: 01772 672 630
Age range: 5–12
Special needs catered for:
ASC, SEMH

Roselyn House School
Moss Lane, Off Wigan Road,
Leyland, Lancashire PR25 4SE
Tel: 01772 435948
Age range: 11–16
No. of pupils: 21
Special needs catered for: AUT, EBD

Waterloo Lodge School
173 Preston Road, Chorley,
Lancashire PR6 7AX
Tel: 01257 230 894
Age range: 11–18
Special needs catered for: SEMH

Merseyside

Olsen House School
85-87 Liverpool Road, Liverpool,
Merseyside L23 5TD
Tel: 01519 240234
Age range: 7–16
Special needs catered for:
ADHD, ASC, LD, SEMH

Warrington

Chaigeley
Thelwall, Warrington WA4 2TE
Tel: 01925 752357
Age range: B8–16
No. of pupils: 75
Special needs catered for:
ADD, ADHD, ASC, ASP, AUT,
BESD, DYS, EBD, GLD, HA, LD,
MLD, SCD, SEMH, SLD, SP&LD

Cornerstones
2 Victoria Road, Grappenhall,
Warrington WA4 2FN
Tel: 01925 211056
Age range: B7–18
No. of pupils: 11
Special needs catered for: AUT, EBD

South-East

Berkshire

Beech Lodge School
13 Home Farm, Honey Lane,
Hurley, Berkshire SL6 6TG
Tel: 01628 879384
Special needs catered for:
ADHD, BESD, DYS, SEMH

Cressex Lodge (SWAAY)
Terrace Road South, Binfield,
Bracknell, Berkshire RG42 4DE
Tel: 01344 862221
Age range: B11–16
No. of pupils: 9
Special needs catered for: BESD

High Close School
Wiltshire Road, Wokingham,
Berkshire RG40 1TT
Tel: 0118 9785767
Age range: 7–18
Special needs catered for: ADHD,
ASC, ASP, BESD, EBD, MLD

Buckinghamshire

Unity College
150 West Wycombe
Road, High Wycombe,
Buckinghamshire HP12 3AE
Tel: 01494 446371
Age range: 11–16
No. of pupils: 25
Special needs catered for:
BESD, MLD, SEMH

East Sussex

Headstart School
Crouch Lane, Ninfield, Battle,
East Sussex TN33 9EG
Tel: 01424 893803
Age range: 7–18
Special needs catered for:
ASC, BESD, SEMH, SP&LD

Mountfield Heath School
Vinehall Road, Robertsbridge,
East Sussex TN32 5JN
Tel: 01323 914 600
Age range: 5–11
Special needs catered for:
ASC, ASP, AUT, SEMH

Springboard Junior
39 Whippingham Road, St
Wilfred's Upper Hall, Brighton,
East Sussex BN2 3PS
Tel: 01273 885109
Age range: 7–13
Special needs catered for:
ADHD, BESD

The Lioncare School
87 Payne Avenue, Hove,
East Sussex BN3 5HD
Tel: 01273 734164
Age range: 7–16
No. of pupils: 15
Special needs catered for: ADHD,
ASC, BESD, EBD, MLD, SLD

The Mount Camphill Community
Faircrouch Lane, Wadhurst,
East Sussex TN5 6PT
Tel: 01892 782025
Age range: 16–24
No. of pupils: 35
Special needs catered for: ADD,
ADHD, ASC, ASP, AUT, BESD, CLD,
CP, DEL, DYS, DYSP, EBD, EPI, GLD,
HI, LD, MLD, MSI, PD, Phe, PH,
PNI, SCD, SLD, SP&LD, SPLD, SLI

Hampshire

Coxlease Abbeymead
Palace Lane, Beaulieu,
Hampshire SO42 7YG
Tel: 02380 283 633
Age range: 9–16
No. of pupils: 5
Special needs catered for: EBD

Coxlease School
Clay Hill, Lyndhurst,
Hampshire SO43 7DE
Tel: 023 8028 3633
Age range: 9–18
No. of pupils: 55
Special needs catered for: BESD, LD

Hillcrest Jubilee School
84-86 Jubilee Road, Waterlooville,
Hampshire PO7 7RE
Tel: 02392 250963
Age range: 8–16 years
No. of pupils: 22
Special needs catered for: ADD,
ADHD, BESD, EBD, SCD, SEMH

St Edward's School
Melchet Court, Sherfield English,
Romsey, Hampshire SO51 6ZR
Tel: 01794 885252
Age range: B9–18
No. of pupils: 38
Special needs catered for: ADD,
ADHD, ASC, ASP, AUT, BESD, DYS,
EBD, MLD, SCD, SEMH, SPLD

The Serendipity School
399 Hinkler Road, Southampton,
Hampshire SO19 6DS
Tel: 023 8042 2255
Age range: G9–19
No. of pupils: 15
Special needs catered for:
BESD, EBD, SEMH

Kent

Brewood School
86 London Road, Deal,
Kent CT14 9TR
Tel: 01304 363000
Age range: 11–18
Special needs catered for: ADD,
ADHD, ASC, ASP, AUT, BESD, CLD,
DEL, EBD, EPI, GLD, HA, HI, LD,
MLD, PH, SCD, SLD, SP&LD, SLI

Browns School
Cannock House, Hawstead Lane,
Chelsfield, Orpington, Kent BR6 7PH
Tel: 01689 876816
Age range: 7–12
No. of pupils: 32
Special needs catered for:
EBD, SPLD
✔

Caldecott Foundation School
Hythe Road, Smeeth,
Ashford, Kent TN25 6PW
Tel: 01303 815678
Age range: 5–18
No. of pupils: 56
Special needs catered for: EBD
🏫 16+ ✔

Esland School
Units 12-13, Oare Gunpowder
Works, Off Bysingwood Road,
Faversham, Kent ME13 7UD
Tel: 01795 531730
Age range: 12–17
No. of pupils: 9
Special needs catered for: BESD
✔

Greenfields School
Tenterden Road, Biddenden,
Kent TN27 8BS
Tel: 01580 292523
Age range: 5–11
No. of pupils: 13
Fees: Day £29,004
Special needs catered for: EBD
✔

Heath Farm School
Egerton Road, Charing Heath,
Ashford, Kent TN27 0AX
Tel: 01233 712 030
Age range: 5–18
Special needs catered for: ADHD,
ASC, ASP, BESD, DYS, DYSP
16+ ✔

Hope View School
Station Approach, Chilham,
Canterbury, Kent CT4 8EG
Tel: 01227 738000
Age range: 11–17
No. of pupils: 16
Special needs catered for:
ADD, ADHD, ASC, ASP, BESD
✔

ISP Sittingbourne School
Church Street, Sittingbourne,
Kent ME10 3EG
Tel: 01795 422 044
Age range: 11–16
Special needs catered for:
BESD, SCD, SEMH
✔

Learning Opportunities Centre
Ringwould Road, Ringwould,
Deal, Kent CT14 8DN
Tel: 01304 381906
Age range: 11–16
No. of pupils: 40
Special needs catered for: EBD
🏫 ✔

Little Acorns School
London Beach Farm,
Ashford Road, St Michael's,
Tenterden, Kent TN30 6SR
Tel: 01233 850422
Age range: 4–14
No. of pupils: 7
Special needs catered for: EBD
🏫 ✔

Meadows School and Meadows 16+
London Road, Southborough,
Kent TN4 0RJ
Tel: 01892 529144
Age range: 11–19
No. of pupils: 45
Special needs catered for: ADHD,
ASP, AUT, DYS, DYSP, EBD, MLD, SEMH
🏫 ✔

Ripplevale School
Chapel Lane, Ripple,
Deal, Kent CT14 8JG
Tel: 01304 373866
Age range: B9–16
No. of pupils: 30
Special needs catered for: ADD,
ADHD, ASC, ASP, AUT, BESD, CLD,
DYS, DYSP, EBD, GLD, HA, LD, MLD,
PMLD, SCD, SCLD, SP&LD, SPLD
👦 🏫 ✔

Small Haven School
146 Newington Road,
Ramsgate, Kent CT12 6PT
Tel: 01843 597088
Age range: 5–13
No. of pupils: 8
Fees: Day £23,863
Special needs catered for: ADD,
ADHD, ASC, ASP, AUT, BESD, CLD,
DEL, EBD, EPI, GLD, HA, HI, LD,
MLD, PH, SCD, SLD, SP&LD, SLI

The Davenport School
Foxborough Hill, Eastry,
Sandwich, Kent CT13 0NY
Tel: 01843 589018
Age range: B7–11
Special needs catered for: EBD
👦 ✔

The Lighthouse School
24 Clarendon Road,
Margate, Kent CT9 2QL
Tel: 01843 482043
Age range: 5–18
No. of pupils: 5
Special needs catered for:
BESD, SEMH
16+ ✔

The Old Priory School
Priory Road, Ramsgate,
Kent CT11 9PG
Tel: 01843 599322
Age range: B10–15
Special needs catered for: EBD
👦 ✔

WEST HEATH SCHOOL
For further details see p. 95
Ashgrove Road, Sevenoaks,
Kent TN13 1SR
Tel: 01732 460553
Email: admissions@
westheathschool.com
Website:
www.westheathschool.com
Principal: Mr James Nunns
Age range: 10–20
No. of pupils: 135
Fees: Day £52,500
Special needs catered for: ADD,
ADHD, ASC, ASP, BESD, DEL,
EBD, SCD, SEMH, SP&LD, SPLD
🏫 16+ ✔

Surrey

Cornfield School
53 Hanworth Road, Redhill,
Surrey RH1 5HS
Tel: 01737 779578
Age range: G11–18
No. of pupils: 25
Special needs catered for: EBD
🏫 16+ ✔

Grafham Grange School
Nr Bramley, Guildford,
Surrey GU5 0LH
Tel: 01483 892214
Age range: B10–19
Special needs catered for:
ADHD, ASC, BESD, EBD, SP&LD
👦 🏫 ✔

West Sussex

Brantridge School
Staplefield Place, Staplefield,
Haywards Heath, West
Sussex RH17 6EQ
Tel: 01444 400228
Age range: B6–13
No. of pupils: 27
Special needs catered for:
ADHD, ASC, ASP, BESD, EBD, LD
👦 🏫 ✔

Farney Close School
Bolney Court, Bolney,
West Sussex RH17 5RD
Tel: 01444 881811
Age range: 10–18 years
No. of pupils: 78
Fees: Day £55,222.10
Special needs catered for: ADHD,
ASP, DYS, EBD, MLD, SP&LD
🏫 16+ ✔

Hillcrest Slinfold School
Stane Street, Slinfold, Horsham,
West Sussex RH13 0QX
Tel: 01403 790939
Age range: B11–16 years
No. of pupils: 20
Special needs catered for:
ADD, ADHD, ASC, AUT,
BESD, EBD, SCD, SEMH
🏫

Muntham House School Ltd
Barns Green, Muntham Drive,
Horsham, West Sussex RH13 0NJ
Tel: 01403 730302
Age range: B8–18
No. of pupils: 51 VIth12
Special needs catered for:
ADD, ADHD, ASC, BESD, DYS,
EBD, MLD, SP&LD, SPLD
👦 🏫 16+ ✔

PHILPOTS MANOR SCHOOL
For further details see p. 94
West Hoathly, East Grinstead,
West Sussex RH19 4PR
Tel: 01342 810268
Email: info@
philpotsmanorschool.co.uk
Website: www.philpots
manorschool.co.uk/
Education Co-ordinator: Mr
Darin Nobes BA (Hons),
PGCE, NPQH
Age range: 7–19
No. of pupils: 43
Special needs catered for:
ADD, ADHD, ASC, ASP, AUT,
BESD, DEL, DYS, EBD, EPI, GLD,
LD, MLD, SCD, SEMH, SP&LD
🏫 16+ ✔

Springboard Senior
55 South Street, Lancing,
West Sussex BN15 8HA
Tel: 01903 605980
Age range: 11–18
No. of pupils: 10
Special needs catered for: ADD,
ADHD, ASC, ASP, AUT, BESD, EBD
16+ ✔

South-West

Cornwall

Oak Tree School
Truro Business Park, Threemilestone,
Truro, Cornwall TR4 9NH
Tel: 01872 264 221
Age range: 7–16
Special needs catered for:
SCD, SEMH

Devon

Cambian Devon School
Intek House, 52 Borough Road,
Paignton, Devon TQ4 7DQ
Tel: 01803 524537
Age range: 10–18
No. of pupils: 30
Special needs catered for:
EBD, LD, SEMH
16+ ✔

Oakwood Court College
7/9 Oak Park Villas, Dawlish,
Devon EX7 0DE
Tel: 01626 864066
Age range: 16–25
Special needs catered for: ADHD,
ASP, DYS, DYSP, EBD, EPI, MLD, SLD
♿ 16+

The Libra School
Edgemoor Court, South Radworthy,
South Molton, Devon EX36 3LN
Tel: 01598 740044
Age range: 8–18
Special needs catered for: EBD
16+ ✔

Gloucestershire

Marlowe Education Unit
Hartpury Old School,
Gloucester Road, Hartpury,
Gloucestershire GL19 3BG
Tel: 01452 700855
Age range: 8–16
No. of pupils: 8
Special needs catered for:
EBD, MLD
✔

Somerset

Cambian Somerset School
Creech Court, Mill Lane, Creech St.
Michael, Taunton, Somerset TA3 5PX
Tel: 01823 443133
Age range: 10–18
No. of pupils: 40
Special needs catered for:
ASC, ASP, AUT, EBD, SEMH
16+ ✔

Inaura School
Moorview House, Burrowbridge,
Bridgwater, Somerset TA7 0RB
Tel: 01823 690211
Age range: 8–18
No. of pupils: 26
Fees: Day £53,990
Special needs catered for: ADHD,
ASC, BESD, CLD, EBD, LD, SCD
16+ ✔

Newbury Manor School
Newbury, Mells, Nr. Frome,
Somerset BA11 3RG
Tel: 01373 814 980
Age range: 7–19
Special needs catered for:
ASC, ASP, AUT, SPLD
16+

Phoenix Academy
Newton Road, North Petherton,
Somerset TA6 6NA
Tel: 01271 318 110
Age range: 11–16
Special needs catered for: EBD
✔

Somerset Progressive School
Bath House Farm, West Hatch,
Taunton, Somerset TA3 5RH
Tel: 01823 481902
Age range: 9–19
No. of pupils: 22
Special needs catered for: ASC
16+ ✔

The Marchant-Holliday School
North Cheriton, Templecombe,
Somerset BA8 0AH
Tel: 01963 33234
Age range: B5–13
No. of pupils: 38
Special needs catered for:
ADD, ADHD, ASC, ASP, BESD,
DYS, DYSP, EBD, SCD
♿ ♿ ✔

Wiltshire

The Faringdon Centre
School Lane, Salisbury,
Wiltshire SP1 3YA
Tel: 01722 820 970
Age range: 11–16
No. of pupils: 8
Special needs catered for:
EBD, MLD

Wessex College
Boreham Mill, Bishopstrow,
Wiltshire BA12 9HQ
Tel: 01985 218486
Age range: 11–16
No. of pupils: 6
Special needs catered for: EBD
✔

West Midlands

Cheshire

Aidenswood
48 Parson Street, Congleton,
Cheshire CW12 4ED
Tel: 01260 281 353
Age range: B11–17
No. of pupils: 6
Special needs catered for:
EBD, MLD
♿ ♿ ✔

Herefordshire

Cambian Hereford School
Coningsby Road, Leominster,
Herefordshire HR6 8LL
Tel: 01568 620443
Age range: 11–19
No. of pupils: 20
Special needs catered for:
ADHD, EBD, SEMH, SPLD
16+ ✔

Queenswood School
Callows Hills Farm, Hereford Road,
Ledbury, Herefordshire HR8 2PZ
Tel: 01531 670 632
Age range: 11–18
No. of pupils: 15
Special needs catered for: ADD,
ADHD, ASC, BESD, DYS, DYSP,
MLD, SEMH, SP&LD, SPLD
♿ 16+ ✔

Shropshire

Care UK Children's Services
46 High Street, Church
Stretton, Shropshire SY6 6BX
Tel: 01694 724488
Age range: 10–18
No. of pupils: 24
Special needs catered for: EBD
16+

Hillcrest Shifnal School
Lamledge Lane, Shifnal,
Shropshire TF11 8SD
Tel: 01952 468220
Age range: 7–19 years
No. of pupils: 55
Special needs catered for:
ADD, ADHD, BESD, EBD, SEMH
♿ 16+

Smallbrook School
Unit 1-4, Sleap, Harmer Hill,
Shrewsbury, Shropshire SY4 3HE
Tel: 01939 233042
Age range: 11–19
Special needs catered for:
BESD, EBD, SEMH
16+

Staffordshire

Bloomfield College
Bloomfield Road, Tipton,
Staffordshire DY4 9ER
Tel: 0121 520 9408
Age range: 11–16
Special needs catered for: EBD

Draycott Moor College
Draycott Old Road, Draycott-
in-the-Moors, Stoke-on-Trent,
Staffordshire ST11 9AH
Tel: 01782 399 849
Age range: 11–16
Special needs catered for:
EBD, SCLD

Hillcrest Glebedale School
Grove Road, Heron Cross, Stoke-
on-Trent, Staffordshire ST4 3AY
Tel: 01782 320773
Age range: 7–19 years
No. of pupils: 30
Special needs catered for: ADD,
ADHD, BESD, EBD, SCD, SEMH
16+

Longdon Hall School
Longdon Green, Near Lichfield,
Staffordshire WS15 4PT
Tel: 01543 491 051
Age range: 7–18
Special needs catered for:
BESD, EBD, SEMH
16+ ✔

Emotional, behavioural and/or social difficulties (EBSD)

Warwickshire

Arc School Ansley
Ansley Lane, Ansley, Nuneaton, Warwickshire CV10 9ND
Tel: 01676 543 810
Age range: 11–16
Special needs catered for: ADHD, ASC, SEMH

Arc School Napton
Vicarage Road, Coventry, Warwickshire CV47 8NA
Tel: 01926 817547
Age range: 5–11
Special needs catered for: ADHD, ASC, SEMH

Arc School Old Arley
Old Arley, Ansley, Nuneaton, Warwickshire CV7 8NU
Tel: 01676 543200
Age range: 7–16
Special needs catered for: ADHD, ASC, SEMH

Wathen Grange School
Church Walk, Mancetter, Atherstone, Warwickshire CV9 1PZ
Tel: 01827 714454
Age range: 11–16
No. of pupils: 15
Special needs catered for: EBD

West Midlands

Blue River Academy
Sara Park, 160 Herbert Road, Small Heath, Birmingham, West Midlands B10 0PR
Tel: 0121 753 1933
Age range: B14–16
Special needs catered for: BESD

Fairways School
Redhill Road, Kings Norton, Birmingham, West Midlands B38 9EL
Tel: 07974 256232
Age range: 11–17
No. of pupils: 25
Special needs catered for: ADHD, ASC, DYS, MLD, SEMH

The Wenlock School
Fossil View, Wrens Hill Road, Dudley, West Midlands DY1 3SS
Tel: 01384 884 883
Age range: 7–18
Special needs catered for: ASC, ASP, AUT, SEMH

Values Academy Birmingham
15 Key Hill, Hockley Hill, Hockley, Birmingham, West Midlands B18 5AQ
Tel: 0121 5230222
Age range: 11–17
No. of pupils: 25
Special needs catered for: BESD, EBD, SEMH

Woodbury School
Hellier Road, Wolverhampton, West Midlands WV10 8ED
Tel: 01902 507 052
Special needs catered for: SEMH

Worcestershire

The Corner House School
Laurel Farm, Dagnall End Lane, Bowley, Redditch, Worcestershire B98 9BD
Tel: 01527 63327
Age range: 9–19
Special needs catered for: SEMH

Yorkshire & Humberside

East Riding of Yorkshire

Cambian Beverley School
Units 19 & 20, Priory Road, Beverley, East Riding of Yorkshire HU17 0EW
Tel: 01482 307830
Age range: 9–18
No. of pupils: 16
Special needs catered for: ADHD, ASC, ASP, AUT, SEMH

Horton House School
Hilltop Farm, Sutton Road, Wawne, Kingston upon Hull, East Riding of Yorkshire HU7 5YY
Tel: 01482 875191
Age range: 8–23
Fees: Day £25,000–£50,000 WB £75,000–£150,000 FB £180,000
Special needs catered for: ADD, ADHD, ASC, ASP, AUT, BESD, CLD, DYS, DYSP, EBD, EPI, GLD, LD, MLD, SCD, SCLD, SEMH, SLD, SPLD

North Yorkshire

Breckenbrough School
Sandhutton, Thirsk, North Yorkshire YO7 4EN
Tel: 01845 587238
Age range: B9–19
No. of pupils: 49
Special needs catered for: ADD, ADHD, ASP, BESD, DEL, DYS, EBD, HA

Cambian Scarborough School
Unit 11, Plaxton Park Industrial Estate, Cayton Low Road, Scarborough, North Yorkshire YO11 3BQ
Tel: 01723 582073
Age range: 8–18
No. of pupils: 18
Special needs catered for: ADHD, ASC, ASP, AUT, EBD, SEMH

Cambian Spring Hill School
Palace Road, Ripon, North Yorkshire HG4 3HN
Tel: 01765 603320
Age range: 8–19
No. of pupils: 23
Special needs catered for: ASC, ASP, AUT, LD

Clervaux
Clow Beck Centre, Jolby Lane, Croft-on-Tees, North Yorkshire DL2 2TF
Tel: 01325 729860
Age range: 16–25+
Special needs catered for: ASC, ASP, AUT, BESD, CLD

Tees Valley College
Sotherby Road, Middlesbrough, North Yorkshire TS3 8BT
Tel: 01642 218776
Age range: 14–16
No. of pupils: 75
Special needs catered for: BESD

South Yorkshire

Brantwood Specialist School
1 Kenwood Bank, Nether Edge, Sheffield, South Yorkshire S7 1NU
Tel: 0114 258 9062
Age range: 7–19
Special needs catered for: ADD, ADHD, ASC, ASP, BESD, CLD, EBD, GLD, LD, MLD, PMLD, SCD, SCLD, SEMH, SPLD

Park House School
Wentworth Way, Tankersley, Barnsley, South Yorkshire S75 3DH
Tel: 01706 227226
Age range: 7–17
No. of pupils: 24
Special needs catered for: BESD

West Yorkshire

Broadwood School
252 Moor End Road, Halifax, West Yorkshire HX2 0RU
Tel: 01422 355925
Age range: 7–18
No. of pupils: 45
Special needs catered for: EBD

Denby Grange School
Stocksmoor Road, Midgley, Wakefield, West Yorkshire WF4 4JG
Tel: 01924 830096
Age range: 11–18
No. of pupils: 36
Special needs catered for: EBD, SCD

Meadowcroft School
24 Bar Lane, Wakefield, West Yorkshire WF1 4AD
Tel: 01924 366 242
Age range: 5–19
Special needs catered for: ASC, AUT, BESD, EBD, SEMH

The Grange School
2 Milner Way, Ossett, Wakefield, West Yorkshire WF5 9JE
Tel: 01924 378957
Age range: 7–14
No. of pupils: 16
Special needs catered for: BESD

William Henry Smith School
Boothroyd, Brighouse, West Yorkshire HD6 3JW
Tel: 01484 710123
Age range: B8–19
No. of pupils: 64
Fees: Day £57,810 FB £70,435
Special needs catered for: ADD, ADHD, ASC, BESD, CLD, GLD, SCD, SEMH, SPLD

Northern Ireland

County Down

Camphill Community Glencraig
Craigavad, Holywood,
County Down BT18 0DB
Tel: 028 9042 3396
Age range: 7–19
No. of pupils: 32
Fees: FB £66,500
Special needs catered for: ADHD,
ASP, AUT, CP, DYSP, EBD, EPI, HI, MLD,
PH, PMLD, SLD, SP&LD, SPLD, VIS

16⁺ 🏛 16⁺

Scotland

Edinburgh

Harmeny Education Trust Ltd
Harmeny School, Balerno,
Edinburgh EH14 7JY
Tel: 0131 449 3938
Age range: 6–13
No. of pupils: 36
Special needs catered for: ADD,
ADHD, ASP, DYS, EBD, SPLD
🏛

Fife

Falkland House School
Falkland Estate, Cupar,
Fife KY15 7AE
Tel: 01337 857268
Age range: B5–18
No. of pupils: 30
Fees: FB £70,000
Special needs catered for:
ADD, ADHD, ASP, BESD,
DYS, EBD, EPI, SCD, SPLD
🧍 🏛 ⬦ 16⁺

Hillside School
Hillside, Aberdour, Fife KY3 0RH
Tel: 01383 860731
Age range: B10–16
No. of pupils: 39
Fees: Day £10,830
FB £26,594–£58,959
Special needs catered for:
DYS, EBD, SPLD
🧍 🏛

Starley Hall School
Aberdour Road, Burntisland,
Fife KY3 0AG
Tel: 01383 860314
Age range: 10–16
No. of pupils: 48
Special needs catered for:
EBD, MLD
🏛

North Lanarkshire

St Philip's School
10 Main Street, Plains, Airdrie,
North Lanarkshire ML6 7SF
Tel: 01236 765407
Age range: B12–16
No. of pupils: 61
Special needs catered for: EBD
🧍 🏛

Perth & Kinross

Balnacraig School
Fairmount Terrace, Perth,
Perth & Kinross PH2 7AR
Tel: 01738 636456
Age range: 12–16
No. of pupils: 24
Special needs catered for:
BESD, EBD

Seamab School
Rumbling Bridge, Kinross,
Perth & Kinross KY13 0PT
Tel: 01577 840307
Age range: 5–12
No. of pupils: 15
Special needs catered for: EBD
🏛

Renfrewshire

Kibble Education and Care Centre
Goudie Street, Paisley,
Renfrewshire PA3 2LG
Tel: 0141 889 0044
Age range: 12–16
No. of pupils: 93
Special needs catered for:
EBD, MLD, SCD, SLD, SPLD
🏛

Spark of Genius
Trojan House, Phoenix Business
Park, Paisley, Renfrewshire PA1 2BH
Tel: 0141 587 2710
Age range: 5–18
No. of pupils: 120
Special needs catered for: ADHD,
ASC, DYS, DYSP, EBD, SEMH

The Good Shepherd Secure/Close Support Unit
Greenock Road, Bishopton,
Renfrewshire PA7 5PW
Tel: 01505 864500
Age range: G12–17
Special needs catered for:
EBD, MLD
🧍 🏛

Stirling

Ballikinrain Residential School
Fintry Road, Balfron, Stirling G63 0LL
Tel: 01360 440244
Age range: B8–14
No. of pupils: 40
Special needs catered for: BESD
🧍 🏛

Snowdon School
31 Spittal Street, Stirling FK8 1DU
Tel: 01786 464746
Age range: G13–17
Special needs catered for: BESD
🧍 🏛

West Lothian

Moore House School
21 Edinburgh Road, Bathgate,
West Lothian EH48 1EX
Tel: 01506 652312
Age range: 8–16
No. of pupils: 37
Special needs catered for:
ADHD, EBD
🏛

Wales

Denbighshire

The Branas School
Branas Isaf, Llandrillo, Corwen,
Denbighshire LL21 0TA
Tel: 01490 440545
Age range: B12–17
No. of pupils: 12
Special needs catered for: EBD

Monmouthshire

Talocher School
Talocher Farm, Wonastow
Road, Monmouth,
Monmouthshire NP25 4DN
Tel: 01600 740 777
Age range: 9–19
No. of pupils: 25
Special needs catered for:
ADD, ADHD, BESD, DYS,
DYSP, MLD, SEMH, SPLD

Pembrokeshire

Marlowe St David's Education Unit
Pembroke House, Brawdy
Business Park, Haverfordwest,
Pembrokeshire SA62 6NP
Tel: 01437 721234
Age range: 8–17
No. of pupils: 7
Special needs catered for: EBD

Wrexham

Woodlands
27 Pentrefelyn Road,
Wrexham LL13 7NB
Tel: 01978 262777
Age range: B11–18
No. of pupils: 14
Special needs catered for:
ADD, ADHD, ASC, ASP, AUT,
BESD, DYS, DYSP, EBD, GLD,
HA, HI, LD, MLD, SCD, SLD

Schools and colleges specialising in learning difficulties (including dyslexia/SPLD)

Abbreviations

ACLD	Autism, Communication and Associated Learning Difficulties
ADD	Attention Deficit Disorder
ADHD	Attention Deficit and Hyperactive Disorder (Hyperkinetic Disorder)
ASC	Autistic Spectrum Conditions
ASP	Asperger Syndrome
AUT	Autism
BESD	Behavioural, Emotional and Social Difficulties
CCD	Complex Communication Difficulties
CLD	Complex Learning Difficulties
CP	Cerebral Palsy
D	Deaf
DEL	Delicate
DYS	Dyslexia
DYSP	Dyspraxia
EBD	Emotional and Behavioural Difficulties
EBSD	Emotional, Behavioural and/ or Social Difficulties
EPI	Epilepsy
GLD	General Learning Difficulties
HA	High Ability
HI	Hearing Impairment
HS	Hospital School
LD	Learning Difficulties
MLD	Moderate Learning Difficulties
MSI	Multi-sensory Impairment
OCD	Obsessive Compulsive Disorder
PD	Physical Difficulties
PH	Physical Impairment
Phe	Partially Hearing
PMLD	Profound and Multiple Learning Difficulties
PNI	Physical Neurological Impairment
PRU	Pupil Referral Unit
SCD	Social and Communication Difficulties
SCLD	Severe and Complex Learning Difficulties
SEBD	Severe Emotional and Behavioural Disorders
SEBN	Social, Emotional and Behavioural Needs
SLD	Severe Learning Difficulties
SLI	Specific Language Impairment
SPLD	Specific Learning Difficulties
SP&LD	Speech and Language Difficulties
SLCN	Speech Language & Communication Needs
VIS	Visually Impaired

Key to Symbols

Type of school:

♂	Boys' school
♀	Girls' school
🌐	International school

School offers:

Ⓐ	A levels
🏠	Residential
16+	Entrance at 16+
✿	Vocational qualifications
✎	Learning support
✓	This is a DfE approved independent or non-maintained school under section 41 of the Children and Families Act 2014 or section 342 of the 1996 Education Act

Please note: Unless otherwise indicated, all schools are coeducational day schools. Single-sex and boarding schools will be indicated by the relevant icon.

England – Central & West

Bristol

Aurora St Christopher's School
Westbury Park, Bristol BS6 7JE
Tel: 0117 973 3301
Age range: 5–19
Special needs catered for:
ASC, AUT, CLD, CP, EPI, PD, Phe,
PMLD, SCLD, SLD, SP&LD

Belgrave School
10 Upper Belgrave Road,
Clifton, Bristol BS8 2XH
Tel: 0117 974 3133
Age range: 5–13
Fees: Day £6,000
Special needs catered for: ADD,
DEL, DYS, DYSP, SP&LD, SLI

Bristol Dyslexia Centre
10 Upper Belgrave Road,
Clifton, Bristol BS8 2XH
Tel: 0117 973 9405
Special needs catered for:
DYS, DYSP, SLD

Sheiling School, Thornbury
Thornbury Park, Thornbury,
Bristol BS35 1HP
Tel: 01454 412194
Age range: 6–19
No. of pupils: 22
Fees: Day £66,419–£83,428
WB £125,931–£172,096
FB £140,578–£197,157
Special needs catered for: ADD,
ADHD, ASC, ASP, AUT, BESD, CLD,
CP, DEL, DYS, DYSP, EBD, EPI, GLD,
HA, HI, LD, MLD, MSI, PD, Phe, SCD,
SCLD, SEMH, SLD, SP&LD, SPLD, SLI

Buckinghamshire

MacIntyre Wingrave School
Leighton Road, Wingrave,
Buckinghamshire HP22 4PA
Tel: 01296 681274
Age range: 10–19
No. of pupils: 38
Fees: FB £182,000
Special needs catered for:
ASC, SCD, SLD

Gloucestershire

Bredon School
Pull Court, Bushley, Tewkesbury,
Gloucestershire GL20 6AH
Tel: 01684 293156
Age range: 7–18
No. of pupils: 215
Fees: Day £11,040–£21,945
WB £15,440–£26,345
FB £15,440–£26,345
Special needs catered for:
DYS, DYSP, SPLD

Ruskin Mill College
The Fisheries, Horsley,
Gloucestershire GL6 0PL
Tel: 01453 837502
Age range: 16–25
Special needs catered for: ADHD,
ASC, ASP, BESD, CLD, EBD, GLD, LD,
MLD, PMLD, SCD, SCLD, SEMH, SPLD

William Morris College
Eastington, Stonehouse,
Gloucestershire GL10 3SH
Tel: 01453 824025
Age range: 16–25
No. of pupils: 30
Special needs catered for:
ASP, AUT, DYSP, EBD, EPI, MLD

Oxfordshire

Bruern Abbey School
Chesterton, Bicester,
Oxfordshire OX26 1UY
Tel: 01869 242448
Age range: B7–13
No. of pupils: 44
Fees: Day £5,703 WB £7,791
Special needs catered for:
DYS, DYSP

The Unicorn School
20 Marcham Road, Abingdon,
Oxfordshire OX14 1AA
Tel: 01235 530222
Age range: 6–16 years
No. of pupils: 74
Fees: Day £19,500
Special needs catered for:
DYS, DYSP

Wiltshire

Calder House School
Thickwood Lane, Colerne,
Wiltshire SN14 8BN
Tel: 01225 743566
Age range: 6–13
No. of pupils: 48
Fees: Day £16,200
Special needs catered for: DEL,
DYS, DYSP, SP&LD, SPLD, SLI

FAIRFIELD FARM COLLEGE
For further details see p. 98
43 High Street, Dilton Marsh,
Wiltshire BA13 4DL
Tel: 01373 823028
Email: admissions@ffc.ac.uk
Website: www.ffc.ac.uk
CEO/Principal: Dr Tina Pagett
Age range: 16–26
No. of pupils: 105
Special needs catered for:
LD, MLD

On Track Education Centre, Westbury
Broadway House, Headquarters
Road, Westbury, Wiltshire BA13 4JX
Tel: 01373 859803
Age range: 11–19
No. of pupils: 32
Special needs catered for:
ASC, MLD, SCLD, SEMH, SPLD

Tumblewood Project School
The Laurels, 4 Hawkeridge
Road, Heywood, Westbury,
Wiltshire BA13 4LF
Tel: 01373 824 466
Age range: G11–18
No. of pupils: 12
Special needs catered for:
ADHD, DYS, DYSP, LD

East

Bedfordshire

On Track Education Centre, Silsoe
Building 53, Wrest Park, Silsoe,
Bedfordshire MK45 4HS
Tel: 01525 864961
Age range: 11–19
No. of pupils: 32
Special needs catered for:
ASC, MLD, SCLD, SEMH, SPLD

Cambridgeshire

Holme Court School
Abington Woods, Church
Lane, Little Abington,
Cambridgeshire CB21 6BQ
Tel: 01223 778030
Age range: 5–16
No. of pupils: 27
Special needs catered for: ADD,
ADHD, ASP, CLD, DYS, DYSP, GLD,
HA, LD, MLD, SCD, SP&LD, SPLD, VIS

Essex

Doucecroft School
Abbots Lane, Eight Ash Green,
Colchester, Essex CO6 3QL
Tel: 01206 771234
Age range: 3–19
No. of pupils: 46
Fees: Day £52,779–£54,291
WB £86,211–£88,211
Special needs catered for:
ASC, ASP, AUT

Woodcroft School
Whitakers Way, Loughton,
Essex IG10 1SQ
Tel: 020 8508 1369
Age range: 2–11
No. of pupils: 36
Special needs catered for:
ADD, ADHD, ASC, ASP, AUT,
CLD, CP, DEL, DYSP, EBD, EPI,
LD, MLD, MSI, PH, PMLD, SCLD,
SLD, SP&LD, SPLD, SLI, VIS

Learning difficulties (including dyslexia/SPLD)

Hertfordshire

Egerton Rothesay School
Durrants Lane, Berkhamsted,
Hertfordshire HP4 3UJ
Tel: 01442 865275
Age range: 5–19
No. of pupils: 179
Fees: Day £16,020–£22,800
Special needs catered for:
ASC, AUT, DYS, DYSP, SP&LD

Lincolnshire

Kisimul Upper School
Acacia Hall, Shortwood
Lane, Friesthorpe, Lincoln,
Lincolnshire LN3 5AL
Tel: 01673 880022
Age range: 8–19
Special needs catered for: ASC, SLD

Norfolk

Copperfield School
22 Euston Road, Great
Yarmouth, Norfolk NR30 1DX
Tel: 01493 849 499
Age range: 11–16
No. of pupils: 12
Special needs catered for:
ADD, ADHD, ASP, BESD, CLD,
DYS, DYSP, EBD, GLD, LD, MLD,
SCD, SCLD, SEMH, SPLD

Suffolk

Centre Academy East Anglia
Church Road, Brettenham,
Ipswich, Suffolk IP7 7QR
Tel: 01449 736404
Age range: 4–19
Fees: Day £18,000–£25,875
WB £24,999–£36,225
Special needs catered for:
ADHD, ASP, CLD, DYS, DYSP,
GLD, HA, LD, SP&LD, SPLD

Riverwalk School
Chevington Close, Bury St
Edmunds, Suffolk IP33 3JZ
Tel: 01284 764280
Age range: 3–19
Special needs catered for: SCLD

East Midlands

Derbyshire

Alderwasley Hall School & Sixth Form Centre
Alderwasley, Belper,
Derbyshire DE56 2SR
Tel: 01629 822586
Age range: 5–19
Special needs catered for:
ADHD, ASC, ASP, AUT, DYSP, GLD,
HA, LD, SCD, SP&LD, SPLD, SLI

Pegasus School
Caldwell Hall, Main Street,
Caldwell, Derbyshire DE12 6RS
Tel: 01283 761352
Age range: 8–19
Special needs catered for: ADHD,
ASC, AUT, CLD, EPI, HI, LD, PMLD,
SCLD, SLD, SP&LD, SPLD, SLI, VIS

Lincolnshire

KISIMUL SCHOOL
For further details see p. 100
The Old Vicarage, 61 High
Street, Swinderby, Lincoln,
Lincolnshire LN6 9LU
Tel: 01522 868279
Email: admissions@kisimul.co.uk
Website: www.kisimul.co.uk
Director of Education: Ms
Emma Sanderson
Age range: 8–19
No. of pupils: 60
Special needs catered for: ASC,
AUT, CLD, EBD, EPI, LD, MSI, PMLD,
SCLD, SEMH, SLD, SP&LD, SPLD

Linkage College – Toynton Campus
Toynton All Saints, Spilsby,
Lincolnshire PE23 5AE
Tel: 01790 752499
Age range: 16–25
Special needs catered for:
ADD, ADHD, ASC, ASP, AUT, CLD,
CP, D, DEL, DYS, DYSP, EPI, GLD,
HI, LD, MLD, PD, Phe, PH, SCD,
SCLD, SLD, SP&LD, SPLD, VIS

Nottinghamshire

I CAN'S DAWN HOUSE SCHOOL
For further details see p. 99
Helmsley Road, Rainworth,
Mansfield, Nottinghamshire
NG21 0DQ
Tel: 01623 795361
Email: enquiries@dawnhouse-
ican.notts.sch.uk
Website:
www.dawnhouseschool.org.uk
Principal: Jenny McConnell
Age range: 5–19
No. of pupils: 66
Special needs catered for:
ASP, CLD, DYS, DYSP, SCD,
SLD, SP&LD, SPLD

Sutherland House – Continuing Education Centre
8 Clinton Avenue, Nottingham,
Nottinghamshire NG5 1AW
Tel: 0115 9693373
Age range: 11–19
Special needs catered for:
ASC, AUT

Sutherland House School
Bath Street, Sneinton, Nottingham,
Nottinghamshire NG1 1DA
Tel: 0115 960 9263
Age range: 3–19
No. of pupils: 84
Fees: Day £41,525–£45,473
Special needs catered for:
ASC, ASP, AUT

Greater London

Essex

St John's RC Special School
Turpins Lane, Woodford
Bridge, Essex IG8 8AX
Tel: 020 8504 1818
Age range: 5–19
No. of pupils: 100
Special needs catered for:
AUT, MLD, SLD, SP&LD

Middlesex

Pield Heath House School
Pield Heath Road, Uxbridge,
Middlesex UB8 3NW
Tel: 01895 258507
Age range: 7–19
No. of pupils: 96
Special needs catered for:
MLD, SLD, SP&LD

Surrey

Blossom Lower School and Upper House (Motspur Park)
Station Road, Motspur Park,
New Malden, Surrey KT3 6JJ
Tel: 020 8946 7348
Age range: 3–19
Special needs catered for:
ADD, ADHD, ASC, DYS,
DYSP, SCD, SP&LD, SPLD

Rutherford School
1A Melville Avenue, South
Croydon, Surrey CR2 7HZ
Tel: 020 8688 7560
Age range: 3–19
No. of pupils: 26
Fees: Day £50,400
Special needs catered for:
CP, D, EPI, HI, MSI, PD, Phe, PH,
PMLD, PNI, SLD, SP&LD, VIS

The Link Primary School
138 Croydon Road, Beddington,
Croydon, Surrey CR0 4PG
Tel: 020 8688 5239
Age range: 4–11
No. of pupils: 50
Special needs catered for:
ASC, ASP, DYSP, GLD, LD,
MLD, SCD, SP&LD, SLI
✔

London

East London

Side by Side Special School
9 Big Hill, London E5 9HH
Tel: 020 8880 8300
Age range: 2–16
No. of pupils: 60
Special needs catered for:
MLD, SLD, SP&LD
✔

North London

Limespring School
Park House, 16 High Road, East
Finchley, London N2 9PJ
Tel: 020 8444 1387
Age range: 7–11
Special needs catered for:
DYS, DYSP
✔

North-West London

Abingdon House School
Broadley Terrace, London NW1 6LG
Tel: 020 3750 5526
Age range: 5–16
Special needs catered for: ADD,
ADHD, ASP, DYS, DYSP, SP&LD, SPLD
🌐 ✏ ✔

Blossom Lower School and Upper House
1-5 Christopher Place, Chalton
Street, London NW1 1JF
Tel: 020 7383 3834
Age range: 3–11
No. of pupils: 17
Special needs catered for:
ADD, ADHD, ASP, DYS,
DYSP, SCD, SP&LD, SPLD
✔

Kisharon School
1011 Finchley Road,
London NW11 7HB
Tel: 020 8455 7483
Age range: 4–19
No. of pupils: 35
Fees: Day £27,000–£42,000
Special needs catered for: ADD,
ADHD, ASC, ASP, AUT, BESD, CLD,
CP, D, DEL, DYS, DYSP, EBD, EPI,
GLD, HA, HI, LD, MLD, MSI, PD,
Phe, PH, PMLD, PNI, SCD, SCLD,
SEMH, SLD, SP&LD, SPLD, SLI, VIS
✔

South-East London

Octavia House School, Kennington
214b Kennington Road,
London SE11 6AU
Tel: 020 3651 4396 (Option:3)
Special needs catered for: ADD,
ADHD, BESD, EBD, SCD, SEMH

South-West London

Centre Academy London
92 St John's Hill, Battersea,
London SW11 1SH
Tel: 020 7738 2344
Age range: 9–19
Fees: Day £27,600–£40,100
Special needs catered for:
ADD, ADHD, ASC, ASP, AUT,
CLD, DYS, DYSP, HA, SP&LD
£ ✏ 16 ✔

Fairley House School
30 Causton Street,
London SW1P 4AU
Tel: 020 7976 5456
Age range: 5–16
No. of pupils: 203
Fees: Day £30,300
Special needs catered for:
DYS, DYSP, SPLD
🌐 ✔

Frederick Hugh House
48 Old Church Street,
London SW3 5BY
Tel: 0207 349 8833
Age range: 10–16
Special needs catered for:
ADHD, ASC, AUT, CLD, CP,
DEL, DYSP, EPI, GLD, LD, MLD,
MSI, PD, SCD, SP&LD, SPLD
✔

Parayhouse School
Hammersmith and Fulham College,
Gliddon Road, London W14 9BL
Tel: 020 8741 1400
Age range: 7–16
No. of pupils: 46
Fees: Day £27,540
Special needs catered for: ADD,
BESD, CLD, CP, DEL, EBD, EPI, MLD,
Phe, SCD, SCLD, SLD, SP&LD
✔

The Dominie
55 Warriner Gardens,
Battersea, London SW11 4DX
Tel: 020 7720 8783
Age range: 6–13
No. of pupils: 30
Special needs catered for:
DYS, DYSP, SP&LD
✔

The Moat School
Bishops Avenue, Fulham,
London SW6 6EG
Tel: 020 7610 9018
Age range: 9–16
Fees: Day £30,000
Special needs catered for:
DYS, DYSP, SPLD
🌐 ✏ ✔

North-East

Northumberland

Cambian Dilston College
Dilston Hall, Corbridge,
Northumberland NE45 5RJ
Tel: 01434 632692
Age range: 16–25
No. of pupils: 60
Special needs catered for:
ASC, LD, SCD
♿ 16

Nunnykirk School
Nunnykirk Hall, Netherwitton,
Morpeth, Northumberland
NE61 4PB
Tel: 01670 772685
Age range: 9–18
No. of pupils: 50
Fees: Day £5,200
Special needs catered for:
ASC, DYS, SEMH, SPLD
Ⓐ ♿ 16 ✔

North-West

Cheshire

The David Lewis School
Mill Lane, Warford, Alderley
Edge, Cheshire SK9 7UD
Tel: 01565 640066
Age range: 14–19
No. of pupils: 20
Special needs catered for:
AUT, CP, EPI, HI, PD, PMLD,
SCD, SLD, SP&LD, SPLD, VIS

Greater Manchester

Birtenshaw School (Bolton)
Darwen Road, Bolton, Greater
Manchester BL7 9AB
Tel: 01204 306043
Age range: 3–19
No. of pupils: 35 VIth25
Fees: Day £49,757–£71,084
Special needs catered for: ADD,
ADHD, ASC, ASP, AUT, CLD, CP,
DEL, EPI, GLD, HI, LD, MLD, MSI,
PD, Phe, PH, PMLD, PNI, SCD,
SCLD, SLD, SP&LD, SLI, VIS

Bridge College
Openshaw Campus, Whitworth
Street, Manchester, Greater
Manchester M11 2GR
Tel: 0161 487 4293
Age range: 16–25
Special needs catered for: ASC,
AUT, CLD, LD, PH, PMLD, SCD

Langdon College
9 Leicester Avenue, Salford,
Greater Manchester M7 4HA
Tel: 0161 740 5900
Age range: 16–25
Special needs catered for:
ASC, ASP, AUT, BESD, DYS, DYSP,
EBD, GLD, HI, LD, MLD, Phe, PH,
SCD, SP&LD, SPLD, SLI, VIS

Lancashire

Pontville School
Black Moss Lane, Ormskirk,
Lancashire L39 4TW
Tel: 01695 578734
Age range: 5–19
Special needs catered for:
ADHD, ASC, ASP, CLD, MLD,
SCD, SEMH, SP&LD, SPLD, SLI

Progress School
Gough Lane, Bamber Bridge,
Preston, Lancashire PR26 7TZ
Tel: 01772 334832
Age range: 7–19
No. of pupils: 17
Fees: WB £3,269 FB £170,000
Special needs catered for:
AUT, PMLD, SCLD, SLD

Merseyside

Birtenshaw School (Merseyside)
82 Higher Lane, Liverpool,
Merseyside L9 7AB
Tel: 0151 317 8277
Age range: 3–19
Special needs catered for:
ASC, MSI, PD, SCD

Liverpool Progressive School
Rice Lane, Liverpool,
Merseyside L9 1NR
Tel: 0151 525 4004
Age range: 8–19
No. of pupils: 22
Special needs catered for:
ASC, PMLD

Wargrave House School
449 Wargrave Road, Newton-le-
Willows, Merseyside WA12 8RS
Tel: 01925 224899
Age range: 5–19
No. of pupils: 70
Special needs catered for: ASP, AUT

South-East

East Sussex

Frewen College
Brickwall, Rye Road, Northiam,
Rye, East Sussex TN31 6NL
Tel: 01797 252 494
Age range: 7–19
No. of pupils: 103
Fees: Day £13,686–£21,801
WB £21,078–£30,264
FB £21,078–£30,264
Special needs catered for:
DYS, DYSP, SP&LD, SPLD

Northease Manor School
Rodmell, Lewes, East Sussex BN7 3EY
Tel: 01273 472915
Age range: 10–17
No. of pupils: 95
Special needs catered for:
ADD, ADHD, ASC, ASP, DYS,
DYSP, SCD, SP&LD, SPLD

Owlswick School
Newhaven Road, Kingston,
Lewes, East Sussex BN7 3NF
Tel: 01273 473078
Age range: 10–17
Special needs catered for: ADD,
ADHD, ASC, ASP, BESD, DYS,
DYSP, EBD, GLD, LD, MLD, SCD

St John's School & College
Business Centre, 17 Walpole Road,
Brighton, East Sussex BN2 0AF
Tel: 01273 244000
Age range: 7–25
No. of pupils: 118
Fees: Day £50,000 FB £100,000
Special needs catered for: ADD,
ADHD, ASC, ASP, AUT, BESD, CLD,
CP, D, DEL, DYS, DYSP, EBD, EPI,
GLD, HA, LD, MLD, PD, PNI, SCD,
SCLD, SEMH, SLD, SP&LD, SPLD, SLI

Hampshire

Chiltern Tutorial School
Otterbourne New Hall,
Cranbourne Drive, Otterbourne,
Winchester, Hampshire SO21 2ET
Tel: 01962 717696
Age range: 7–12
No. of pupils: 20
Fees: Day £8,850
Special needs catered for:
DYS, DYSP

Clay Hill School
Clay Hill, Lyndhurst,
Hampshire SO43 7DE
Tel: 023 8028 3633
Age range: 5–19
Special needs catered for: ASC, LD

Minstead Training Project
Minstead Lodge, Minstead,
Lyndhurst, Hampshire SO43 7FT
Tel: 023 80812254
Age range: 18+
No. of pupils: 14
Special needs catered for:
GLD, LD, MLD

Sheiling College
Horton Road, Ashley, Ringwood,
Hampshire BH24 2EB
Tel: 01425 477488
Age range: 19–25
No. of pupils: 32
Special needs catered for: ASC,
AUT, CLD, EPI, GLD, LD, MLD,
SCD, SCLD, SLD, SP&LD, SPLD

Sheiling School
Horton Road, Ashley, Ringwood,
Hampshire BH24 2EB
Tel: 01425 477488
Age range: 6–19
No. of pupils: 31
Fees: Day £39,070
WB £88,260 FB £106,008
Special needs catered for: ASC,
AUT, CLD, EBD, EPI, GLD, LD, MLD,
SCD, SCLD, SLD, SP&LD, SPLD

THE LODDON SCHOOL
For further details see p. 108
Wildmoor Lane, Sherfield-
on-Loddon, Hook,
Hampshire RG27 0JD
Tel: 01256 884600
Email: info@loddonschool.co.uk
Website:
www.loddonschool.co.uk
Principal: Dr Gill Barrett PhD,
MEd, BA(Hons), NPQH, PCGE
Age range: 8–19
No. of pupils: 30
Special needs catered for:
ADHD, ASC, AUT, SLD, SP&LD

Isle of Wight

St Catherine's School
Grove Road, Ventnor, Isle
of Wight PO38 1TT
Tel: 01983 852722
Age range: 7–19+
No. of pupils: 64 VIth33
Special needs catered for:
ADD, ADHD, ASC, ASP, AUT, DYS,
DYSP, SCD, SLD, SP&LD, SLI

Kent

Great Oaks Small School
Ebbsfleet Farmhouse,
Ebbsfleet Lane, Minster,
Ramsgate. Kent CT12 5DI
Tel: 01843 822 022
Age range: 10–18
No. of pupils: 18 VIth3
Special needs catered for: SPLD
(A)(✓)

West London

Trinity School & College
10-13 New Road, Rochester,
Kent ME1 1BG
Tel: 01634 812233
Age range: 6–25
Special needs catered for:
ASC, ASP, AUT, DYS, DYSP
(✏)(16+)

Surrey

I CAN'S MEATH SCHOOL
For further details see p. 104
Brox Road, Ottershaw,
Surrey KT16 0LF
Tel: 01932 872302
Email: meath@meath-ican.org.uk
Website:
www.meathschool.org.uk
Headteacher: Rob Walton
B.Ed (Hons) Primary
No. of pupils: 60
Special needs catered for:
ASC, ASP, AUT, SCD, SP&LD
(🏢)(✓)

KISIMUL SCHOOL – WOODSTOCK HOUSE
For further details see p. 102
Woodstock Lane North, Long
Ditton, Surbiton, Surrey KT6 5HN
Tel: 020 8335 2570
Email: admissions@kisimul.co.uk
Website: www.kisimul.co.uk
Director of Education: Ms
Emma Sanderson
Age range: 8–19
No. of pupils: 40
Special needs catered for:
ASC, AUT, BESD, CLD, EBD,
EPI, LD, MSI, PMLD, SCLD,
SEMH, SLD, SP&LD, SPLD
(🏢)(16+)(✓)

Knowl Hill School
School Lane, Pirbright,
Woking, Surrey GU24 0JN
Tel: 01483 797032
Age range: 7–16
No. of pupils: 57
Fees: Day £15,606
Special needs catered for:
DYS, DYSP, SPLD
(£)(✏)(✓)

Moon Hall College
Burys Court, Flanchford Road,
Leigh, Reigate, Surrey RH2 8RE
Tel: 01306 611372
Age range: 3–16
Fees: Day £6,630–£17,220
Special needs catered for:
DYS, LD, SPLD

Moon Hall School
Pasturewood Road, Holmbury St
Mary, Dorking, Surrey RH5 6LQ
Tel: 01306 731464
Age range: 7–13
Fees: Day £14,400–£16,470
WB £16,015–£18,085
Special needs catered for:
DYS, SPLD
(🌐)(🏢)(✓)

MORE HOUSE SCHOOL
For further details see p. 105
Moons Hill, Frensham,
Farnham, Surrey GU10 3AP
Tel: 01252 792303
Email: schooloffice@
morehouseschool.co.uk
Website:
www.morehouseschool.co.uk
Headmaster: Jonathan
Hetherington BA(Hons),
MSc(ed), QTS
Age range: B8–18
No. of pupils: 470
Fees: Day £4,524–£6,341
WB £8,046–£9,112
FB £8,803–£9,869
Special needs catered for:
LD, SCD, SPLD
(♂)(🌐)(🏢)(16+)(✓)

Orchard Hill College and Academy Trust
BedZED, 20 Sandmartin Way,
Hackbridge, Surrey SM6 7DF
Tel: 0345 402 0453
Age range: 16+
Special needs catered for: ADD,
ADHD, ASC, ASP, AUT, BESD, CLD,
CP, DEL, DYS, DYSP, EBD, EPI,
GLD, HA, HI, LD, MLD, MSI, PD,
Phe, PH, PMLD, PNI, SCD, SCLD,
SEMH, SLD, SP&LD, SPLD, SLI, VIS

St Dominic's School
Hambledon, Godalming,
Surrey GU8 4DX
Tel: 01428 684693/682741
Age range: 7–19
No. of pupils: // VIth19
Special needs catered for: ADD,
ADHD, ASC, ASP, BESD, CLD, DEL,
DYS, DYSP, EPI, HA, SCD, SP&LD, SPLD
(🏢)(✏)(✓)

ST JOSEPH'S SPECIALIST TRUST
For further details see p. 106
Amlets Lane, Cranleigh,
Surrey GU6 7DH
Tel: 01483 272449
Email: admissions@st-josephscranleigh.surrey.sch.uk
Website: www.st-josephs
cranleigh.surrey.sch.uk
Principal: Mrs Annie Sutton
Age range: 5–19
No. of pupils: 65
Fees: Day £57,905 FB £83,898
Special needs catered for:
ADHD, ASC, ASP, AUT, CLD,
DYS, DYSP, EPI, MLD,
SCLD, SEMH, SLD, SP&LD
(🏢)(✏)(16+)(✓)

Wiltshire

Appleford School
Shrewton, Salisbury,
Wiltshire SP3 4HL
Tel: 01980 621020
Age range: 7–18
No. of pupils: 126
Fees: Day £16,608 FB £25,491
Special needs catered for:
ADD, ADHD, ASP, DYS, DYSP,
HA, MLD, SP&LD, SPLD
(🌐)(🏢)(16+)(✓)

South-West

Devon

Highgate Hill House School
Whitstone, Holsworthy,
Devon EX22 6TJ
Tel: 01288 341998
Age range: 5–16
Special needs catered for: ASC,
ASP, AUT, BESD, LD, MSI, PD, PH

Kingsley School
Northdown Road, Bideford,
Devon EX39 3LY
Tel: 01237 426200
Age range: 0–18
No. of pupils: 395
Fees: Day £1,950 WB £5,495 FB £7,095
Special needs catered for:
DYS, DYSP
(🌐)(A)(🏢)(£)(✏)(16+)

On Track Education Centre, Barnstaple
16a Castle Park Road, Whiddon
Valley, Barnstaple, Devon EX32 8PA
Tel: 01271 372269
Age range: 11–19
No. of pupils: 36
Special needs catered for:
ASC, MLD, SCLD, SEMH, SPLD
(16+)

Dorset

KINGSTON MAURWARD COLLEGE
For further details see p. 109
Dorchester, Dorset DT2 8PY
Tel: 01305 215000
Email: fulltimecourses@
kmc.ac.uk
Website: www.kmc.ac.uk
Principal: Luke Rake
No. of pupils: 53
Special needs catered for: ASC,
ASP, AUT LD, MLD, SEMH, SPLD
(16+)(16+)

Somerset

Cambian Lufton College
Lufton, Yeovil, Somerset BA22 8ST
Tel: 01935 403120
Age range: 16–25
No. of pupils: 120
Special needs catered for:
ASC, LD, SCD
(🏢)(16+)

Foxes Academy
Selbourne Place, Minehead,
Somerset TA24 5TY
Tel: 01643 708529
Age range: 16–25
No. of pupils: 80
Special needs catered for: ADD,
ADHD, ASC, ASP, AUT, CLD, CP,
DYS, DYSP, EPI, GLD, HI, LD, MLD,
Phe, PMLD, SCD, SLD, SP&LD, SPLD
(🏢)(16+)

Mark College
Highbridge, Somerset TA9 4NP
Tel: 01278 641 632
Age range: 10–19
Special needs catered for:
DYS, DYSP, LD, SP&LD, SPLD
🌐 🏫 16+

Shapwick School
Shapwick Manor, Station Road,
Shapwick, Somerset TA7 9NJ
Tel: 01458 210384
Age range: 8–19
No. of pupils: 84
Fees: Day £18,519–£19,386
WB £24,258 FB £25,560–£27,858
Special needs catered for:
DYS, DYSP
🌐 🏫 ✔

West Midlands

Herefordshire

Rowden House School
Rowden, Bromyard,
Herefordshire HR7 4LS
Tel: 01885 488096
Age range: 11–19
Special needs catered for: ADHD,
ASC, AUT, CLD, EPI, HI, LD, PMLD,
SCLD, SLD, SP&LD, SPLD, SLI, VIS
🏫 16+

Shropshire

Access School
Holbrook Villa Farm, Harmer
Hill, Broughton, Shrewsbury,
Shropshire SY4 3EW
Tel: 01939 220797
Age range: 5–16
No. of pupils: 10
Special needs catered for:
EBD, GLD, MLD
✔

Queensway HLC
Hadley, Telford, Shropshire TF1 6AJ
Tel: 01952 388555
Age range: 11–16
Special needs catered for:
EBD, SPLD
✔

Staffordshire

Bladon House School
Newton Solney, Burton upon
Trent, Staffordshire DE15 0TA
Tel: 01283 563787
Age range: 5–19
Special needs catered for: ADD,
ADHD, ASC, AUT, CLD, EPI, HI,
LD, MLD, SP&LD, SPLD, SLI, VIS
🏫 16+

Maple Hayes Dyslexia School
Abnalls Lane, Lichfield,
Staffordshire WS13 8BL
Tel: 01543 264387
Age range: 7–17
No. of pupils: 118
Fees: Day £15,165–£20,259
Special needs catered for:
DYS, DYSP, SPLD
🌐 £ ✔

Regent College
77 Shelton New Road, Shelton,
Stoke-on-Trent, Staffordshire ST4 7AA
Tel: 01782 263326
Age range: 16–25
No. of pupils: 30
Special needs catered for:
CLD, EPI, PD, SLD, SP&LD

West Midlands

Argent College
New Standard Works, 43-47
Vittoria Street, Birmingham,
West Midlands B1 3PE
Tel: 01453 837502
Age range: 16–25
Special needs catered for:
ASC, ASP, AUT, BESD, CLD,
EBD, LD, SCLD, SEMH
16+

Glasshouse College
Wollaston Road, Amblecote,
Stourbridge, West Midlands DY8 4HF
Tel: 01453 837502
Age range: 16–25
Special needs catered for: ADHD,
ASC, ASP, BESD, CLD, EBD, GLD, LD,
PMLD, SCD, SCLD, SEMH, SLD, SPLD
16+ 🏫

OVERLEY HALL SCHOOL
For further details see p. 110
Overley, Wellington, Telford,
West Midlands TF6 5HE
Tel: 01952 740262
Email: info@overleyhall.com
Website: www.overleyhall.com
Headteacher: Mrs
Beverley Doran
Age range: 8–19
No. of pupils: 21
Special needs catered for:
ADD, ADHD, ASC, ASP, AUT,
CLD, DYSP, EPI, GLD, LD, PMLD,
SCD, SCLD, SLD, SP&LD
🏫 16+ ✔

Sunfield School
Clent Grove, Woodman Lane,
Stourbridge, West Midlands DY9 9PB
Tel: 01562 882253
Age range: 6–19
Special needs catered for: ADD,
ADHD, ASC, AUT, BESD, CLD, DYS,
EPI, GLD, LD, MLD, MSI, PMLD,
SCD, SCLD, SEMH, SLD, SP&LD, SLI
🏫 16+ ✔

Worcestershire

Our Place School
The Orchard, Bransford,
Worcestershire WR6 5JE
Tel: 01886 833378
Special needs catered for:
ASC, MLD, PMLD, SLD

Yorkshire & Humberside

North-East Lincolnshire

Linkage College – Weelsby Campus
Weelsby Road, Grimsby, North-
East Lincolnshire DN32 9RU
Tel: 01472 241044
Age range: 16–25
No. of pupils: 220
Special needs catered for:
ADD, ADHD, ASC, ASP, AUT,
CLD, CP, D, DEL, DYS, DYSP, EPI,
GLD, HI, LD, MLD, Phe, PH, SCD,
SCLD, SLD, SP&LD, SPLD, VIS
16+ 🏫

South Yorkshire

Freeman College
Sterling Works, 88 Arundel Street,
Sheffield, South Yorkshire S1 2NG
Tel: 01453 837502
Age range: 16–25
Special needs catered for: ADHD,
ASC, ASP, BESD, CLD, EBD, GLD, LD,
MLD, PMLD, SCD, SCLD, SEMH, SLD
16+ 🏫 ✔

FULLERTON HOUSE COLLEGE
For further details see p. 112
Tickhill Square, Denaby,
Doncaster, South
Yorkshire DN12 4AR
Tel: 01709 861663
Email: enquiries@
hesleygroup.co.uk
Website:
www.hesleygroup.co.uk
General Manager: Heidi
Dugdale-Dawkes
Age range: 18–25
No. of pupils: 12
Special needs catered for:
ASC, ASP, AUT, CLD, DYS, DYSP,
GLD, LD, MLD, SCLD, SLD, SPLD
🏫

FULLERTON HOUSE SCHOOL
For further details see p. 111
Tickill Square, Denaby,
Doncaster, South
Yorkshire DN12 4AR
Tel: 01709 861663
Email: enquiries@
hesleygroup.co.uk
Website:
www.fullertonhouseschool.co.uk
General Manager: Heidi
Dugdale-Dawkes
Age range: 8–19
Special needs catered for:
ASC, ASP, AUT, CLD, DYS, DYSP,
GLD, LD, MLD, SCLD, SLD, SPLD
🏫 16+ ✔

WILSIC HALL COLLEGE
For further details see p. 112
Wadworth, Doncaster,
South Yorkshire DN11 9AG
Tel: 01302 856382
Age range: 18–25
No. of pupils: 8
Special needs catered for:
ASC, ASP, AUT, CLD, DYS, DYSP,
GLD, LD, MLD, SCLD, SLD, SPLD

WILSIC HALL SCHOOL
For further details see p. 113
Wadworth, Doncaster,
South Yorkshire DN11 9AG
Tel: 01302 856382
Email: enquiries@
hesleygroup.co.uk
Website:
www.wilsichallschool.co.uk
Head: Geoff Turner
Age range: 11–19
No. of pupils: 32
Special needs catered for:
ASC, ASP, AUT, CLD, DYS, DYSP,
GLD, LD, MLD, SCLD, SLD, SPLD

West Yorkshire

Hall Cliffe School
Dovecote Lane, Horbury,
Wakefield, West Yorkshire WF4 6BB
Tel: 01924 663 420
Age range: 8–16
Special needs catered for:
ADHD, ASC, ASP, AUT, BESD,
MLD, SCD, SLD, SPLD

Pennine Camphill Community
Wood Lane, Chapelthorpe,
Wakefield, West Yorkshire WF4 3JL
Tel: 01924 255281
Age range: 16–25
No. of pupils: 56
Fees: Day £14,000–£45,000
FB £26,000–£69,000
Special needs catered for: ADHD,
ASC, ASP, AUT, CLD, DYSP, EBD,
EPI, LD, MLD, SCLD, SLD, SPLD

Northern Ireland

County Tyrone

Parkanaur College
57 Parkanaur Road, Dungannon,
County Tyrone BT70 3AA
Tel: 028 87761272
Age range: 18–65
Special needs catered for: ADD,
ADHD, ASP, AUT, BESD, CLD, CP,
DYS, DYSP, EBD, EPI, GLD, HA,
HI, LD, MLD, PD, Phe, PH, PMLD,
PNI, SCD, SCLD, SLD, SPLD, VIS

Scotland

Aberdeen

VSA Linn Moor Campus
Peterculter, Aberdeen AB14 0PJ
Tel: 01224 732246
Age range: 5–18
No. of pupils: 25
Fees: Day £38,326
FB £76,650–£239,114
Special needs catered for:
ASC, AUT, CLD, GLD, LD,
MLD, SCD, SCLD, SPLD

Clackmannanshire

New Struan School
100 Smithfield Loan, Alloa,
Clackmannanshire FK10 1NP
Tel: 01259 222000
Age range: 5–17
Special needs catered for:
ASC, AUT

Glasgow

East Park
1092 Maryhill Road,
Glasgow G20 9TD
Tel: 0141 946 2050
Age range: 0–25
Fees: Day £12,298 FB £22,958
Special needs catered for:
AUT, CP, DEL, EPI, HI, MLD,
PH, PMLD, SLD, SP&LD, VIS

Perth & Kinross

Ochil Tower
140 High Street, Auchterarder,
Perth, Perth & Kinross PH3 1AD
Tel: 01764 662416
Age range: 5–18
No. of pupils: 35
Fees: Day £23,500 FB £41,100
Special needs catered for: ADD,
ADHD, ASC, BESD, CLD, EBD, EPI, LD,
MLD, MSI, PMLD, SCD, SCLD, SP&LD

Wales

Denbighshire

Cambian Pengwern College
Sarn Lane, Rhuddlan, Rhyl,
Denbighshire LL18 5UH
Tel: 01745 592300
Age range: 16–25
No. of pupils: 60
Special needs catered for:
ASC, LD, SCD

Gwynedd

Aran Hall School
Rhydymain, Dolgellau,
Gwynedd LL40 2AR
Tel: 01341 450641
Age range: B11–19
Special needs catered for:
ADHD, ASC, ASP, AUT, CLD,
EPI, GLD, LD, MLD, PMLD, SCD,
SCLD, SP&LD, SPLD, SLI

Pembrokeshire

Coleg Plas Dwbl
Mynachlog-ddu, Clunderwen,
Pembrokeshire SA66 7SE
Tel: 01453 837502
Age range: 16–25
Special needs catered for:
ASC, ASP, CLD, EBD

Powys

Trefnanney School
Gaer Lane, Meifod, Powys SY22 6XX
Age range: 11–17
No. of pupils: 12
Special needs catered for: LD

Vale of Glamorgan

Action for Children Headlands School
2 St Augustine's Road, Penarth,
Vale of Glamorgan CF64 1YY
Tel: 02920 709771
Age range: 8–19
Special needs catered for: ADD,
ADHD, ASC, ASP, AUT, BESD,
DYS, EBD, MLD, SP&LD, SPLD

Schools and colleges specialising in sensory or physical impairment

Abbreviations

ACLD	Autism, Communication and Associated Learning Difficulties
ADD	Attention Deficit Disorder
ADHD	Attention Deficit and Hyperactive Disorder (Hyperkinetic Disorder)
ASC	Autistic Spectrum Conditions
ASP	Asperger Syndrome
AUT	Autism
BESD	Behavioural, Emotional and Social Difficulties
CCD	Complex Communication Difficulties
CLD	Complex Learning Difficulties
CP	Cerebral Palsy
D	Deaf
DEL	Delicate
DYS	Dyslexia
DYSP	Dyspraxia
EBD	Emotional and Behavioural Difficulties
EBSD	Emotional, Behavioural and/or Social Difficulties
EPI	Epilepsy
GLD	General Learning Difficulties
HA	High Ability
HI	Hearing Impairment
HS	Hospital School
LD	Learning Difficulties
MLD	Moderate Learning Difficulties
MSI	Multi-sensory Impairment
OCD	Obsessive Compulsive Disorder
PD	Physical Difficulties
PH	Physical Impairment
Phe	Partially Hearing
PMLD	Profound and Multiple Learning Difficulties
PNI	Physical Neurological Impairment
PRU	Pupil Referral Unit
SCD	Social and Communication Difficulties
SCLD	Severe and Complex Learning Difficulties
SEBD	Severe Emotional and Behavioural Disorders
SEBN	Social, Emotional and Behavioural Needs
SLD	Severe Learning Difficulties
SLI	Specific Language Impairment
SPLD	Specific Learning Difficulties
SP&LD	Speech and Language Difficulties
SLCN	Speech Language & Communication Needs
VIS	Visually Impaired

Key to Symbols

Type of school:

(symbol)	Boys' school
(symbol)	Girls' school
(symbol)	International school

School offers:

Ⓐ	A levels
(symbol)	Residential
(16·)	Entrance at 16+
(symbol)	Vocational qualifications
(symbol)	Learning support
✔	This is a DfE approved independent or non-maintained school under section 41 of the Children and Families Act 2014 or section 342 of the 1996 Education Act

Please note: Unless otherwise indicated, all schools are coeducational day schools. Single-sex and boarding schools will be indicated by the relevant icon.

England – Central & West

Buckinghamshire

THE PACE CENTRE
For further details see p. 117
Coventon Road, Aylesbury,
Buckinghamshire HP19 9JL
Tel: 01296 392739
Email: info@thepacecentre.org
Website:
www.thepacecentre.org
Head Teacher: Mrs Claire Smart
Age range: 3–16
Special needs catered for:
CLD, CP, DYSP, HI, LD, MLD, MSI,
PD, PNI, SCLD, SLD, SP&LD, VIS
✓

Gloucestershire

NATIONAL STAR COLLEGE
For further details see p. 116
Ullenwood Manor Road,
Ullenwood, Cheltenham,
Gloucestershire GL53 9QU
Tel: 01242 527631
Email: admissions@
nationalstar.org
Website: www.nationalstar.org
Principal: Pauline Bayliss-Jones
Age range: 16–25
No. of pupils: 242
Special needs catered for: ASC,
ASP, AUT, CLD, CP, DYS, DYSP,
EPI, GLD, HI, LD, MLD, MSI,
PD, Phe, PH, PMLD, PNI, SCD,
SCLD, SLD, SP&LD, SPLD, VIS
🏛 16+

St Rose's School
Stratford Lawn, Stroud,
Gloucestershire GL5 4AP
Tel: 01453 763793
Age range: 2–25
No. of pupils: 54
Special needs catered for: CLD,
CP, D, DEL, DYS, DYSP, EPI, GLD, HI,
LD, MLD, MSI, PD, Phe, PH, PMLD,
PNI, SCD, SCLD, SLD, SP&LD, SLI, VIS
🏛 16+ ✓

West Berkshire

Mary Hare Primary School
Mill Hall, Pigeons Farm Road,
Thatcham, Newbury, West
Berkshire RG19 8XA
Tel: 01635 573800
Age range: 5–12
Special needs catered for:
D, HI, SP&LD, SLI
🏛

**Mary Hare Secondary
School**
Arlington Manor, Snelsmore
Common, Newbury, West
Berkshire RG14 3BQ
Tel: 01635 244200
Age range: 11–19
No. of pupils: 220
Special needs catered for: D, HI
🏛 16+ ✓

East

Hertfordshire

**Aurora Meldreth
Manor School**
Fenny Lane, Meldreth, Royston,
Hertfordshire SG8 6LG
Tel: 01763 268 000
Age range: 6–19
Special needs catered for: CP,
D, EPI, GLD, HI, LD, MLD, MSI, PD,
Phe, PH, PMLD, SCLD, SP&LD, VIS
🏛 16+

St Elizabeth's School
South End, Much Hadham,
Hertfordshire SG10 6EW
Tel: 01279 844270
Age range: 5–19
Special needs catered for:
AUT, CP, DYS, DYSP, EBD, EPI,
MLD, SLD, SP&LD, SPLD
🏛 16+ ✓

East Midlands

Derbyshire

**Royal School for
the Deaf Derby**
Ashbourne Road, Derby,
Derbyshire DE22 3BH
Tel: 01332 362512
Age range: 3–19
Special needs catered for: D, HI
🏛 16+ ✓

Leicestershire

Homefield College
42 St Mary's Road,
Sileby, Loughborough,
Leicestershire LE12 7TL
Tel: 01509 815696
Age range: 16–25
No. of pupils: 54 VIth54
Special needs catered for:
ASC, BESD, LD, SCD
£

**RNIB COLLEGE
LOUGHBOROUGH**
For further details see p. 118
Radmoor Road, Loughborough,
Leicestershire LE11 3BS
Tel: 01509 611077
Email: enquiries@
rnibcollege.ac.uk
Website: www.rnibcollege.ac.uk
Principal: June Murray
Age range: 16–65
No. of pupils: 108
Special needs catered for:
ADD, ADHD, ASC, ASP, AUT,
BESD, CLD, CP, DYS, DYSP, EBD,
EPI, GLD, HA, HI, LD, MLD, MSI,
PD, Phe, PH, PNI, SCD, SCLD,
SEMH, SLD, SP&LD, SPLD, SLI, VIS
16+ 🏛 ✓

Nottinghamshire

Portland College
Nottingham Road,
Mansfield, Nottingham,
Nottinghamshire NG18 4TJ
Tel: 01623 499111
Age range: 16–59
No. of pupils: 230
Special needs catered for:
ASC, ASP, AUT, CP, D, DYS,
DYSP, EBD, EPI, GLD, HI, MLD,
MSI, PD, Phe, PH, PMLD, PNI,
SCLD, SP&LD, SPLD, SLI, VIS
🏛

Rutland

The Shires School
Shires Lane, Stretton,
Rutland LE15 7GT
Tel: 01780 411 944
Age range: 11–19
Special needs catered for:
ASC, ASP, AUT, LD
🏛 16+ ✓

Greater London

Kent

Nash College
Croydon Road, Bromley,
Kent BR2 7AG
Tel: 020 8315 4844
Age range: 18–25
Special needs catered for: AUT,
CP, EPI, MLD, PH, PMLD, PNI, SCD,
SCLD, SLD, SP&LD, SPLD, VIS
♿

Middlesex

RNIB SUNSHINE HOUSE SCHOOL
For further details see p. 119
33 Dene Road, Northwood,
Middlesex HA6 2DD
Tel: 01923 822538
Email: sunshinehouse@
rnib.org.uk
Website:
www.rnib.org.uk/sunshinehouse
Head: Jackie Seaman
and Mark Fuel
Age range: 2–14
Special needs catered for: CLD,
CP, D, EPI, GLD, HI, LD, MSI, PD,
Phe, PH, PMLD, SCLD, SPLD, VIS
♿ ✓

London

North London

Woodstar School
143 Coppetts Road,
London N10 1JP
Tel: 020 8444 7242
Age range: 3–11
Special needs catered for: CP, PD
✓

North-East

Tyne & Wear

Hedleys College
Station Road, Forest Hall, Newcastle
upon Tyne, Tyne & Wear NE12 8YY
Tel: 0191 266 5491
Age range: 14–19
No. of pupils: 170
Fees: Day £19,944 FB £42,134
Special needs catered for: HI
♿ 16+ ✓

Hedleys Northern Counties School
Tankerville Terrace, Jesmond,
Newcastle upon Tyne,
Tyne & Wear NE12 7BH
Tel: 0191 281 5821
Age range: 3–19
Fees: Day £13,767–£29,772
FB £19,134–£33,162
Special needs catered for:
AUT, HI, PMLD, SLD, VIS
79D

Percy Hedley School
West Lane, Killingworth, Newcastle
upon Tyne, Tyne & Wear NE12 7BH
Tel: 0191 2161811
Age range: 3–14
Special needs catered for: CP, SCD
♿

North-West

Lancashire

Beaumont College
Slyne Road, Lancaster,
Lancashire LA2 6AP
Tel: 01524 541400
Age range: 18–25
Special needs catered for:
GLD, LD, PD, PH
♿ 16+

Merseyside

Royal School for the Blind
Church Road North, Wavertree,
Liverpool, Merseyside L15 6TQ
Tel: 0151 733 1012
Age range: 2–19
No. of pupils: 51
Special needs catered for: ASC,
AUT, BESD, CLD, CP, D, EBD, EPI, HI,
MLD, MSI, PD, Phe, PH, PMLD, PNI,
SCLD, SLD, SP&LD, SPLD, SLI, VIS
♿ 16+ ✓

St Vincent's School for the Visually Handicapped
Yew Tree Lane, West Derby,
Liverpool, Merseyside L12 9HN
Tel: 0151 228 9968
Age range: 3–17
Fees: Day £19,566 FB £27,363
Special needs catered for: MLD, VIS
♿ ✓

South-East

East Sussex

CHAILEY HERITAGE SCHOOL
For further details see p. 120
Haywards Heath Road,
North Chailey, Lewes,
East Sussex BN8 4EF
Tel: 01825 724444
Email: office@chf.org.uk
Website: www.chf.org.uk
Charity Chief Executive: Helen Hewitt
Age range: 3–19
No. of pupils: 95
Special needs catered for:
ASC, AUT, CLD, CP, D, EBD, EPI,
HI, MLD, MSI, PD, PH, PMLD,
PNI, SCLD, SLD, SP&LD, VIS
(♿) (16+) (✓)

Hamilton Lodge School
9 Walpole Road, Brighton,
East Sussex BN2 0LS
Tel: 01273 682362
Age range: 5–16
Special needs catered for: D, HI
(♿) (✓)

St Mary's School & 6th Form College
Wrestwood Road, Bexhill-on-Sea, East Sussex TN40 2LU
Tel: 01424 730740
Age range: 7–19
No. of pupils: 63
Special needs catered for: ASC,
ASP, AUT, CLD, CP, D, DEL, DYS,
DYSP, EPI, GLD, HI, LD, MLD, MSI, PD,
Phe, PH, SCD, SP&LD, SPLD, SLI, VIS
(♿) (16+) (✓)

Hampshire

TRELOAR SCHOOL
For further details see p. 122
Holybourne, Alton,
Hampshire GU34 4GL
Tel: 01420 547400
Email: admissions@treloar.org.uk
Website: www.treloar.org.uk
Age range: 2–19
No. of pupils: 81 VIth21
Special needs catered for:
CLD, CP, DEL, DYSP, EPI, HA, HI,
MLD, MSI, PD, Phe, PH, PNI,
SCLD, SP&LD, SPLD, SLI, VIS
(♿) (✓)

Kent

Dorton College of Further Education
Seal Drive, Seal, Sevenoaks,
Kent TN15 0AH
Tel: 01732 592600
Age range: 16–19
No. of pupils: 60
Special needs catered for: VIS
(16+) (♿)

Surrey

St Piers School and College
St Piers Lane, Lingfield,
Surrey RH7 6PW
Tel: 01342 832243
Age range: 5–25
No. of pupils: 181
Special needs catered for: ADD,
ADHD, ASP, AUT, CP, EPI, MLD,
PMLD, PNI, SCD, SCLD, SLD, SP&LD
(♿) (16+) (✓)

Stepping Stones School
Tower Road, Hindhead,
Surrey GU26 6SU
Tel: 01428 609083
Age range: 8–19
No. of pupils: 40
Fees: Day £11,000–£14,800
Special needs catered for: ASC,
ASP, AUT, MLD, PD, SP&LD
(✓)

THE CHILDREN'S TRUST SCHOOL
For further details see p. 121
Tadworth Court, Tadworth,
Surrey KT20 5RU
Tel: 01737 365810
Email: school@
thechildrenstrust.org.uk
Website:
www.thechildrenstrust.org.uk/
the-childrens-trust-school
Head Teacher: Samantha
Newton
Age range: 2–19
No. of pupils: 44
Special needs catered for:
CLD, CP, EPI, HI, MSI, PD, PH,
PMLD, PNI, SLD, SP&LD, VIS
(♿) (16+) (✓)

West Sussex

Ingfield Manor School
Ingfield Manor Drive, Five Oaks,
Billingshurst, West Sussex RH14 9AX
Tel: 01403 782294
Age range: 3–19
Special needs catered for:
CP, GLD, LD, PD, PH
(♿) (16+) (✓)

South-West

Devon

Dame Hannah Rogers School
Woodland Road, Ivybridge,
Devon PL21 9HQ
Tel: 01752 892461
Age range: 3–18
No. of pupils: 2
Special needs catered for:
ASC, MLD, PD, PMLD, SLD
(♿) (16+) (✓)

Exeter Royal Academy for Deaf Education
50 Topsham Road, Exeter,
Devon EX2 4NF
Tel: 01392 267023
Age range: 5–25
No. of pupils: VIth68
Fees: Day £23,007–£39,195
WB £31,779–£46,800
FB £36,360–£48,990
Special needs catered for: AUT, CP,
D, EPI, HI, MLD, MSI, Phe, SP&LD, VIS
(♿) (16+) (✓)

On Track Education Centre, Totnes
Parragon Building, Ford Road,
Totnes, Devon TQ9 5LQ
Tel: 01803 866462
Age range: 7–19
No. of pupils: 48
Special needs catered for:
ASC, MLD, SCLD, SEMH, SPLD
(16+) (✓)

Vranch House
Pinhoe Road, Exeter,
Devon EX4 8AD
Tel: 01392 468333
Age range: 2–12
Fees: Day £19,425
Special needs catered for: CP,
EPI, MLD, PD, PH, PMLD, SP&LD
(✓)

WESC Foundation – The Specialist College for Visual Impairment
Countess Wear, Exeter,
Devon EX2 6HA
Tel: 01392 454200
Age range: 16+
Special needs catered for:
EPI, PH, PMLD, VIS
(16+) (♿) (✓)

WESC Foundation – The Specialist School for Visual Impairment
Countess Wear, Exeter,
Devon EX2 6HA
Tel: 01392 454200
Age range: 5–16
Special needs catered for:
EPI, PH, PMLD, VIS
(♿) (✓)

Dorset

Langside School
Langside Avenue, Parkstone,
Poole, Dorset BH12 5BN
Tel: 01202 518635
Age range: 2–19
No. of pupils: 23
Special needs catered for: CLD, CP,
EPI, MSI, PD, PMLD, SCD, SCLD, SLD
(16+) (✓)

The Fortune Centre of Riding Therapy
Avon Tyrrell, Bransgore,
Christchurch, Dorset BH23 8EE
Tel: 01425 673297
Age range: 16–25
No. of pupils: 47
Special needs catered for: AUT,
CP, DEL, DYS, EBD, EPI, HI, MLD,
PH, PMLD, SLD, SP&LD, SPLD, VIS
(♿) (16+)

Victoria Education Centre
12 Lindsay Road, Branksome
Park, Poole, Dorset BH13 6AS
Tel: 01202 763697
Age range: 3–19
No. of pupils: 90
Special needs catered for:
DEL, EPI, PH, SP&LD
(♿) (16+) (✓)

West Midlands

Herefordshire

The Royal National College for the Blind (RNC)
Venns Lane, Hereford,
Herefordshire HR1 1DT
Tel: 01432 376621
Age range: 16–65
Special needs catered for: ASP,
AUT, DYS, HA, MLD, PD, Phe, VIS
16⊕ 🏛

Shropshire

Derwen College
Oswestry, Shropshire SY11 3JA
Tel: 01691 661234
Age range: 16–25
No. of pupils: 160
Fees: FB £17,928
Special needs catered for:
CP, DEL, DYS, EPI, HI, MLD, PH,
PMLD, SLD, SP&LD, SPLD, VIS
🏛

West Midlands

Hereward College of Further Education
Bramston Crescent, Tile Hill Lane,
Coventry, West Midlands CV4 9SW
Tel: 024 7646 1231
Age range: 16+
No. of pupils: 400
Special needs catered for: ASP,
AUT, CP, DEL, DYS, DYSP, EBD,
EPI, HA, HI, MLD, PH, SPLD, VIS
🏛

National Institute for Conductive Education
Cannon Hill House, Russell
Road, Moseley, Birmingham,
West Midlands B13 8RD
Tel: 0121 449 1569
Age range: 0–11
No. of pupils: 18
Fees: Day £25,000
Special needs catered for:
CP, DYSP, PNI
✔

RNIB Three Spires Academy
Kingsbury Road, Coundon,
Coventry, West Midlands CV6 1PJ
Tel: 024 7659 4952
Age range: 4–11
Special needs catered for:
ASC, AUT, VIS

Worcestershire

NEW COLLEGE WORCESTER
For further details see p. 123
Whittington Road, Worcester,
Worcestershire WR5 2JX
Tel: 01905 763933
Email: office@ncw.co.uk
Website: www.ncw.co.uk
Principal: Miss Nicki Ross
Age range: 11–19
No. of pupils: 80
Special needs catered for: VIS
🏛 16⊕ ✔

Yorkshire & Humberside

North Yorkshire

Henshaws College
Bogs Lane, Harrogate,
North Yorkshire HG1 4ED
Tel: 01423 886451
Age range: 16–25
Special needs catered for: CLD,
CP, D, EPI, HI, LD, MLD, MSI, PD,
Phe, SCD, SLD, SP&LD, VIS
16⊕ 🏛

South Yorkshire

Communication Specialist College
Leger Way, Doncaster,
South Yorkshire DN2 6AY
Tel: 01302 386700
Age range: 16–59
No. of pupils: 185
Special needs catered for: HI
🏛

Doncaster School for the Deaf
Leger Way, Doncaster,
South Yorkshire DN2 6AY
Tel: 01302 386733
Age range: 4–19
No. of pupils: 32
Special needs catered for: BESD,
CP, D, DYS, GLD, HI, MLD, PH,
PMLD, SLD, SP&LD, SPLD, VIS
🏛 ✔

Paces High Green School for Conductive Education
Paces High Green Centre, Pack
Horse Lane, High Green, Sheffield,
South Yorkshire S35 3HY
Tel: 0114 284 5298
Age range: 1–18
No. of pupils: 30
Fees: Day £27,452
Special needs catered for: CP, PD
16⊕ ✔

West Yorkshire

Holly Bank School
Roe Head, Far Common Road,
Mirfield, West Yorkshire WF14 0DQ
Tel: 01924 490833
Age range: 5–19
No. of pupils: 20 VIth10
Fees: Day £35,000–£45,000
WB £70,000–£75,000
FB £99,000–£105,000
Special needs catered for: CLD, CP,
MSI, PD, PH, PMLD, PNI, SCLD, SLD
🏛 16⊕

ST JOHN'S CATHOLIC SCHOOL FOR THE DEAF
For further details see p. 124
Church Street, Boston
Spa, Wetherby, West
Yorkshire LS23 6DF
Tel: 01937 842144
Email: info@stjohns.org.uk
Website: www.stjohns.org.uk
Headteacher: Mrs A Bradbury
BA(Hons), MSc, NPQH
Age range: 4–19
Special needs catered for: ADD,
ADHD, ASC, ASP, AUT, BESD, CP,
D, DEL, DYS, DYSP, EBD, EPI,
HI, LD, MLD, MSI, PD, Phe, PH,
PMLD, SCD, SLD, SP&LD, SLI, VIS
🏛 16⊕ ✔

Northern Ireland

County Antrim

Jordanstown School
85 Jordanstown Road,
Newtownabbey, County
Antrim BT37 0QE
Tel: 028 9086 3541
Age range: 4–19
No. of pupils: 79
Special needs catered for: ASC, D,
EBD, GLD, HI, LD, MSI, PD, SP&LD, VIS
16⊕

County Tyrone

Buddy Bear Trust Conductive Education School
Killyman Road, Dungannon,
County Tyrone BT71 6DE
Tel: 02887 752 025
Special needs catered for: CP

Scotland

Aberdeen

Camphill School Aberdeen
Murtle House, Bieldside,
Aberdeen AB15 9EP
Tel: 01224 867935
Age range: 3–19
Fees: Day 25,198–50,397
FB 50,397–100,794
Special needs catered for:
ADD, ADHD, ASC, ASP, AUT,
BESD, CLD, CP, D, DEL, DYS, DYSP,
EBD, EPI, GLD, LD, MLD, MSI, PD,
PMLD, PNI, SCD, SCLD, SEMH,
SLD, SP&LD, SPLD, SLI, VIS
♿ 16·

Edinburgh

**THE ROYAL BLIND
SCHOOL**
For further details see p. 126
43 Canaan Lane,
Edinburgh EH10 4SG
Tel: 0131 446 3120
Email: office@
royalblindschool.org.uk
Website:
www.royalblind.org/education
Head Teacher: Elaine
Brackenridge (BEd)
Age range: 5–19
Special needs catered for:
AUT, CP, DEL, EPI, MLD, PH,
PMLD, SLD, SP&LD, SPLD, VIS
♿ ✏ 16·

Renfrewshire

Corseford School
Milliken Park, Johnstone,
Renfrewshire PA10 2NT
Tel: 01505 702141
Age range: 3–18
No. of pupils: 50
Special needs catered for:
CP, DEL, DYSP, EPI, HI, MLD,
PH, SP&LD, SPLD, VIS
♿ 16·

South Lanarkshire

Stanmore House School
Lanark, South Lanarkshire ML11 7RR
Tel: 01555 665041
Age range: 0–18
No. of pupils: 47
Special needs catered for:
CP, PH, SCLD, SP&LD, VIS
♿ 16·

West Lothian

Donaldson's School
Preston Road, Linlithgow,
West Lothian EH49 6HZ
Tel: 01506 841900
Age range: 2–19
No. of pupils: 12
Special needs catered for:
ASP, AUT, D, HI, Phe, PMLD,
SCD, SLD, SP&LD, SLI
♿ ✏ 16·

Wales

Glamorgan

Craig-y-Parc School
Heol y Parc, Pentyrch, Cardiff,
Glamorgan CF15 9NB
Tel: 029 2089 0397
Age range: 3–19
Special needs catered for:
CP, EPI, PD, PH
♿ 16·

Special Educational Needs and the independent and non-maintained schools and colleges that cater for them

Attention Deficit Disorder (AD)

Attention Deficit and Hyperactive Disorder (ADHD)

Autistic Spectrum Conditions (ASC) (also Autistic Spectrum Disorders – ASD)

Schools and colleges by category

Asperger Syndrome (ASP)

Autism (AUT)

175

Behaviour, Emotional and Social Difficulties (BESD) – see also EBSD and SEBD

Complex Learning Difficulties (CLD)

Cerebral Palsy (CP)

Deaf (D) – see also Hearing Impairment (HI)

Dyslexia (DYSL) – see also SPLD

Dyspraxia (DYSP)

Emotional, Behavioural Difficulties (EBD) – see also BESD and SEMH

Epilepsy (EPI)

General Learning Difficulties (GLD)

High Ability (HA)

Hearing Impairment (HI)

Learning Difficulties (LD)

Moderate Learning Difficulties (MLD)

Schools and colleges by category

Multi-sensory Impairment (MSI)

Partially Hearing (Phe)

Physical Difficulties (PD)

Physical Impairment (PH)

Profound and Multiple Learning Difficulties (PMLD)

Physical Neurological Impairment (PNI)

Social and Communication Difficulties (SCD)

Severe and Complex Learning Difficulties (SCLD)

Social, Emotional and Mental Health needs (SEMH) – see also BESD and EBD

Schools and colleges by category

Severe Learning Difficulties (SLD)

Speech and Language Difficulties (SP&LD)

Specific Learning Difficulties (SPLD)

Specific Language Impairment (SLI)

Visually Impaired (VIS)

Maintained special schools and colleges

ENGLAND

BEDFORD

Borough Council

Bedford SENDIASS, 5th Floor, Borough Hall, Cauldwell Street, Bedford, MK42 9AP
Tel: 01234 276 267 Email: sendadvice@bedford.gov.uk Website: www.bedford.gov.uk

BEDFORD

Ridgeway School
Hill Rise, Kempston,
BEDFORD MK42 7EB
Tel: 01234 402402
Category: PD LD LDD (Coed 3-19)

St. John's Special School & College
Bedford Road, Kempston,
BEDFORD MK42 8AA
Tel: 01234 345565
Category: SLD PMLD (Coed 2-19)

CENTRAL BEDFORDSHIRE

Council

Central Bedfordshire SEND Team, Priory House, Monks Walk, Chicksands Shefford, SG17 5TQ
Tel: 0300 300 8088 Email: cbcsendpypps@centralbedfordshire.gov.uk Website: www.centralbedfordshire.gov.uk

BIGGLESWADE

Ivel Valley College
The Baulk, BIGGLESWADE,
Bedfordshire SG18 0PT
Tel: 01767 601010
Category: ASD PMLD SLD
SpEd (Coed 16-19)

Ivel Valley School
Hitchmead Road, BIGGLESWADE,
Bedfordshire SG18 0NL
Tel: 01767 601010
Category: ASD PMLD SLD
SpEd (Coed 3-16)

DUNSTABLE

The Chiltern School – Beech Road Campus
Beech Road, DUNSTABLE,
Bedfordshire LU6 3LY
Tel: 01582 667106
Category: ASC SLD
PMLD (Coed 3-19)

HOUGHTON REGIS

The Chiltern School – Kingsland Campus
Parkside Drive, HOUGHTON
REGIS, Bedfordshire LU5 5PX
Tel: 01582 866972
Category: ASC SLD
PMLD (Coed 7-19)

LEIGHTON BUZZARD

Oak Bank School
Sandy Lane, LEIGHTON BUZZARD,
Bedfordshire LU7 3BE
Tel: 01525 374559
Category: ADHD, ASD, ASP, BESD,
DYSL, OCD, ODD, PDA (Coed 9-18)

WEST BERKSHIRE

Council

West Berkshire SENDIASS, Rose Road Association, The Bradbury Centre, 300 Aldermoor Road Southampton, SO16 5NA
Tel: 0300 303 2644 Email: westberksiass@roseroad.org.uk Website: www.westberkssendiass.info

NEWBURY

The Castle School
Love Lane, Donnington,
NEWBURY, Berkshire RG14 2JG
Tel: 01635 42976
Category: ASD CLD SLD SpEd
SPLD GLD PH (Coed 2-19)

READING

Brookfields School: Specialist SEN School
Sage Road, Tilehurst, READING,
Berkshire RG31 6SW
Tel: 01189 421382
Category: ADHD, AUT, CB, CP, HI,
MSI Complex Needs, SLCN, VIS

BLACKBURN WITH DARWEN
Borough Council

Blackburn SENDIASS, Boulevard Centre, Cathedral Quarter, 45 Railway Road Blackburn, Lancashire, BB1 1EZ
Tel: 01254 503049 Website: www.blackburn.gov.uk

BLACKBURN

**Crosshill Special
School with BCHS**
Haslingden Road, BLACKBURN,
Lancashire BB2 3HJ
Tel: 01254 667713
Category: ASD, GLD, HI, MLD, SEMH,
SLCN, SLD, VIS (Coed Day 11-16)

Newfield School
Old Bank Lane, BLACKBURN,
Lancashire BB1 2PW
Tel: 01254 588600
Category: ASC, ASD,
Complex (Coed Day 2-19)

St. Thomas's Centre
Lambeth Street, BLACKBURN,
Lancashire BB1 1NA
Tel: 01254 680523
Category: ADD, ADHD, Pupil
Referral Unit, SEMH (Coed Day 5-16)

DARWEN

Sunnyhurst Centre
Salisbury Road, DARWEN,
Lancashire BB3 1HZ
Tel: 01254 702317
Category: ADHD, ASD, ODD, Pupil
Referral Unit (Coed Day 5-11)

BLACKPOOL
Council

Blackpool SENDIASS, PO Box 4, Town Hall, Municipal Buildings Blackpool, FY1 1NA
Tel: 01253 477083 Email: sendiass@blackpool.gov.uk Website: www.blackpool.gov.uk

BLACKPOOL

Highfurlong School
Blackpool Old Road, BLACKPOOL,
Lancashire FY3 7LR
Tel: 01253 392188
Category: ASD, HI, MLD,
MSI, PH (Coed 2-19)

Woodlands School
Whitegate Drive, BLACKPOOL,
Lancashire FY3 9HF
Tel: 01253 316722
Category: SLD PMLD
MSI (Coed 2-19)

BOURNEMOUTH
Borough Council

Bournemouth SENDIASS, Bournemouth Learning Centre, Ensbury Avenue, Bournemouth, Dorset, BH10 4HG
Tel: 01202 451970 Email: local.offer@bournemouth.gov.uk Website: www.bournemouth.gov.uk

BOURNEMOUTH

Linwood School
Alma Road, Winton,
BOURNEMOUTH, Dorset BH9 1AJ
Tel: 01202 525107
Category: ASD MLD SLD
PMLD (Coed 3-19)

Tregonwell Academy
Petersfield Road, BOURNEMOUTH,
Dorset BH7 6QP
Tel: 01202 424361
Category: ASC, ASD,
BESD (Coed 5-16)

BRACKNELL FOREST
Borough Council

Bracknell SENDIASS, Time Square, Market Street, Bracknell, Berkshire, RG12 1JD
Tel: 01344 354011 Email: send.support@bracknell-forest.gov.uk Website: www.bracknell-forest.gov.uk

BRACKNELL

Kennel Lane School
Kennel Lane, BRACKNELL,
Berkshire RG42 2EX
Tel: 01344 483872
Category: MLD SLD AUT PMLD

BRADFORD
Council

Bradford SENDIASS, Barnardo's, 40-42 Listerhills Science Park, Bradford, West Yorkshire, BD7 1HR
Tel: 01274 513300 Email: bradfordsendiass@barnardos.org.uk Website: localoffer.bradford.gov.uk

BRADFORD

Chellow Heights School
Thorn Lane, Bingley Road,
BRADFORD, West Yorkshire BD9 6AL
Tel: 01274 484242
Category: ADS, AUT, HI, MSI,
PMLD, SLD, VIS (Primary 2-11)

Delius Special School
Barkerend Road, BRADFORD,
West Yorkshire BD3 8QX
Tel: 01274 666472
Category: SLD PMLD ASD
(Nursery & Primary 2-11)

Oastler's School
Flockton Road, BRADFORD,
West Yorkshire BD4 7RH
Tel: 01274 307456
Category: (Coed Day 11-19)

KEIGHLEY

Beechcliffe School
Greenhead Road, Utley, KEIGHLEY,
West Yorkshire BD20 6ED
Tel: 01535 603041
Category: SLD PMLD
ASD (Secondary)

BRIGHTON & HOVE
City Council

Brighton & Hove SENDIASS, Amaze, Community Base, 113 Queens Road Hove, East Sussex, BN1 3XG
Tel: 01273 772289 Email: sendiass@amazesussex.org.uk Website: www.amazesussex.org.uk

BRIGHTON

**Downs View School
Hollingdean**
Lynchet Close, Hollingdean,
BRIGHTON, East Sussex BN1 7FP
Tel: 01273 558622
Category: ADHD, ASC,
MLD (Coed 3-19)

**Downs View School
Woodingdean**
Warren Road, BRIGHTON,
East Sussex BN2 6BB
Tel: 01273 601680
Category: ASD, HI, SLD,
VIS (Coed 3-19)

Hill Park School – Lower Site
Foredown Road, Portslade,
BRIGHTON, East Sussex BN41 2FU
Tel: 01273 416979
Category: ASC, MLD,
SLD (Coed 2-11)

**Hill Park School
– Upper site**
Foredown Road, Portslade,
BRIGHTON, East Sussex BN41 2FU
Tel: 01273 422855
Category: ASD (Coed 11-16)

Homewood College
Queensdown Road, BRIGHTON,
East Sussex BN1 7LA
Tel: 01273 604472
Category: ADHD, SEBD,
SPLD, SP&LD (Coed 5-16)

Patcham House School
Old London Road, Patcham,
BRIGHTON, East Sussex BN1 8XR
Tel: 01273 551028
Category: PD Del ASP
MLD SPLD (11-16)

BRISTOL

City Council

Bristol SENDIASS, Supportive Parents, 3rd Floor, Royal Oak House, Royal Oak Avenue Bristol, BS1 4GB
Tel: 0117 9897725 Email: support@supportiveparents.org.uk Website: www.bristol.gov.uk

BRISTOL

Briarwood School
Briar Way, Fishponds,
BRISTOL BS16 4EA
Tel: 01173 532651
Category: SLD PMLD
AUT (Coed 3-19)

Bristol Gateway School
Long Cross, Lawrence
Weston, BRISTOL BS11 0QA
Tel: 01173 772275
Category: SEMH (Coed 11-19)

Claremont School
Henleaze Park, Westbury-
on-Trym, BRISTOL BS9 4LR
Tel: 01173 533622
Category: MSI, PD, PMLD,
SLCN, SLD (Coed 2-19)

**Elmfield School for
Deaf Children**
Greystoke Avenue, Westbury-
on-Trym, BRISTOL BS10 6AY
Tel: 01179 030366
Category: D HI (Coed 2-16)

Kingsweston School
Napier Miles Road, Kingsweston,
BRISTOL BS11 0UT
Tel: 01179 030400
Category: MLD SLD AUT (Coed 2-19)

Knowle DGE Academy
Leinster Avenue, Knowle,
BRISTOL BS4 1NN
Tel: 01173 708030
Category: ASC, CLD, MLD, SEMH,
SLCN, Complex Needs (Coed 7-19)

New Fosseway School
Teyfant Road, Hartcliffe,
BRISTOL BS13 0RG
Tel: 01179 030220
Category: ASD, AUT, PMLD,
SLD (Coed 4-19)

Notton House School
28 Notton, Lacock,
BRISTOL SN15 2NF
Tel: 01249 730407
Category: SEMH (Boys 9-19)

Woodstock School
Rectory Gardens, Henbury,
BRISTOL BS10 7AH
Tel: 01173 772175
Category: SEMH (Coed 5-11)

BUCKINGHAMSHIRE

County Council

Buckinghamshire SENDIASS, Annex A, Walton Street, Aylesbury, Buckinghamshire, HP20 1UX
Tel: 01296 383754 Email: sendias@buckscc.gov.uk Website: www.buckscc.gov.uk

AMERSHAM

Stony Dean School
Orchard End Avenue, Off
Pineapple Road, AMERSHAM,
Buckinghamshire HP7 9JW
Tel: 01494 762538
Category: ASD, MLD Language &
Communication, SLCN (Coed 11-19)

AYLESBURY

Booker Park School
Stoke Leys Close, Kynaston
Avenue, AYLESBURY,
Buckinghamshire HP21 9ET
Tel: 01296 427221
Category: ASD MLD
SLD (Coed 3-11)

**Chiltern Way Federation
– Wendover Campus**
Church Lane, Wendover,
AYLESBURY, Buckinghamshire
HP22 6NL
Tel: 01296 622157
Category: BESD (Boys
Day/boarding 11-16)

Pebble Brook School
Churchill Avenue, AYLESBURY,
Buckinghamshire HP21 8LZ
Tel: 01296 415761
Category: ADHD, ASC, MLD SLC
(Coed Day/boarding 11-19)

Stocklake Park School
Stocklake, AYLESBURY,
Buckinghamshire HP20 1DP
Tel: 01296 423507
Category: SLD (Coed 11-19)

BEACONSFIELD

Alfriston School
Penn Road, Knotty
Green, BEACONSFIELD,
Buckinghamshire HP9 2TS
Tel: 01494 673740
Category: MLD (Girls Day/
boarding 11-19)

CHESHAM

Heritage House School
Cameron Road, CHESHAM,
Buckinghamshire HP5 3BP
Tel: 01494 771445
Category: SLD (Coed 2-19)

GREAT MISSENDEN

**Chiltern Way Federation
– Prestwood Campus**
Nairdwood Lane, Prestwood,
GREAT MISSENDEN,
Buckinghamshire HP16 0QQ
Tel: 01494 863514
Category: BESD (Boys
Day/boarding 11-16)

HIGH WYCOMBE

Chiltern Wood School
Verney Avenue, HIGH WYCOMBE,
Buckinghamshire HP12 3NE
Tel: 01494 532621
Category: ASD, SLCN (Coed 3-19)

Westfield School
Highfield Road, Bourne
End, HIGH WYCOMBE,
Buckinghamshire SL8 5BE
Tel: 01628 533125
Category: ASD, ADHD,
BESD, SP&LD (Coed 4-11)

WINSLOW

Furze Down School
Verney Road, WINSLOW,
Buckinghamshire MK18 3BL
Tel: 01296 711380
Category: ASD, MLD, SLCN,
SPLD (Coed 2-19)

CAMBRIDGESHIRE
County Council

Cambridgeshire SENDIASS, SH1212, Shire Hall, Cambridge, CB3 0AP
Tel: 01223 699214 Email: pps@cambridgeshire.gov.uk Website: www.cambridgeshire.gov.uk

CAMBRIDGE

Castle School
Courtney Way,
CAMBRIDGE CB4 2EE
Tel: 01223 442400
Category: ASC MLD PMLD
SLD SP&LD (Coed 3-19)

Granta School
Cambridge Road, Linton,
CAMBRIDGE CB21 4NN
Tel: 01223 896890
Category: ASD PMLD SLD
MLD (Coed 3-19)

Samuel Pepys School
Cromwell Road, St.
Neots, CAMBRIDGE,
Cambridgeshire PE19 2EZ
Tel: 01480 375012
Category: ASD HI PMLD SLD VIS
Complex needs (Coed 2-19)

**TBAP Unity Academy
– St Neots**
Almond Road, St.
Neots, CAMBRIDGE,
Cambridgeshire PE19 1EA
Tel: 01223 712995
Category: ACLD, EBSP,
SEAL (Coed 11-16)

COTTENHAM

The Centre School
High Street, COTTENHAM,
Cambridgeshire CB24 8UA
Tel: 01954 288789
Category: SEMH (Coed 11-16)

ELY

Highfield Ely Academy
Downham Road, ELY,
Cambridgeshire CB6 1BD
Tel: 01353 662085
Category: ASD MLD PD
PMLD SLD VIS (Coed 2-19)

The Harbour School
Station Road, Wilburton, ELY,
Cambridgeshire CB6 3RR
Tel: 01353 740229
Category: ADD EBD MLD
SEBN (Boys 5-16)

WISBECH

Meadowgate School
Meadowgate Lane, WISBECH,
Cambridgeshire PE13 2JH
Tel: 01945 461836
Category: AUT MLD SLD
SP&LD (Coed 2-19)

**TBAP Unity Academy
– Fenland**
2 Algores Way, WISBECH,
Cambridgeshire PE13 2TQ
Tel: 01223 712995
Category: ACLD, EBSP,
SEAL (Coed 11-16)

CHESHIRE EAST
Council

Cheshire East SENDIASS (CEIAS), c/o Municipal Buildings, Earle Street, Crewe, CW1 2BJ
Tel: 0300 123 5166 Email: ceias@cheshireeast.gov.uk Website: www.ceias.cheshireeast.gov.uk

CREWE

Springfield School
Crewe Green Road, CREWE,
Cheshire CW1 5HS
Tel: 01270 685446
Category: ASC PMLD
SLD (Coed 4-19)

MACCLESFIELD

Park Lane School
Park Lane, MACCLESFIELD,
Cheshire SK11 8JR
Tel: 01625 801964
Category: AUT HI SLD VIS
(Coed Day 2-19)

CHESHIRE WEST & CHESTER
Council

Cheshire West & Chester SENDIASS, Council Offices, 4 Civic Way, Ellesmere Port, CH65 0BE
Tel: 0300 123 7001 Email: iasservice@cheshirewestandchester.gov.uk Website: www.westcheshirelocaloffer.co.uk

CHESTER

Dee Banks School
Dee Banks, Sandy Lane,
CHESTER, Cheshire CH3 5UX
Tel: 01244 981030
Category: ASD SLD PMLD
(Coed Day 2-19)

**Dorin Park School &
Specialist SEN College**
Wealstone Lane, Upton,
CHESTER, Cheshire CH2 1HD
Tel: 01244 981191
Category: PD Complex
needs (Coed Day 2-19)

ELLESMERE PORT

Archers Brook School
Chester Road, Great
Sutton, ELLESMERE PORT,
Cheshire CH66 2NA
Tel: 01513 382141
Category: BESD (Coed 11-16)

Hinderton School
Capenhurst Lane,
Whitby, ELLESMERE PORT,
Cheshire CH65 7AQ
Tel: 01513 382203
Category: ASD with complex
learning needs (Coed Day 3-11)

NORTHWICH

Greenbank School
Greenbank Lane, Hartford,
NORTHWICH, Cheshire CW8 1LD
Tel: 01606 288028
Category: ASD MLD
(Coed Day 11-18)

Rosebank School
Townfield Lane, Barnton,
NORTHWICH, Cheshire CW8 4QP
Tel: 01606 74975
Category: ASD with complex
learning needs (Coed Day 4-11)

The Russett School
Middlehurst Avenue, Weaverham,
NORTHWICH, Cheshire CW8 3BW
Tel: 01606 853005
Category: MSI PMLD SLD
(Coed Day 2-19)

WINSFORD

**Hebden Green
Community School**
Woodford Lane West,
WINSFORD, Cheshire CW7 4EJ
Tel: 01606 594221
Category: PD Complex needs
(Coed Day/Residential 2-19)

Oaklands School
Montgomery Way, WINSFORD,
Cheshire CW7 1NU
Tel: 01606 551048
Category: HI MLD SEMH
SP&LD (Coed Day 11-17)

CORNWALL
Council

Cornwall SENDIASS, Units 1G/H, Guildford Road Industrial Estate, Hayle, Cornwall, TR27 4QZ
Tel: 01736 751921 Email: sendiass@disabilitycornwall.org.uk Website: www.cornwallsendiass.org.uk

PENZANCE

Nancealverne School
Madron Road, PENZANCE,
Cornwall TR20 8TP
Tel: 01736 365039
Category: HI PD PMLD
SLD VIS (Coed 2-19)

REDRUTH

Curnow School
Drump Road, REDRUTH,
Cornwall TR15 1LU
Tel: 01209 215432
Category: PMLD SLD (Coed 3-19)

ST AUSTELL

Doubletrees School
St Blazey Gate, St Blazey, Par, ST
AUSTELL, Cornwall PL24 2DS
Tel: 01726 812757
Category: ASD PD PMLD
SLD (Coed 2-19)

CUMBRIA
County Council

Cumbria SEND Team, Cumbria House, 117 Botchergate, Carlisle, Cumbria, CA1 1RD
Tel: 01228 226582 Email: localoffer@cumbria.gov.uk Website: localoffer.cumbria.gov.uk

KENDAL

Sandgate School
Sandylands Road, KENDAL,
Cumbria LA9 6JG
Tel: 01539 792100
Category: PMLD SLD (3-19 Coed)

ULVERSTON

Sandside Lodge School
Sandside Road, ULVERSTON,
Cumbria LA12 9EF
Tel: 01229 588825
Category: PMLD SLD (2-19 Coed)

WHITEHAVEN

Mayfield School
Red Lonning, WHITEHAVEN,
Cumbria CA28 8UG
Tel: 01946 691253
Category: PMLD SLD (3-19 Coed)

DERBYSHIRE
County Council

Derbyshire SENDIASS, The Register Office, New Beetwell Street, Chesterfield, Derbyshire, S40 1QJ
Tel: 01629 533660 Email: ias.service@derbyshire.gov.uk Website: www.derbyshireiass.co.uk

ALFRETON

**Alfreton Park Community
Special School**
Wingfield Road, Alfreton Park,
ALFRETON, Derbyshire DE55 7AL
Tel: 01773 832019
Category: ASD SLD (2-19)

**Swanwick School and
Sports College**
Hayes Lane, Swanwick,
ALFRETON, Derbyshire DE55 1AR
Tel: 01773 602198
Category: ASD MLD PD SEMH
SLCN SLD SpLD (5-16)

BELPER

Holbrook School for Autism
Port Way, Holbrook, BELPER,
Derbyshire DE56 0TE
Tel: 01332 880208
Category: AUT (4-19)

BUXTON

Peak School
Buxton Road, Chinley, High Peak,
BUXTON, Derbyshire SK23 6ES
Tel: 01663 750324
Category: PMLD SLD (2-19)

CHESTERFIELD

Ashgate Croft School
Ashgate Road, CHESTERFIELD,
Derbyshire S40 4BN
Tel: 01246 275111
Category: AUT EBD MLD
PMLD SLD (2-19)

Holly House School
Church Street North, Old
Whittington, CHESTERFIELD,
Derbyshire S41 9QR
Tel: 01246 450530
Category: EBD SEBD (7-14 Coed)

ILKESTON

**Bennerley Fields
Specialist Speech &
Language College**
Stratford Street, ILKESTON,
Derbyshire DE7 8QZ
Tel: 01159 326374
Category: ASD MLD SLCN SLD (2-16)

LONG EATON

**Brackenfield
Special School**
Bracken Road, LONG
EATON NG10 4DA
Tel: 01159 733710
Category: ADHD ASD
MLD SEBN (4-16)

Stanton Vale School
Thoresby Road, LONG
EATON NG10 3NP
Tel: 01159 72 9769
Category: ASD AUT CB MLD
MSI PH PMLD SLD (2-19)

SHIREBROOK

Stubbin Wood School
Common Lane, SHIREBROOK,
Derbyshire NG20 8QF
Tel: 01623 742795
Category: MLD PMLD SLD (2-19)

DERBY CITY
Council

Derby SENDIASS, The Council House, Corporation Street, Derby, Derbyshire, DE1 2FS
Tel: 01332 641414 Email: sendiass@derby.gov.uk Website: derbysendiass.org.uk

DERBY

Ivy House School
Moorway Lane, Littleover,
DERBY DE23 2FS
Tel: 01332 777920
Category: SLD PMLD (Coed 2-19)

St Andrew's School
St Andrew's View, Breadsall
Hilltop, DERBY DE21 4EW
Tel: 01332 832746
Category: ASD MLD
SLD (Coed 11-19)

St Clare's School
Rough Heanor Road,
Mickleover, DERBY DE3 9AZ
Tel: 01332 511757
Category: AUT MLD HI PD SLD
SP&LD VIS (Coed 11-16)

St Giles' School
Hampshire Road, Chaddesden,
DERBY DE21 6BT
Tel: 01332 343039
Category: ASD CLD MLD
SLD (Coed 4-11)

St Martin's School
Bracknell Drive, Alvaston,
DERBY DE24 0BT
Tel: 01332 571151
Category: ASD CLD EBD
MLD SLD (Coed 11-16)

The Kingsmead School
Bridge Street, DERBY DE1 3LB
Tel: 01332 973830
Category: EBD (Coed 11-16)

DEVON
County Council

Devon SENDIASS, Great Moor House, Bittern Road, Sowton Exeter, Devon, EX2 7NL
Tel: 01392 383080 Email: devonias@devon.gov.uk Website: www.devonias.org.uk

BARNSTAPLE

Pathfield School
Abbey Road, Pilton,
BARNSTAPLE, Devon EX31 1JU
Tel: 01271 342423
Category: ASD PMLD SLD (3-19)

**The Lampard
Community School**
St John's Lane, BARNSTAPLE,
Devon EX32 9DD
Tel: 01271 345416
Category: Complex and
difficulties with communication
and interaction (including
SLCN and/or ASC) (5-16)

BUDLEIGH SALTERTON

Mill Water School
Bicton, East Budleigh, BUDLEIGH
SALTERTON, Devon EX9 7BJ
Tel: 01395 568890
Category: ASC CD PD
PMLD SLD (3-19)

DAWLISH

Orchard Manor School
John Nash Drive, DAWLISH,
Devon EX7 9SF
Tel: 01626 862363
Category: ASD (3-19)

EXETER

Barley Lane School
Barley Lane, St Thomas,
EXETER, Devon EX4 1TA
Tel: 01392 430774
Category: ADHD ASD BESD (7-16)

Ellen Tinkham School
Hollow Lane, EXETER,
Devon EX1 3RW
Tel: 01392 467168
Category: ASC PMLD SLD (3-19)

Southbrook School
Bishop Westall Road,
EXETER, Devon EX2 6JB
Tel: 01392 258373
Category: ASC EBSD MLD PD (11-16)

TORRINGTON

Marland School
Petersmarland, TORRINGTON,
Devon EX38 8QQ
Tel: 01805 601324
Category: BESD SEBD (10-16 boys)

TOTNES

Bidwell Brook School
Shinner's Bridge, Dartington,
TOTNES, Devon TQ9 6JU
Tel: 01803 864120
Category: SLD PMLD (3-19)

DORSET
County Council

Dorset SENDIASS, County Hall, Colliton Park, Dorchester, DT1 1XJ
Email: sendiass@dorsetcc.gov.uk Website: www.dorsetforyou.gov.uk

BEAMINSTER

Mountjoy School
Tunnel Road, BEAMINSTER,
Dorset DT8 3HB
Tel: 01308 861155
Category: ASD SLD MLD
PMLD Complex (2-19)

STURMINSTER NEWTON

Yewstock School
Honeymead Lane, STURMINSTER
NEWTON, Dorset DT10 1EW
Tel: 01258 472796
Category: ASC MLD/
Comlex PMLD SLD (3-19)

WEYMOUTH

Westfield Arts College
Littlemoor Road, Preston,
WEYMOUTH, Dorset DT3 6AA
Tel: 01305 833518
Category: ASD MLD/Complex (4-19)

WIMBORNE

Beaucroft Foundation School
Wimborne Road, Colehill,
WIMBORNE, Dorset BH21 2SS
Tel: 01202 886083
Category: ASD MLD/Complex (4-19)

DURHAM
County Council

Durham SENDIASS, Lee House, Lee Terrace, Easington Village Peterlee, County Durham, SR8 3AB
Tel: 0191 5873541 Website: www.durhamsendiass.info

BISHOP AUCKLAND

Evergreen Primary School
Warwick Road, BISHOP
AUCKLAND, Durham DL14 6LS
Tel: 01388 459721
Category: MLD SLD PMLD AUT (2-11)

CONSETT

Villa Real School
Villa Real Road, CONSETT,
Durham DH8 6BH
Tel: 01207 503651
Category: AUC BESD
PMLD SLD (2-19)

DURHAM

Durham Trinity School and Sports College
Dunholme Close, Aykley
Heads, DURHAM DH1 5WB
Tel: 01913 864612
Category: ASD ASP MLD
PMLD SLD SP&LD (2-19)

FERRYHILL

Windlestone School
Chilton, FERRYHILL,
Durham DL17 0HP
Tel: 01388 720337
Category: AUT ASP
SEBD SP&LD (11-16)

NEWTON AYCLIFFE

Walworth School
Bluebell Way, NEWTON
AYCLIFFE, Durham DL5 7LP
Tel: 01325 300194
Category: SEBD (4-11)

SHERBURN

Elemore Hall School
Pittington, SHERBURN,
Durham DH6 1QD
Tel: 01913 720275
Category: SEBD (11-16)

SPENNYMOOR

The Meadows School
Whitworth Lane, SPENNYMOOR,
Durham DL16 7QW
Tel: 01388 811178
Category: SEBD (11-16)

The Oaks Secondary School
Rock Road, SPENNYMOOR,
Durham DL16 7DB
Tel: 01388 827380
Category: ASD MLD PMLD
SLD (11-19 coed)

STANLEY

Croft Community School
Greencroft Road End, Annfield
Plain, STANLEY, Durham DH9 8PR
Tel: 01207 234547
Category: ASD MLD SLCN
SLD (4-16 coed)

ESSEX
County Council

Essex SENDIASS, County Hall, Market Road, Chelmsford, Essex, CM1 1QH
Tel: 03330 138913 Email: send.iass@essex.gov.uk Website: www.essex.gov.uk

BASILDON

Castledon School
Bromfords Drive, Wickford,
BASILDON, Essex SS12 0PW
Tel: 01268 761252
Category: ASD MLD (5-16)

The Pioneer School
Ghyllgrove, BASILDON,
Essex SS14 2LA
Tel: 01268 243300
Category: CLD PMLD SLD (3-19)

BENFLEET

Cedar Hall School
Hart Road, Thundersley,
BENFLEET, Essex SS7 3UQ
Tel: 01268 774723
Category: AUT CD MLD (4-16)

Glenwood School
Rushbottom Lane, New
Thundersley, BENFLEET,
Essex SS7 4LW
Tel: 01268 792575
Category: ASD SLD (3-19)

BILLERICAY

Ramsden Hall School
Heath Road, Ramsden Heath,
BILLERICAY, Essex CM11 1HN
Tel: 01277 624580
Category: BESD (Boys 11-16)

BRAINTREE

The Edith Borthwick School
Springwood Drive, BRAINTREE,
Essex CM7 2YN
Tel: 01376 529300
Category: ASD MLD PH
SLD SP&LD (3-19)

BRENTWOOD

Grove House School
Sawyers Hall Lane, BRENTWOOD,
Essex CM15 9DA
Tel: 01277 361498
Category: SP&LD Communication
Difficulties (9-19)

The Endeavour School
Hogarth Avenue, BRENTWOOD,
Essex CM15 8BE
Tel: 01277 217330
Category: MLD (5-16)

CHELMSFORD

Columbus School
Oliver Way, CHELMSFORD,
Essex CM1 4ZB
Tel: 01245 491492
Category: SpLD (3-19 coed)

Thriftwood School
Slades Lane, Galleywood,
CHELMSFORD, Essex CM2 8RW
Tel: 01245 266880
Category: LD (5-19)

CHIGWELL

Wells Park School
School Lane, Lambourne Road,
CHIGWELL, Essex IG7 6NN
Tel: 02085 026442
Category: BESD (5-11 boys)

CLACTON ON SEA

Shorefields School
114 Holland Road, CLACTON
ON SEA, Essex CO15 6HF
Tel: 01255 424412
Category: ASD MLD SLD (3-19)

COLCHESTER

Kingswode Hoe School
Sussex Road, COLCHESTER,
Essex CO3 3QJ
Tel: 01206 576408
Category: ASD ASP MLD
PI SP&LD (5-16)

Langham Oaks School
School Road, Langham,
COLCHESTER, Essex CO4 5PA
Tel: 01206 271571
Category: SEMH (Boys 10-16)

Lexden Springs School
Halstead Road, Lexden,
COLCHESTER, Essex CO3 9AB
Tel: 01206 563321
Category: ASD MLD
PMLD SLD (3-19)

Market Field School
School Road, Elmstead Market,
COLCHESTER, Essex CO7 7ET
Tel: 01206 825195
Category: ASD MLD SLD (4-16)

HARLOW

**Harlow Fields School
& College**
Tendring Road, HARLOW,
Essex CM18 6RN
Tel: 01279 423670
Category: ASD HI MLD PD
SLD SP&LD VIS (3-19)

LOUGHTON

Oak View School
Whitehills Road, LOUGHTON,
Essex IG10 1TS
Tel: 02085 084293
Category: MLD SLD (3-19)

WITHAM

Southview School
Conrad Road, WITHAM,
Essex CM8 2TA
Tel: 01376 503505
Category: PNI (3-19 coed)

GLOUCESTERSHIRE
County Council

Gloucestershire SENDIASS, 2nd Floor, Messenger House, 35 St. Michael's Square, Gloucester, GL1 1HX
Tel: 0800 158 3603 Email: sendiass@carersgloucestershire.org.uk Website: sendiassglos.org.uk

CHELTENHAM

**Battledown Centre for
Children & Families**
Harp Hill, Battledown,
CHELTENHAM,
Gloucestershire GL52 6PZ
Tel: 01242 525472
Category: VI SLCN ASD SEMH
PD MLD SLD (Coed 2-7)

Belmont School
Warden Hill Road, CHELTENHAM,
Gloucestershire GL51 3AT
Tel: 01242 216180
Category: MLD (Coed 4-16)

Bettridge School
Warden Hill Road, CHELTENHAM,
Gloucestershire GL51 3AT
Tel: 01242 514934
Category: ASD PMLD SLCN
SLD VI (Coed 2-19)

CIRENCESTER

Paternoster School
Watermoor Road, CIRENCESTER,
Gloucestershire GL7 1JR
Tel: 01285 652480
Category: PMLD SLD (Coed 2-16)

COLEFORD

**Heart of the Forest
Community School**
Speech House, Coalway,
COLEFORD, Gloucestershire
GL16 7EJ
Tel: 01594 822175
Category: PMLD SLD (Coed 3-19)

GLOUCESTER

The Milestone School
Longford Lane, GLOUCESTER,
Gloucestershire GL2 9EU
Tel: 01452 874000
Category: ASD PD PMLD MLD
SEMH SLCN SLD VI (Coed 2-16)

STONEHOUSE

The Shrubberies School
Oldends Lane, STONEHOUSE,
Gloucestershire GL10 2DG
Tel: 01453 822155
Category: SLD (Coed 2-19)

TEWKESBURY

Alderman Knight School
Ashchurch Road, TEWKESBURY,
Gloucestershire GL20 8JJ
Tel: 01684 295639
Category: ASD MLD
SLD (Coed 5-19)

SOUTH GLOUCESTERSHIRE

Council

South Gloucestershire SENDIASS, Supportive Parents, 3rd floor, Royal Oak House,
Royal Oak Avenue Bristol, South Gloucestershire, BS1 4GB

Tel: 0117 989 7725 Email: support@supportiveparents.org.uk Website: www.southglos.gov.uk

BRISTOL

SGS Pegasus School
Hempton Lane, BRISTOL, South
Gloucestershire BS32 4AJ
Tel: 01454 862057
Category: (4-18)

DOWNEND

Pathways Learning Centre
Overndale Road, DOWNEND,
South Gloucestershire BS16 2RQ
Tel: 01454 862630
Category: (Day 4-16)

KINGSWOOD

**New Horizons
Learning Centre**
Mulberry Drive, KINGSWOOD,
South Gloucestershire BS15 4EA
Tel: 01454 865340
Category: BESD

THORNBURY

New Siblands School
Easton Hill Road, THORNBURY,
South Gloucestershire BS35 2JU
Tel: 01454 862888
Category: SLD

Sheiling School
Thornbury Park, Park
Road, THORNBURY, South
Gloucestershire BS35 1HP
Tel: 01454 412194
Category: (Day & Boarding)

WARMLEY

Warmley Park School
Tower Road North, WARMLEY,
South Gloucestershire BS30 8XL
Tel: 01454 867272
Category: SLD (Day 3-19)

YATE

Culverhill School
Kelston Close, YATE, South
Gloucestershire BS37 8SZ
Tel: 01454 866930
Category: CLD (Day 7-16)

HALTON

Borough Council

Halton SEND Partnership, Brookvale Children's Centre, Woodhatch Road, Runcorn, Cheshire, WA7 1BY
Tel: 01515 117733 Email: sendpartnership@halton.gov.uk Website: sendiasshalton.co.uk

WIDNES

Ashley School
Cawfield Avenue, WIDNES,
Cheshire WA8 7HG
Tel: 01514 244892
Category: MLD Complex
emotional needs (11-16)

Brookfields School
Moorfield Road, WIDNES,
Cheshire WA8 0JA
Tel: 01514 244329
Category: SLD (2-11)

**Chesnut Lodge School &
Specialist SEN College**
Green Lane, WIDNES,
Cheshire WA8 7HF
Tel: 01514 240679
Category: PH (2-16)

HAMPSHIRE
County Council

Hampshire SENDIASS, Elizabeth II Court, The Castle, Winchester, Hampshire, SO23 8UG
Tel: 0808 164 5504 Email: info@hampshiresendiass.co.uk Website: www.hampshiresendiass.co.uk

ANDOVER

Icknield School
River Way, ANDOVER,
Hampshire SP11 6LT
Tel: 01264 365297
Category: SLD (Coed 2-19)

Norman Gate School
Vigo Road, ANDOVER,
Hampshire SP10 1JZ
Tel: 01264 323423
Category: MLD ASD (Coed 2-11)

The Mark Way School
Batchelors Barn Road, ANDOVER,
Hampshire SP10 1HR
Tel: 01264 351835
Category: MLD ASD (Coed 11-16)

**Wolverdene
Special School**
22 Love Lane, ANDOVER,
Hampshire SP10 2AF
Tel: 01264 362350
Category: BESD (Coed 5-11)

BASINGSTOKE

Limington House School
St Andrews Road, BASINGSTOKE,
Hampshire RG22 6PS
Tel: 01256 322148
Category: SLD (Coed 2-19)

Maple Ridge School
Maple Crescent, BASINGSTOKE,
Hampshire RG21 5SX
Tel: 01256 323639
Category: MLD ASD (Coed 4-11)

Saxon Wood School
Rooksdown, Barron
Place, BASINGSTOKE,
Hampshire RG24 9NH
Tel: 01256 356635
Category: PD (Coed 2-11)

BORDON

Hollywater School
Mill Chase Road, BORDON,
Hampshire GU35 0HA
Tel: 01420 474396
Category: LD (Coed 2-19)

CHANDLERS FORD

Lakeside School
Winchester Road, CHANDLERS
FORD, Hampshire SO53 2DW
Tel: 02380 266633
Category: BESD (Boys 11-16)

FAREHAM

Baycroft School
Gosport Road, Stubbington,
FAREHAM, Hampshire PO14 2AE
Tel: 01329 664151
Category: MLD ASD (Coed 11-16)

Heathfield School
Oldbury Way, FAREHAM,
Hampshire PO14 3BN
Tel: 01329 845150
Category: MLD ASD PD (Coed 2-11)

St Francis Special School
Patchway Drive, Oldbury Way,
FAREHAM, Hampshire PO14 3BN
Tel: 01329 845730
Category: SLD (Coed 2-19)

FARNBOROUGH

Henry Tyndale School
Ship Lane, FARNBOROUGH,
Hampshire GU14 8BX
Tel: 01252 544577
Category: LD ASD (Coed 2-19)

**Samuel Cody Specialist
Sports College**
Ballantyne Road, FARNBOROUGH,
Hampshire GU14 8SS
Tel: 01252 514194
Category: MLD ASD (Coed 11-16)

HAVANT

Prospect School
Freeley Road, HAVANT,
Hampshire PO9 4AQ
Tel: 02392 485140
Category: BESD (Boys 11-16)

PORTSMOUTH

Glenwood School
Washington Road,
Emsworth, PORTSMOUTH,
Hampshire PO10 7NN
Tel: 01243 373120
Category: MLD ASD (Coed 11-16)

SOUTHAMPTON

Forest Park School
Ringwood Road,
Totton, SOUTHAMPTON,
Hampshire SO40 8DZ
Tel: 02380 864949
Category: LD (Coed 2-19)

Oak Lodge School
Roman Road, Dibden
Purlieu, SOUTHAMPTON,
Hampshire SO45 4RQ
Tel: 02380 847213
Category: MLD ASD (Coed 11-16)

WATERLOOVILLE

Rachel Madocks School
Eagle Avenue, Cowplain,
WATERLOOVILLE,
Hampshire PO8 9XP
Tel: 02392 241818
Category: SLD (Coed 2-19)

**Riverside Community
Special School**
Scratchface Lane,
Purbrook, WATERLOOVILLE,
Hampshire PO7 5QD
Tel: 02392 250138
Category: MLD ASD (Coed 3-11)

The Waterloo School
Warfield Avenue, WATERLOOVILLE,
Hampshire PO7 7JJ
Tel: 02392 255956
Category: BESD (Boys 4-11)

WINCHESTER

Osborne School
Athelstan Road, WINCHESTER,
Hampshire SO23 7GA
Tel: 01962 854537
Category: LD ASD (Coed 11-19)

**Shepherds Down
Special School**
Shepherds Lane, Compton,
WINCHESTER, Hampshire SO21 2AJ
Tel: 01962 713445
Category: LD ASD (Coed 4-11)

HARTLEPOOL
Borough Council

Hartlepool SENIAS, Civic Centre, Victoria Road, Hartlepool, TS24 8AY
Tel: 01429 284876 Email: hartlepooliass@hartlepool.gov.uk Website: www.hartlepool.gov.uk

HARTLEPOOL

Springwell School
Wiltshire Way, HARTLEPOOL TS26 0TB
Tel: 01429 280600
Category: MLD SLD PMLD
ASD BESD (Coed 3-11)

HEREFORDSHIRE
Council

Herefordshire SENDIAS, Town Hall, 10 St Owen Street, Hereford, Herefordshire, HR1 2PJ
Tel: 01432 260955 Email: sendias@herefordshire.gov.uk Website: www.herefordshire.gov.uk

HEREFORD

Blackmarston School
Honddu Close, HEREFORD HR2 7NX
Tel: 01432 272376
Category: SLD ASD
PMLD(Coed 3-11)

LEOMINSTER

Westfield School
Westfield Walk,
LEOMINSTER HR6 8NZ
Tel: 01568 613147
Category: SLD ASD
PMLD (Coed 2-19)

HERTFORDSHIRE
County Council

Hertfordshire SENDIASS, County Hall, Pegs Lane, Hertford, SG13 8DF
Tel: 01992 555847 Email: sendiass@hertfordshire.gov.uk Website: www.hertsdirect.org

BALDOCK

Brandles School
Weston Way, BALDOCK,
Hertfordshire SG7 6EY
Tel: 01462 892189
Category: EBD (Boys 11-16)

BUSHEY

Meadow Wood School
Cold Harbour Lane, BUSHEY,
Hertfordshire WD23 4NN
Tel: 02084 204720
Category: PI (Coed Day 3-12)

HATFIELD

Southfield School
Woods Avenue, HATFIELD,
Hertfordshire AL10 8NN
Tel: 01707 276504
Category: MLD (Coed Day 3-11)

HEMEL HEMPSTEAD

Haywood Grove School
St Agnells Lane, HEMEL HEMPSTEAD,
Hertfordshire HP2 7BG
Tel: 01442 250077
Category: EBD (Coed Day 5-11)

The Collett School
Lockers Park Lane, HEMEL
HEMPSTEAD, Hertfordshire HP1 1TQ
Tel: 01442 398988
Category: MLD AUT (Coed 4-16)

Woodfield School
Malmes Croft, Leverstock
Green, HEMEL HEMPSTEAD,
Hertfordshire HP3 8RL
Tel: 01442 253476
Category: SLD AUT (Coed Day 3-19)

RADLETT

Forest House Education Centre
9 Forest Lane, Kingsley Green,
Harper Lane, RADLETT,
Hertfordshire WD7 9HQ
Tel: 01923 633241
Category: (13-18)

REDBOURN

St Luke's School
Crouch Hall Lane, REDBOURN,
Hertfordshire AL3 7ET
Tel: 01582 626727
Category: MLD (Coed Day 9-16)

ST ALBANS

Batchwood School
Townsend Drive, ST ALBANS,
Hertfordshire AL3 5RP
Tel: 01727 868021
Category: EBD (Coed 11-16)

Heathlands School
Heathlands Drive, ST ALBANS,
Hertfordshire AL3 5AY
Tel: 01727 807807
Category: HI (Coed Day
& boarding 3-16)

Watling View School
Watling View, ST ALBANS,
Hertfordshire AL1 2NU
Tel: 01727 850560
Category: SLD (Coed Day 2-19)

STEVENAGE

Greenside School
Shephall Green, STEVENAGE,
Hertfordshire SG2 9XS
Tel: 01438 315356
Category: SLD AUT (Coed Day 2 19)

Lonsdale School
Brittain Way, STEVENAGE,
Hertfordshire SG2 8UT
Tel: 01438 726999
Category: PH (Coed Day
& boarding 5-19)

The Valley School
Valley Way, STEVENAGE,
Hertfordshire SG2 9AB
Tel: 01438 747274
Category: MLD (Coed Day 11-19)

WARE

Amwell View School & Specialist Sports College
Stanstead Abbotts, WARE,
Hertfordshire SG12 8EH
Tel: 01920 870027
Category: SLD AUT (Coed Day 2-19)

Middleton School
Walnut Tree Walk, WARE,
Hertfordshire SG12 9PD
Tel: 01920 485152
Category: MLD AUT
(Coed Day 5-11)

WATFORD

Breakspeare School
Gallows Hill Lane, Abbots Langley,
WATFORD, Hertfordshire WD5 0BU
Tel: 01923 263645
Category: SLD (Coed Day 3-19)

Colnbrook School
Hayling Road, WATFORD,
Hertfordshire WD19 7UY
Tel: 02084 281281
Category: MLD AUT
(Coed Day 4-11)

Falconer School
Falconer Road, Bushey, WATFORD,
Hertfordshire WD23 3AT
Tel: 02089 502505
Category: EBD (Boys Day/
boarding 10-19)

Garston Manor School
Horseshoe Lane, Garston,
WATFORD, Hertfordshire WD25 7HR
Tel: 01923 673757
Category: MLD (Coed Day 11-16)

WELWYN GARDEN CITY

Lakeside School
Stanfield, Lemsford Lane,
WELWYN GARDEN CITY,
Hertfordshire AL8 6YN
Tel: 01707 327410
Category: SLD PD (Coed Day 2-19)

ISLE OF WIGHT
Council

Isle of Wight SENDIASS, 11 Orchard Street, Newport, Isle of Wight, PO30 1JZ
Tel: 01983 825548 Email: sendiass@iow.gov.uk Website: iowsendiass.co.uk

NEWPORT

Medina House School
School Lane, NEWPORT,
Isle of Wight PO30 2HS
Tel: 01983 522917
Category: Severe & complex
needs (Coed 2-11)

St George's School
Watergate Road, NEWPORT,
Isle of Wight PO30 1XW
Tel: 01983 524634
Category: Severe complex
needs (Coed 11-19)

KENT
County Council

Kent SENDIASS, Shepway Centre, Oxford Road, Maidstone, Kent, ME15 8AW
Tel: 03000 412412 Email: iask@kent.gov.uk Website: www.kent.gov.uk

ASHFORD

Goldwyn School
Godinton Lane, Great Chart,
ASHFORD, Kent TN23 3BT
Tel: 01233 622958
Category: BESD (Coed 11-16)

The Wyvern School
Great Chart Bypass,
ASHFORD, Kent TN23 4ER
Tel: 01233 621468
Category: PMLD SLD
CLD PD (Coed 3-19)

BROADSTAIRS

Stone Bay School
70 Stone Road, BROADSTAIRS,
Kent CT10 1EB
Tel: 01843 863421
Category: SLD AUT SLCN MLD C&I
(Coed Day & Residential 11-19)

CANTERBURY

St Nicholas' School
Holme Oak Close, Nunnery Fields,
CANTERBURY, Kent CT1 3JJ
Tel: 01227 464316
Category: PMLD SLD CLD
PSCN (Coed 3-19)

The Orchard School
Cambridge Road,
CANTERBURY, Kent CT1 3QQ
Tel: 01227 769220
Category: MLD CLD
B&L (Coed 11-16)

DARTFORD

Rowhill School
Main Road, Longfield,
DARTFORD, Kent DA3 7PW
Tel: 01474 705377
Category: B&L AUT LD
Complex needs Behavioural
difficulties (Coed Day 4-16)

DOVER

Elms School
Elms Vale Road, DOVER,
Kent CT17 9PS
Tel: 01304 201964
Category: BESD ASD MLD
B&L (Coed 4-16)

Portal House School
Sea Street, St Margarets-at-
Cliffe, DOVER, Kent CT15 6SS
Tel: 01304 853033
Category: BESD (Coed 11-16)

FOLKESTONE

The Beacon School
Park Farm Road, FOLKESTONE,
Kent CT19 5DN
Tel: 01303 847555
Category: MLD CLD Complex
needs (Coed 4-17)

GRAVESEND

The Ifield School
Cedar Avenue, GRAVESEND,
Kent DA12 5JT
Tel: 01474 365485
Category: CLD PMLD SLD
MLD PSCN (Coed 4-18)

MAIDSTONE

Bower Grove School
Fant Lane, MAIDSTONE,
Kent ME16 8NL
Tel: 01622 726773
Category: BESD MLD ASD
B&L (Coed Day 5-16)

Five Acre Wood School
Boughton Lane, Loose Valley,
MAIDSTONE, Kent ME15 9QF
Tel: 01622 743925
Category: ASD PMLD SLD PD
CLD PSCN (Coed 4-19)

MARGATE

St Anthony's School
St Anthony's Way, MARGATE,
Kent CT9 3RA
Tel: 01843 292015
Category: MLD ASD LD SEBD
SLCN B&L (Coed 3-11)

RAMSGATE

Foreland Fields School
Newlands Lane, RAMSGATE,
Kent CT12 6RH
Tel: 01843 863891
Category: ASD PMLD SLD
PSCN (Coed 2-19)

Laleham Gap School
Ozengell Place, RAMSGATE,
Kent CT12 6FH
Tel: 01843 570598
Category: AUT ABD PD SLCN C&I
(CoedDay & Residential 3-16)

SEVENOAKS

Grange Park School
Borough Green Road, Wrotham,
SEVENOAKS, Kent TN15 7RD
Tel: 01732 882111
Category: AUT C&I
(Coed Day 11-19)

SITTINGBOURNE

Meadowfield School
Swanstree Avenue,
SITTINGBOURNE, Kent ME10 4NL
Tel: 01795 477788
Category: CLD PMLD SLD ASD
SP&LD PSCN (Coed 4-19)

SWANLEY

**Broomhill Bank
School (North)**
Rowhill Road, Hextable,
SWANLEY, Kent BR8 7RP
Tel: 01322 662937
Category: MLD SP&LD CLD AUT C&I
(Coed Day & Residential 11-19)

TONBRIDGE

Nexus School
Upper Haysden Lane,
TONBRIDGE, Kent TN11 8AA
Tel: 01732 771384
Category: PMLD ASD (Coed 2-19)

**Oakley School
– Tonbridge Site**
Waveney Road, TONBRIDGE,
Kent TN10 3JU
Tel: 01892 823096
Category: PMLD ASD MLD
PSCN (Coed 3-19)

TUNBRIDGE WELLS

**Broomhill Bank
School (West)**
Broomhill Road, Rusthall,
TUNBRIDGE WELLS, Kent TN3 0TB
Tel: 01892 510440
Category: MLD SP&LD CLD AUT C&I
(Coed Day & Residential 11-19)

**Oakley School
– Tunbridge Wells Site**
Pembury Road, TUNBRIDGE
WELLS, Kent TN2 4NE
Tel: 01892 823096
Category: PMLD ASD MLD
PSCN (Coed 3-19)

WESTERHAM

Valence School
Westerham Road, WESTERHAM,
Kent TN16 1QN
Tel: 01959 562156
Category: PD Sensory Medical
(Coed Day & Residential 4-19)

KINGSTON UPON HULL

City Council

Kingston upon Hull SENDIASS, 182 Chanterlands Avenue, Hull, HU5 4DJ
Tel: 01482 467 540 Website: www.hullcc.gov.uk

KINGSTON UPON HULL

Bridgeview School
Pickering Road, KINGSTON
UPON HULL HU4 7AD
Tel: 01482 303300
Category: BESD

Frederick Holmes School
Inglemire Lane, KINGSTON
UPON HULL HU6 8JJ
Tel: 01482 804766
Category: PH

Ganton Primary School
The Compass, 1 Burnham Road,
KINGSTON UPON HULL HU4 7EB
Tel: 01482 564 646
Category: SLD

Ganton Secondary School
294 Anlaby Park Road South,
KINGSTON UPON HULL HU4 7JB
Tel: 01482 564646
Category: SLD

Northcott School
Dulverton Close, Bransholme,
KINGSTON UPON HULL HU7 4EL
Tel: 01482 825311
Category: Vulnerable ASD

Oakfield School
Hopewell Road, KINGSTON
UPON HULL HU9 4HD
Tel: 01482 854588
Category: BESD

Tweendykes School
Midmere Avenue, Leads Road,
KINGSTON UPON HULL HU7 4PW
Tel: 01482 826508
Category: SLD

LANCASHIRE

County Council

Lancashire SENDIASS, County Hall, Preston, Lancashire, PR1 8RJ
Tel: 03001 236706 Email: information.lineteam@lancashire.gov.uk Website: www.lancashire.gov.uk

ACCRINGTON

**Broadfield Specialist
School for SEN**
Fielding Lane, Oswaldtwistle,
ACCRINGTON, Lancashire BB5 3BE
Tel: 01254 381782
Category: AUT SLCN PD
PMLD VI HI (Coed 11-19)

White Ash School
Thwaites Road, Oswaldtwistle,
ACCRINGTON, Lancashire BB5 4QG
Tel: 01254 235772
Category: GLD (Coed 2-11)

BURNLEY

Holly Grove School
Burnley Campus, Barden Lane,
BURNLEY, Lancashire BB10 1JD
Tel: 01282 682278
Category: SLD MLD PMLD ASD
Medical needs (Coed 2-11)

**Ridgewood Community
High School**
Eastern Avenue, BURNLEY,
Lancashire BB10 2AT
Tel: 01282 682316
Category: MSI PD LD (Coed 11-19)

The Rose School
Greenock Street, BURNLEY,
Lancashire BB11 4DT
Tel: 01282 683050
Category: SEMH (Coed 11-16)

CARNFORTH

Bleasdale School
27 Emesgate Lane, Silverdale,
CARNFORTH, Lancashire LA5 0RG
Tel: 01524 701217
Category: PMLD (Coed 2-19)

CHORLEY

Astley Park School
Harrington Road, CHORLEY,
Lancashire PR7 1JZ
Tel: 01257 262227
Category: MLD SLD AUT
SLCN (Coed 4-16)

Mayfield Specialist School
Gloucester Road, CHORLEY,
Lancashire PR7 3HN
Tel: 01257 263063
Category: SLD PMLD AUT
SLCN PD MSI (Coed 2-19)

COLNE

**Pendle View
Primary School**
Gibfield Road, COLNE,
Lancashire BB8 8JT
Tel: 01282 865011
Category: PMLD (Coed 2-11)

HASLINGDEN

**Tor View Community
Special School**
Clod Lane, HASLINGDEN,
Lancashire BB4 6LR
Tel: 01706 214640
Category: AUT (Coed 3-19)

KIRKHAM

Pear Tree School
29 Station Road, KIRKHAM,
Lancashire PR4 2HA
Tel: 01772 683609
Category: SLD PMLD (Coed 2-19)

LANCASTER

**The Loyne Specialist
School**
Sefton Drive, LANCASTER,
Lancashire LA1 2PZ
Tel: 01524 64543
Category: SLD PMLD AUT (2-19)

Wennington Hall School
Lodge Lane, Wennington,
LANCASTER, Lancashire LA2 8NS
Tel: 01524 221333
Category: SEMH (Boys
Day or resident 11-16)

MORECAMBE

Morecambe Road School
Morecambe Road, MORECAMBE,
Lancashire LA3 3AB
Tel: 01524 414384
Category: PD HI VI AUT MLD
PMLD SLD (Coed 3-16)

Maintained special schools and colleges

NELSON

Pendle Community High School and College
Oxford Road, NELSON, Lancashire BB9 8LF
Tel: 01282 682260
Category: MLD BESD ASD (Coed 11-19)

POULTON-LE-FYLDE

Brookfield School
Fouldrey Avenue, POULTON-LE-FYLDE, Lancashire FY6 7HE
Tel: 01253 886895
Category: SEMH (Coed 11-16)

PRESTON

Acorns Primary School
Blackpool Road, Moor Park, PRESTON, Lancashire PR1 6AU
Tel: 01772 792681
Category: AUT SLD PMLD (Coed 2-11)

Hillside Specialist School & College
Ribchester Road, Longridge, PRESTON, Lancashire PR3 3XB
Tel: 01772 782205
Category: AUT (Coed 3-19)

Moor Hey School
Far Croft, off Leyland Road, Lostock Hall, PRESTON, Lancashire PR5 5SS
Tel: 01772 336976
Category: GLD (4-16)

Moorbrook School
Ainslie Road, Fulwood, PRESTON, Lancashire PR2 3DB
Tel: 01772 774752
Category: SEMH (11-16)

Royal Cross Primary School
Elswick Road, Ashton-on-Ribble, PRESTON, Lancashire PR2 1NT
Tel: 01772 729705
Category: Deaf (Coed 4-11)

Sir Tom Finney Community High School
Ribbleton Hall Drive, PRESTON, Lancashire PR2 6EE
Tel: 01772 795749
Category: GLD (Coed 11-19)

The Coppice School
Ash Grove, Bamber Bridge, PRESTON, Lancashire PR5 6GY
Tel: 01772 336342
Category: SLD PMLD AUT MLD VI HI MSI (Coed 2-19)

RAWTENSTALL

Cribden House Community Special School
Haslingden Road, RAWTENSTALL, Lancashire BB4 6RX
Tel: 01706 213048
Category: SEMH (Coed 5-11)

SKELMERSDALE

Elm Tree Community Primary School
Elmers Wood Road, SKELMERSDALE, Lancashire WN8 6SA
Tel: 01695 50924
Category: SEMH (Coed 5-11)

Hope High School
Clay Brow, SKELMERSDALE, Lancashire WN8 9DP
Tel: 01695 721066
Category: SEMH (Coed 11-16)

Kingsbury Primary School
School Lane, Chapel House, SKELMERSDALE, Lancashire WN8 8EH
Tel: 01695 722991
Category: GLD (Coed 2-11)

West Lancashire Community High School
School Lane, Chapel House, SKELMERSDALE, Lancashire WN8 8EH
Tel: 01695 721487
Category: MLD SLD PMLD AUT VI HI (Coed 11-19)

THORNTON-CLEVELEYS

Great Arley School
Holly Road, THORNTON-CLEVELEYS, Lancashire FY5 4HH
Tel: 01253 821072
Category: MLD CLD (Coed Day 4-16)

Red Marsh School
Holly Road, THORNTON-CLEVELEYS, Lancashire FY5 4HH
Tel: 01253 868451
Category: MLD SLD AUT PMLD (Coed 2-19)

LEICESTER CITY
Council

Leicester SENDIASS, Voluntary Action Leicester, 9 Newarke Street, Leicester, LE1 5SN
Tel: 0116 257 5027 Email: info@sendiassleicester.org.uk Website: www.sendiassleicester.org.uk

LEICESTER

Ellesmere College
40 Braunstone Lane East, LEICESTER LE3 2FD
Tel: 0116 289 4242
Category: MLD SCLD ASD SpeechLD Complex Needs (4-19)

Keyham Lodge School
Keyham Lane, LEICESTER LE5 1FG
Tel: 0116 241 6852
Category: ASD ADHD Complex Needs (9-16)

Millgate School
18 Scott Street, LEICESTER LE2 6DW
Tel: 0116 270 4922
Category: BESD Complex Needs (11-16)

Nether Hall School
Keyham Lane West, LEICESTER LE5 1RT
Tel: 0116 241 7258
Category: SCLD PMLD PD ASD (4-19)

Oaklands School
Whitehall Road, LEICESTER LE5 6GJ
Tel: 0116 241 5921
Category: MLD (4-11)

The Children's Hospital School
Leicester Royal Infirmary, Infirmary Square, LEICESTER LE1 5WW
Tel: 0116 229 8137
Category: HS

West Gate School
Glenfield Road, LEICESTER LE3 6DG
Tel: 0116 255 2187
Category: SCLD MLD ASD PMLD Complex Needs (4-19)

LEICESTERSHIRE
County Council

Leicestershire SENDIASS, County Hall, Leicester Road, Glenfield, Leicestershire, LE3 8RA
Tel: 0116 305 5614 Email: sendiass@leics.gov.uk Website: www.leicestershire.gov.uk

LOUGHBOROUGH

Ashmount School
Thorpe Hill, LOUGHBOROUGH, Leicestershire LE11 4SQ
Tel: 01509 268506
Category: SLD PMLD (4-19)

Maplewell Hall School
Maplewell Road, Woodhouse Eaves, LOUGHBOROUGH, Leicestershire LE12 8QY
Tel: 01509 890237
Category: MLD AUT (11-19)

MELTON MOWBRAY

Birch Wood (Melton Area Special School)
Grange Drive, MELTON MOWBRAY, Leicestershire LE13 1HA
Tel: 01664 483340
Category: MLD SLD AUT (4-19)

WIGSTON

Wigston Birkett House Community Special School
Station Road, WIGSTON, Leicestershire LE18 2DT
Tel: 01162 885802
Category: SLD PMLD (4-19)

LINCOLNSHIRE
County Council

Lincolnshire FIS, 2nd Floor, Thomas Parker House, Silver Street, Lincoln, Lincolnshire, LN2 1DY
Tel: 0800 195 1635 Email: fis@lincolnshire.gov.uk Website: www.lincolnshire.gov.uk

BOURNE

Willoughby School
South Road, BOURNE,
Lincolnshire PE10 9JE
Tel: 01778 425203
Category: SLD (2-19)

GRANTHAM

The Phoenix School
Great North Road, GRANTHAM,
Lincolnshire NG31 7US
Tel: 01476 574112
Category: EBD (11-16)

SLEAFORD

The Ash Villa School
Willoughby Road, Greylees,
SLEAFORD, Lincolnshire NG34 8QA
Tel: 01529 488066
Category: HS (8-16)

GAINSBOROUGH

Aegir Community School
Sweyn Lane, GAINSBOROUGH,
Lincolnshire DN21 1PB
Tel: 01427 619360
Category: SLD

LINCOLN

St Christopher's School
Hykeham Road, LINCOLN,
Lincolnshire LN6 8AR
Tel: 01522 528378
Category: MLD (3-16)

NORTH LINCOLNSHIRE
Council

North Lincolnshire SENDIASS, Hewson House, Station Road, Brigg, North Lincolnshire, DN20 8XJ
Tel: 01724 277665 Email: help@nlsendiass.org.uk Website: www.northlincs.gov.uk

SCUNTHORPE

St Hugh's Communication & Interaction Specialist College
Bushfield Road, SCUNTHORPE,
North Lincolnshire DN16 1NB
Tel: 01724 842960
Category: MLD SLD
PMLD (Coed 11-19)

St Luke's Primary School
Grange Lane North, SCUNTHORPE,
North Lincolnshire DN16 1BN
Tel: 01724 844560
Category: PMLD SLD
MLD (Coed 3-11)

London
BARKING & DAGENHAM
Council

Barking & Dagenham Education Inclusion Team, 2nd Floor, Town Hall, 1 Town Square, Barking, Essex, IG11 8LU
Tel: 020 8227 2636 Website: www.lbbd.gov.uk

BARKING

Riverside Bridge School
Renwick Road, BARKING,
Essex IG11 0FU
Tel: 02039 465888

DAGENHAM

Hopewell School
Baden Powell Close,
DAGENHAM, Essex RM9 6XN
Tel: 02085 936610

Trinity School
Heathway, DAGENHAM,
Essex RM10 7SJ
Tel: 02034 355955
Category: SLD ASD
PMLD (Coed 3-19)

Maintained special schools and colleges

London

BARNET
Council

Barnet SENDIASS, North London Business Park, Oakleigh Road South, London, N11 1NP
Tel: 020 8359 7637 Fax: 020 8359 2480 Email: sendiass@barnet.gov.uk Website: www.barnet.gov.uk

LONDON

Mapledown School
Claremont Road, Golders
Green, LONDON NW2 1TR
Tel: 02084 554111
Category: SLD CLD (Mixed 11-19)

Northway School
The Fairway, Mill Hill,
LONDON NW7 3HS
Tel: 02083 595450
Category: CLD AUT (Mixed 5-11)

Oak Lodge School
Heath View, Off East End Road,
Finchley, LONDON N2 0QY
Tel: 02084 446711
Category: MLD ASD SCLN
EBD (Mixed 11-19)

Oakleigh School
Oakleigh Road North,
Whetstone, LONDON N20 0DH
Tel: 02083 685336
Category: SLD AUT
PMLD (Mixed 3-11)

London

LONDON BOROUGH OF BEXLEY
Council

Bexley SENDIASS, Shepway Centre, Oxford Road, Maidstone, ME15 8AW
Tel: 02030 455976 Email: bexleyiass@bexley.gov.uk Website: www.bexleylocaloffer.uk

BEXLEYHEATH

**Endeavour Academy
Bexley**
Woodside Road, BEXLEYHEATH,
Kent DA7 6LB
Tel: 01322 553787
Category: BESD (Coed 11-16)

Pelham Primary School
Pelham Road, BEXLEYHEATH,
Kent DA7 4HL
Tel: 02083 036556

CRAYFORD

Shenstone School
94 Old Road, CRAYFORD,
Kent DA1 4DZ
Tel: 01322 524145
Category: SLD (2-11)

ERITH

Woodside School
Colyers Lane, ERITH, Kent DA8 3PB
Tel: 01322 350123
Category: MLD (Primary/
Secondary)

SIDCUP

Marlborough School
Marlborough Park Avenue,
SIDCUP, Kent DA15 9DP
Tel: 02083 006896
Category: SLD (11-19)

WELLING

Aspire Academy Bexley
South Gipsy Road, WELLING,
Kent DA16 1JB
Tel: 02083 041320
Category: BESD (5-11)

London

BRENT
Council

Brent SENDIASS, Brent Civic Centre, Engineers Way, Wembley, Middlesex, HA9 0FJ
Tel: 020 8937 3434 Email: sendias@brent.gov.uk Website: www.brent.gov.uk

KENSALE RISE

Manor School
Chamberlayne Road, KENSALE
RISE, London NW10 3NT
Tel: 02089 683160
Category: MLD SLD CLD
ASD (Coed 4-11)

KINGSBURY

The Village School
Grove Park, KINGSBURY,
London NW9 0JY
Tel: 02082 045396
Category: LD DD VIS Medical
needs (Coed 2-19)

Woodfield School
Glenwood Avenue, KINGSBURY,
London NW9 7LY
Tel: 02082 051977
Category: MLD BESD
ASD (Coed 11-19)

NEASDEN

Phoenix Arch School
Drury Way, NEASDEN,
London NW10 0NQ
Tel: 02084 516961
Category: BESD LD ADHD
ASD (Coed 5-11)

London

BROMLEY
Council

Bromley SENDIASS, 6th Floor, Central Library, High Street, Bromley, Kent, BR1 1EX
Tel: 020 8461 7630 Email: iass@bromley.gov.uk Website: www.bromley.gov.uk

BECKENHAM

Riverside School Beckenham (Beckenham Site)
2 Hayne Road, BECKENHAM, Kent BR3 4HY
Tel: 020 8639 0079
Category: ASD (Coed 4-19)

CHISLEHURST

Marjorie McClure School
Hawkwood Lane, CHISLEHURST, Kent BR7 5PW
Tel: 02084 670174
Category: PD SLD Medical needs (Coed 3-18)

ORPINGTON

Riverside School (St Paul's Cray Site)
Main Road, St Paul's Cray, ORPINGTON, Kent BR5 3HS
Tel: 01689 870519
Category: ASD (Coed 4-19)

WEST WICKHAM

Glebe School
117 Hawes Lane, WEST WICKHAM, Kent BR4 9AE
Tel: 02087 774540
Category: Complex needs SCD ASD SLD (Coed 11-19)

London Borough

CAMDEN
Council

Camden SENDIASS, Highgate Newtown Community Centre, 25 Bertram Street, London, N19 5DQ
Tel: 0207 974 6264 Email: sendiass@camden.gov.uk Website: www.sendiasscamden.co.uk

LONDON

Cpotential
143 Coppetts Road, LONDON N10 1JP
Tel: 02084 447242
Category: CP

Frank Barnes Primary School for Deaf Children
4 Wollstonecraft Street, LONDON N1C 4BT
Tel: 02073 917040
Category: HI (Coed 2-11)

SEBD Special School
Harmood Street, LONDON NW1 8DP
Tel: 02079 748906
Category: BESD (Coed 11-16)

Swiss Cottage School Development & Research Centre
80 Avenue Road, LONDON NW8 6HX
Tel: 02076 818080
Category: LD (2-16)

The Children's Hospital School
Great Ormond Street, LONDON WC1N 3JH
Tel: 02078 138269
Category: HS (Coed 0-19)

The Royal Free Hospital Children's School
Royal Free Hospital, Pond Street, LONDON NW3 2QG
Tel: 02074 726298
Category: HS (5-16)

London

CROYDON
Council

KIDS Croydon SENDIAS, Carers Support Centre, 24 George Street, Croydon, Surrey, CR0 1PB
Tel: 020 8663 5630 Email: croydon@kids.org.uk Website: www.croydon.gov.uk

BECKENHAM

Beckmead School
Monks Orchard Road, BECKENHAM, Kent BR3 3BZ
Tel: 020 8777 9311
Category: BESD (Boys 5-16)

CROYDON

Bensham Manor School
Ecclesbourne Road, Thornton Heath, CROYDON, Surrey CR7 7BN
Tel: 020 8684 0116
Category: MLD AUT (Coed 11-16)

Chaffinch Brook School
32 Morland Road, CROYDON, Surrey CR0 6NA
Tel: 020 8325 4612
Category: AUT (Coed 5-11)

Red Gates School
Farnborough Avenue, CROYDON, Surrey CR2 8HD
Tel: 020 8651 6540
Category: SLD AUT (Coed 4-12)

St Giles School
207 Pampisford Road, CROYDON, Surrey CR2 6DF
Tel: 020 8680 2141
Category: PD PMLD MLD (Coed 4-19)

Maintained special schools and colleges

PURLEY

St Nicholas School
Reedham Drive, PURLEY,
Surrey CR8 4DS
Tel: 020 8660 4861
Category: MLD AUT (Coed 4-11)

UPPER NORWOOD

Priory School
Hermitage Road, UPPER
NORWOOD, London SE19 3QN
Tel: 020 8653 7879
Category: SLD AUT (Coed 11-19)

London

EALING

Council

Ealing SEN Team, Perceval House, 14-16 Uxbridge Road, London, W5 2HL
Tel: 020 8825 5588 Email: children@ealing.gov.uk Website: www.ealing.gov.uk

EALING

Castlebar School
Hathaway Gardens, EALING,
London W13 0DH
Tel: 02089 983135
Category: MLD SLD ASD
(Coed Day 4-11)

Springhallow School
Compton Close, Cavendish
Ave, EALING, London W13 0JG
Tel: 02088 328979
Category: ASD (Coed Day 4-16/17)

GREENFORD

Mandeville School
Horsenden Lane North,
GREENFORD, Middlesex UB6 0PA
Tel: 02088 644921
Category: SLD ASD PMLD
(Coed Day 2-12)

HANWELL

St Ann's School
Springfield Road, HANWELL,
London W7 3JP
Tel: 02085 676291
Category: SLD MSI PNLD
SLCN Complex medical
conditions (Coed Day 11-19)

NORTHOLT

Belvue School
Rowdell Road, NORTHOLT,
London UB5 6AG
Tel: 02088 455766
Category: MLD SLD ASD
(Coed Day 11-18)

John Chilton School
Bengarth Road, NORTHOLT,
London UB5 5LD
Tel: 02088 421329
Category: PH/Medical
(Coed Day 2-18)

London

ENFIELD

Council

Enfield SENDIASS, Every Parent & Child, Community House, 311 Fore Street London, N9 0PZ
Tel: 020 8373 6243 Email: enquiries@epandc.org.uk Website: www.epandc.org.uk

EDMONTON

West Lea School
Haselbury Road, EDMONTON,
London N9 9TU
Tel: 02088 072656
Category: HA ASD PD
LD (Coed 5-19)

ENFIELD

Durants School
4 Pitfield Way, ENFIELD,
London EN3 5BY
Tel: 02088 041980
Category: CLD ASD
AUT (Coed 11-19)

Fern House School
Keswick Drive, ENFIELD,
London EN3 6NY
Tel: 01992 761229
Category: EBD (Coed 7-19)

Russet House School
11 Autumn Close, ENFIELD,
London EN1 4JA
Tel: 02083 500650
Category: AUT (Coed 3-11)

Waverley School
105 The Ride, ENFIELD,
London EN3 7DL
Tel: 02088 051858
Category: PMLD SLD (Coed 3-19)

SOUTHGATE

Oaktree School
Chase Side, SOUTHGATE,
London N14 4HN
Tel: 02084 403100
Category: Complex
needs (Coed 7-19)

London

ROYAL BOROUGH OF GREENWICH
Council

Greenwich SENDIASS, The Point, 47 Woolwich New Road, London, SE18 6EW
Tel: 020 8921 8402 Email: sendiass@royalgreenwich.gov.uk Website: www.greenwichfamiliesinformation.org.uk

LONDON

King's Oak
Eltham Palace Road,
LONDON SE9 5LX
Tel: 02088 508081
Category: BESD (Boys 11-19)

Waterside School
Robert Street, Plumstead,
LONDON SE18 7NB
Tel: 02083 177659
Category: BESD (Coed 5-11)

Willow Dene School
Swingate Lane, Plumstead,
LONDON SE18 2JD
Tel: 02088 549841
Category: SCLD CLD PMLD
PD ASD (Coed 3-11)

London

HACKNEY
Council

Hackney SEN Team, Hackney Learning Trust, 1 Reading Lane, London, E8 1GQ
Email: localoffer@learningtrust.co.uk Website: www.hackneylocaloffer.co.uk

LONDON

Ickburgh School
Kenworthy Road, LONDON E9 5RB
Tel: 02088 064638
Category: SLD PMLD (3-19)

Stormont House School
Downs Park Road, LONDON E5 8NP
Tel: 02089 854245
Category: Complex
needs (Secondary)

The Garden School
Wordsworth Road,
LONDON N16 8BZ
Tel: 02072 548096
Category: MLD ASD (2-16)

London

HAMMERSMITH & FULHAM
Council

Hammersmith & Fulham SEN Team, 3rd Floor, 145 King Street, Hammersmith London, W6 9XY
Tel: 020 8753 1021 Email: send@lbhf.gov.uk Website: www.lbhf.gov.uk

LONDON

Cambridge School
61 Bryony Road, Hammersmith,
LONDON W12 0SP
Tel: 02087 350980
Category: MLD (11-16)

Jack Tizard School
South Africa Road,
LONDON W12 7PA
Tel: 02087 353590
Category: SLD PMLD
(Coed Day 3-19)

Queensmill School
1 Askham Road, Shepherds
Bush, LONDON W12 0NW
Tel: 02087 408112
Category: ASD (Coed 3-25)

**The Courtyard at
Langford Primary**
The Courtyard, Langford Primary,
Gilstead Road, LONDON SW6 2LG
Tel: 02076 108075
Category: BESD (5-11)

Woodlane High School
Du Cane Road, LONDON W12 0TN
Tel: 02087 435668
Category: SCLN SPLD SEBD MSI
Medical difficulties (Coed 11-16)

London

HARINGEY

Council

Haringey Additional Needs & Disabilities, Alexandra House, 2nd Floor, 10 Station Road, Wood Green London, N22 7TR
Tel: 020 8489 1913 Email: sen@haringey.gov.uk Website: www.haringey.gov.uk

MUSWELL HILL

Blanche Nevile Secondary School
Burlington Road, MUSWELL HILL, London N10 1NJ
Tel: 02084 422750
Category: HI (Coed Day 11-18)

NORTH HILL

Blanche Nevile Primary School
Storey Road, NORTH HILL, London N6 4ED
Tel: 02083 473760
Category: HI (Coed Day 3-10)

TOTTENHAM

Riverside School
Wood Green Inclusive Learning Campus, White Hart Lane, TOTTENHAM, London N22 5QJ
Tel: 02088 897814
Category: PMLD ASD (Coed Day 11-16)

The Brook on Broadwaters
Adams Road, TOTTENHAM, London N17 6HW
Tel: 02088 087120
Category: CP EPI (Coed Day 4-11)

WEST GREEN

The Vale School
Northumberland Park Community School, Trulock Road, WEST GREEN, London N17 0PG
Tel: 02088 016111
Category: PD (Coed Day 2-16)

London

BOROUGH OF HARROW

Council

Harrow SENDIAS, Cedars Hall, Chicheley Road, Harrow Weald, Middlesex, HA3 6QT
Tel: 020 8428 6487 Email: harrowsendias@family-action.org.uk Website: www.harrow.gov.uk

EDGWARE

Woodlands School
Bransgrove Road, EDGWARE, Middlesex HA8 6JP
Tel: 02083 812188
Category: SLD PMLD ASD (Coed 3-11)

HARROW

Alexandra School
Alexandra Avenue, HARROW, Middlesex HA2 9DX
Tel: 02088 642739
Category: MLD EBD ASD (Coed 4-11)

Kingsley High School
Whittlesea Road, HARROW, Middlesex HA3 6ND
Tel: 02084 213676
Category: SLD PMLD (Coed 11-19)

Shaftesbury High School
Long Elmes, Harrow Weald, HARROW, Middlesex HA3 6LE
Tel: 02084 282482
Category: MLD EBD ASD (Coed 11-19)

London Borough of

HAVERING

Council

Havering SENDIASS, Mercury House, Romford, Essex, RM1 3DW
Tel: 01708 433 885 Email: sendiass@havering.gov.uk Website: www.havering.gov.uk

ROMFORD

Forest Approach Academy
Settle Road, Harold Hill, ROMFORD, Essex RM3 9YA
Tel: 01708 343649
Category: MLD

Ravensbourne School
Neave Crescent, Harold Wood, ROMFORD, Essex RM3 8HN
Tel: 01708 341800
Category: SLD PMLD (Coed 2-19)

UPMINSTER

Corbets Tey School
Harwood Hall Lane, Corbets Tey, UPMINSTER, Essex RM14 2YQ
Tel: 01708 225888
Category: MLD/SLD/Complex Needs (Coed 4-19)

London

HILLINGDON
Council

Hillingdon SENDIASS, 4 West 10, Civic Centre, High Street, Uxbridge, Middlesex, UB8 1UW
Tel: 01895 277001 Email: sendiass@hillingdon.gov.uk Website: www.hillingdonsendiass.co.uk

HAYES

**Hedgewood
Special School**
Weymouth Road, HAYES,
Middlesex UB4 8NF
Tel: 02088 456756
Category: MLD ASD
Complex moderate learning
needs (Coed 5-11)

ICKENHAM

Pentland Field School
Pentland Way, ICKENHAM,
Middlesex UB10 8TS
Tel: 01895 609120
Category: MLD SLD (Coed 4-19)

PINNER

Grangewood School
Fore Street, Eastcote, PINNER,
Middlesex HA5 2JQ
Tel: 01895 676401
Category: SLD PMLD
AUT (Coed 3-11)

UXBRIDGE

Meadow High School
Royal Lane, Hillingdon,
UXBRIDGE, Middlesex UB8 3QU
Tel: 01895 443310
Category: CLD ASD
Complex moderate learning
needs (Coed 11-19)

London

HOUNSLOW
Council

Hounslow SENDIASS, Civic Centre, Lampton Road, Hounslow, TW3 4DN
Tel: 020 8583 2607 Email: sendiass@hounslow.gov.uk Website: www.hounslow.gov.uk

BEDFONT

Marjory Kinnon School
Hatton Road, BEDFONT,
London TW14 9QZ
Tel: 02088 908890
Category: MLD AUT (5-16)

FELTHAM

The Rise School
Browells Lane, FELTHAM,
London TW13 7EF
Tel: 02080 990640
Category: AUI (4-18)

ISLEWORTH

Oaklands School
Woodlands Road, ISLEWORTH,
London TW7 6JZ
Tel: 02085 603569
Category: SLD (Secondary)

CRANFORD

The Cedars Primary School
High Street, CRANFORD,
London TW5 9RU
Tel: 02082 300015
Category: EBD (Primary)

HANWORTH

The Lindon Bennett School
Main Street, HANWORTH,
London TW13 6ST
Tel: 02088 980479
Category: SLD (3-11)

London
ISLINGTON
Council

Islington SEND Community Support Service, The Northern Medical Centre, 580 Holloway Road, London, N7 6LB
Tel: 020 3031 6651 Email: islingtonsend@family-action.org.uk Website: www.islington.gov.uk

LONDON

Richard Cloudesley Primary School
Golden Lane Campus,
101 Whitecross Street,
LONDON EC1Y 8JA
Tel: 020 7786 4800
Category: PD (Coed 2-11)

Richard Cloudesley Secondary School
Tudor Rose Building, 1 Prebend Street, LONDON N1 8RE
Tel: 020 7704 8127
Category: PD (Coed 11-19)

Samuel Rhodes Primary School
Montem Community Campus,
Hornsey Road, LONDON N7 7QT
Tel: 020 7281 5114
Category: MLD ASD BESD (Coed 5-11)

Samuel Rhodes Secondary School
11 Highbury New Park,
LONDON N5 2EG
Tel: 020 7704 7490
Category: MLD ASD BESD (Coed 11-18)

The Bridge Primary School
251 Hungerford Road,
LONDON N7 9LD
Tel: 020 7619 1000
Category: ASD SLD PMLD (Coed 2-11)

The Bridge Secondary School
28 Carleton Road, LONDON N7 0EQ
Tel: 020 7715 0320
Category: ASD SLD PMLD (Coed 11-19)

London
ROYAL BOROUGH OF KINGSTON UPON THAMES
Council

Kingston SENDIASS, Achieving for Children Local Offer, 44 York Street, Twickenham, Middlesex, TW1 3BZ
Tel: 020 8547 4722 Website: www.kingston.gov.uk

CHESSINGTON

St Philip's School & Post 16
Harrow Close, Leatherhead Road,
CHESSINGTON, Surrey KT9 2HR
Tel: 02083 972672
Category: MLD SLD ASD (11-19)

KINGSTON UPON THAMES

Bedelsford School
Grange Road, KINGSTON UPON THAMES, Surrey KT1 2QZ
Tel: 02085 469838
Category: PD PMLD MSI CLD (2-19)

SURBITON

Dysart School
190 Ewell Road, SURBITON,
Surrey KT6 6HL
Tel: 02084 122600
Category: SLD ASD PMLD (5-19)

London
LAMBETH
Council

Lambeth SENDIASS, Mary Sheridan Centre, Wooden Spoon House, 5 Dugard Way London, SE11 4TH
Tel: 020 7926 1831 Email: lambethiass@lambeth.gov.uk Website: www.lambeth.gov.uk

RUSKIN PARK

The Michael Tippet School
Heron Road, Herne Hill, RUSKIN PARK, London SE24 0HZ
Tel: 02073 265898
Category: CLD AUT PD SLD PMLD (Coed 11-18)

STOCKWELL

Lansdowne School
49 Combermere Road,
STOCKWELL, London SW9 9QD
Tel: 02077 373713
Category: MLD SEBD ASD CLD SLD (Coed 11-15)

STREATHAM

The Livity School
Adare walk, STREATHAM,
London SW16 2PW
Tel: 02087 691009
Category: SLD PMLD ASD (Coed 2-11)

WEST DULWICH

Turney School
Turney Road, WEST DULWICH,
London SE21 8LX
Tel: 02086 707220
Category: MLD SLD CLD ASD (Coed 5-10)

WEST NORWOOD

Elm Court School
96 Elm Park, WEST NORWOOD,
London SW2 2EF
Tel: 02086 743412
Category: SEBN SLCN (Coed 6-16)

London

LEWISHAM
Council

Lewisham SEN Team, Kaleidoscope Child Development Centre, 32 Rushey Green, London, SE6 4JF
Tel: **02030 491475** Email: **sen@lewisham.gov.uk** Website: **www.lewisham.gov.uk**

BROMLEY

Drumbeat School
Roundtable Road, Downham,
BROMLEY, Kent BR1 5LE
Tel: 02086 989738
Category: ASD (5-19)

DOWNHAM

New Woodlands School
49 Shroffold Road,
DOWNHAM, Kent BR1 5PD
Tel: 02086 952380
Category: BESD (Coed 5-14)

LONDON

Abbey Manor College
40 Falmouth Close, Lee,
LONDON SE12 8PJ
Tel: 02082 977060
Category: BESD (Coed 11-19)

Brent Knoll School
Perry Rise, LONDON SE23 2QU
Tel: 02086 991047
Category: AUT ASP SLCN
Emotionally Vulnerable (Coed 4-16)

Greenvale School
Waters Road, Catford,
LONDON SE6 1UF
Tel: 02084 650740
Category: SLD PMLD (Coed 11-19)

Watergate School
Lushington Road, Bellingham,
LONDON SE6 3WG
Tel: 02086 956555
Category: SLD PMLD (Coed 3-11)

London

MERTON
Council

Merton SENDIASS, Joseph Hood Primary School, Whatley Avenue, London, SW20 9NS
Tel: **020 8543 8854** Website: **www.merton.gov.uk**

MITCHAM

Cricket Green School
Lower Green West, MITCHAM,
Surrey CR4 3AF
Tel: 02086 401177
Category: CLD (Coed 5-19)

Melrose School
Church Road, MITCHAM,
Surrey CR4 3BE
Tel: 02086 462620
Category: SEBD (Coed 11-16)

MORDEN

Perseid School
Bordesley Road, MORDEN,
Surrey SM4 5LT
Tel: 02086 489737
Category: PMLD (Coed 3-19)

London

NEWHAM
Council

Newham SEN Team, Newham Dockside, 1000 Dockside Road, London, E16 2QU
Tel: 02084 302000 Website: www.newham.gov.uk

BECKTON

**Eleanor Smith KS3
Annexe (Secondary)**
90a Lawson Close, BECKTON,
London E16 3LU
Tel: 020 7511 3222
Category: SEBD (11-16)

**John F Kennedy School
– Beckton Campus**
Tollgate Road, BECKTON,
London E16 3LQ
Tel: 020 7474 6326
Category: SLD PMLD ASD Complex
medical needs (Coed 2-19)

PLAISTOW

**Eleanor Smith
School (Primary)**
North Street, PLAISTOW,
London E13 9HN
Tel: 020 8471 0018
Category: SEBD (5-10)

STRATFORD

**John F Kennedy School
– Stratford Campus**
Pitchford Street, STRATFORD,
London E15 4RZ
Tel: 020 8534 8544
Category: SLD PMLD ASD Complex
medical needs (Coed 2-19)

London

REDBRIDGE
Council

Redbridge SENDIASS, c/o Redbridge Drama Centre, Churchfields, London, E18 2RB
Tel: 020 8708 8922 Email: rias@redbridge.gov.uk Website: find.redbridge.gov.uk

GOODMAYES

**Newbridge School
– Barley Lane Campus**
258 Barley Lane, GOODMAYES,
Essex IG3 8XS
Tel: 02085 991768
Category: SLD PMLD ASD
Complex medical needs (11-19)

HAINAULT

New Rush Hall School
Fencepiece Road,
HAINAULT, Essex IG6 2LB
Tel: 02085 013951
Category: SEMH (5-15)

ROMFORD

Little Heath School
Hainault Road, Little Heath,
ROMFORD, Essex RM6 5RX
Tel: 02085 994864
Category: MLD Learning difficulties
& complex needs (11-19)

**Newbridge School
– Gresham Drive Campus**
161 Gresham Drive, Chadwell
Heath, ROMFORD, Essex RM6 4TR
Tel: 02085 907272
Category: SLD PMLD ASD
Complex medical needs (2-11)

WOODFORD GREEN

Hatton School
Roding Lane South, WOODFORD
GREEN, Essex IG8 8EU
Tel: 02085 514131
Category: AUT SP&LD (3-11)

London

RICHMOND UPON THAMES
Council

Richmond SEN Team, Achieving for Children Local Offer, Civic Centre, 44 York Street Twickenham, Middlesex, TW1 3BZ
Tel: 020 8547 4722 Website: www.richmond.gov.uk

HAMPTON

Clarendon School
Hanworth Road, HAMPTON,
Surrey TW12 3DH
Tel: 02089 791165
Category: MLD (7-16)
(offsite EBD 7-16)

RICHMOND

Strathmore School
Meadlands Drive, Petersham,
RICHMOND, Surrey TW10 7ED
Tel: 02089 480047
Category: SLD PMLD (4-19)

London
SOUTHWARK
Council

Southwark SENDIASS, PO Box 64529, London, SE1P 5LX

Tel: 0207 525 3104 Email: sias@southwark.gov.uk Website: localoffer.southwark.gov.uk

BERMONDSEY

Beormund Primary School
Crosby Row, Long Lane,
BERMONDSEY SE1 3PS
Tel: 02075 259027
Category: EBD (Boys 5-11)

Spa School
Monnow Road,
BERMONDSEY SE1 5RN
Tel: 02072 373714
Category: MLD AUT ASP
SLD SCD (Coed 11-19)

CAMBERWELL

Highshore School
Farmers Road,
CAMBERWELL SE5 0TW
Tel: 02077 086790
Category: DYS PD SLCN EBD
Complex needs (Coed 11-16)

PECKHAM

Cherry Garden School
41 Bellenden Road,
PECKHAM SE15 5BB
Tel: 02072 374050
Category: SCLD (Coed 2-11)

Haymerle School
Haymerle Road, PECKHAM SE15 6SY
Tel: 02076 396080
Category: ASD SCD SpeechLD
DD SCLD (Coed 5-11)

Tuke School
Daniels Gardens,
PECKHAM SE15 6ER
Tel: 02075 258002
Category: SLD PMLD
ASD (Coed 11-19)

London
SUTTON
Council

Sutton SENDIASS, Civic Offices, St Nicholas Way, Sutton, Surrey, SM1 1EA

Tel: 020 8770 4541 Email: siass@cognus.org.uk Website: www.sutton.gov.uk

WALLINGTON

Sherwood Park School
Streeters Lane, WALLINGTON,
Surrey SM6 7NP
Tel: 02087 739930
Category: SLD PMLD
ASD (Coed 2-19)

London
TOWER HAMLETS
Council

Tower Hamlets FIS, 30 Greatorex Street, London, E1 5NP

Tel: 020 7364 6486 Email: fis@towerhamlets.gov.uk Website: www.localoffertowerhamlets.co.uk

BOW

Cherry Trees School
68 Campbell Road, BOW,
London E3 4EA
Tel: 02089 834344
Category: SEBD (Boys Day 5-11)

Phoenix School
49 Bow Road, BOW, London E3 2AD
Tel: 02089 804740
Category: ASD (Coed Day 3-19)

BROMLEY-BY-BOW

Ian Mikardo High School
60 William Guy Gardens,
Talwin Street, BROMLEY-BY-
BOW, London E3 3LF
Tel: 02089 812413
Category: SEBD (Boys Day 11-16)

LIMEHOUSE

Stephen Hawking School
2 Brunton Place, LIMEHOUSE,
London E14 7LL
Tel: 02074 239848
Category: PMLD (Coed Day 2-11)

MILE END

Beatrice Tate School
Poplar Day Centre, 40 Southern
Grove, MILE END, London E3 4PX
Tel: 02089 833760
Category: PMLD SLD
(Coed Day 11-19)

SEAFORD

Bowden House School
Firle Road, SEAFORD BN25 2JB
Tel: 01323 893138
Category: SEMH (Weekly Residential)

London

WALTHAM FOREST
Council

Waltham Forest SENDIASS, 220 Hoe Street, Walthamstow London, E17 3AY
Tel: 020 3233 0251 Email: wfsendiass@citizensadvicewalthamforest.org.uk Website: www.walthamforest.gov.uk

HALE END

Joseph Clarke School
31 Vincent Road, Highams Park,
HALE END, London E4 9PP
Tel: 02085 234833
Category: VIS Complex needs (Coed 2-18)

LEYTON

Belmont Park School
101 Leyton Green Road,
LEYTON, London E10 6DB
Tel: 02085 560006
Category: BESD SEMH (Coed 10-18)

London

WANDSWORTH
Council

Wandsworth SENDIASS, Room 223, Wandsworth Town Hall, High Street, Wandsworth London, SW18 2PU
Tel: 020 8871 5237 Email: wiass@wandsworth.gov.uk Website: thrive.wandsworth.gov.uk

BALHAM

Oak Lodge School
101 Nightingale Lane, BALHAM,
London SW12 8NA
Tel: 02086 733453
Category: D (Coed, Day/ boarding 11-19)

BROADSTAIRS

Bradstow School
34 Dumpton Park Drive,
BROADSTAIRS, Kent CT10 1BY
Tel: 01843 862123
Category: PD AUT Challenging behaviour (Coed 5-19)

EARLSFIELD

Garratt Park School
Waldron Road, EARLSFIELD,
London SW18 3TB
Tel: 02089 465769
Category: MLD SP&LD (Coed 11-18)

PUTNEY

Paddock Primary School
St Margaret's Crescent,
PUTNEY, London SW15 6HL
Tel: 02087 885648
Category: ASD MLD SLD (Coed 3-11)

ROEHAMPTON

Paddock Secondary School
Priory Lane, ROEHAMPTON,
London SW15 5RT
Tel: 02088 781521
Category: SCLD ASD with SLD (Coed 11-19)

SOUTHFIELDS

Greenmead School
147 Beaumont Road,
SOUTHFIELDS, London SW19 6RY
Tel: 02087 891466
Category: PD PMLD (Coed 3-11)

Linden Lodge School
61 Princes Way, SOUTHFIELDS,
London SW19 6JB
Tel: 02087 880107
Category: VIS PMLD MSI (Coed 3-11)

TOOTING

Nightingale School
Beechcroft Road, TOOTING,
London SW17 7DF
Tel: 02088 749096
Category: BESD (Boys 11-19)

London

CITY OF WESTMINSTER
Council

Westminster SENDIASS, 1st Floor, 215 Lisson Grove, London, NW8 8LF
Tel: 020 7641 5355 Email: iass@westminster.gov.uk Website: www.westminsteriass.co.uk

LONDON

College Park School
Garway Road, LONDON W2 4PH
Tel: 020 7221 3454
Category: CLD AUT (Coed 4-19)

Queen Elizabeth II Jubilee School
Kennet Road, LONDON W9 3LG
Tel: 020 7641 5825
Category: SLD PMLD (Coed 4-19)

LUTON
Borough Council

Luton SENDIAS, Futures House, The Moakes, Marsh Farm Luton, LU3 3QB
Tel: 01582 548156 Email: sendias@luton.gov.uk Website: www.luton.gov.uk

LUTON

Lady Zia Werner School
Ashcroft Road, LUTON,
Bedfordshire LU2 9AY
Tel: 01582 728705
Category: SLD PMLD (Yr 1-6 & Early Years)

Richmond Hill School
Sunridge Avenue, LUTON,
Bedfordshire LU2 7JL
Tel: 01582 721019
Category: SLD PMLD (Primary Yr 1-6)

Woodlands School
Northwell Drive, LUTON,
Bedfordshire LU3 3SP
Tel: 01582 572880
Category: SLD PMLD (11-19)

Greater Manchester

BOLTON
Council

Bolton SENDIASS, Lowndes Street Day Nursery, Bolton, BL1 4QB
Tel: 01204 848722 Email: pps@boltoncog.co.uk Website: iasbolton.com

BOLTON

Firwood School
Stitch Mi Lane, BOLTON BL2 4HU
Tel: 01204 333044
Category: SLD PMLD ASD (Coed 11-19)

Ladywood School
Masefield Road, Little
Lever, BOLTON BL3 1NG
Tel: 01204 333400
Category: MLD with Complex needs incl ASD PD MSI (Coed 4-11)

Rumworth School
Armadale Road, Ladybridge,
BOLTON BL3 4TP
Tel: 01204 333600
Category: MLD with Complex needs incl ASD PD MSI (Coed 11-19)

Thomasson Memorial School
Devonshire Drive, BOLTON BL1 4PJ
Tel: 01204 333118
Category: HI (Coed 2-16)

FARNWORTH

Green Fold School
Highfield Road,
FARNWORTH BL4 0RA
Tel: 01204 335883
Category: SLD ASD PMLD (Coed 2-11)

Greater Manchester

BURY
Council

Bury SENDIASS, Floor 2, Blue Pit Mill, Castleton, Bury, Greater Manchester, OL11 2YW
Tel: 01706 769 634 Email: bury.sendiass@barnardos.org.uk Website: www.bury.gov.uk

BURY

Elms Bank Specialist Arts College
Ripon Avenue, Whitefield,
BURY M45 8PJ
Tel: 01617 661597
Category: LD (Coed 11-19)

Millwood School
School Street, Radcliffe,
BURY M26 3BW
Tel: 01617 242266
Category: SLD PMLD ASD AUT
Complex needs (Coed 2-11)

PRESTWICH

**Cloughside College
(Hospital Special School)**
Bury New Road,
PRESTWICH M25 3BL
Tel: 01617 724625
Category: HS (Coed 11-19)

Greater Manchester

MANCHESTER
City Council

Manchester SENDIASS, Westwood Street Centre, Westwood Street, Moss Side Manchester, Lancashire, M14 4PH
Tel: 0161 209 8356 Email: parents@manchester.gov.uk Website: www.manchester.gov.uk

MANCHESTER

Ashgate School
Crossacres Road, Peel
Hall, Wythenshawe,
MANCHESTER M22 5DR
Tel: 01612 196642
Category: PMLD SLD AUT (5-11)

Camberwell Park School
Brookside Road, Moston,
MANCHESTER M40 9GJ
Tel: 01616 827537
Category: SLD (5-11)

Grange School
Matthews Lane, Longsight,
MANCHESTER M12 4GR
Tel: 01612 312590
Category: ASD CLD (4-19)

Lancasterian School
Elizabeth Slinger Road, West
Didsbury, MANCHESTER M20 2XA
Tel: 01614 450123
Category: PD (2-16)

**Manchester
Hospital School**
Third Floor School, Royal
Manchester Children's
Hospital, Oxford Road,
MANCHESTER M13 9WL
Tel: 01617 010684
Category: HS

Meade Hill School
Chain Road, Higher Blackley,
MANCHESTER M9 6GN
Tel: 01616 960764
Category: SEBD (11-16)

Melland High School
Gorton Education Village,
50 Wembley Road, Gorton,
MANCHESTER M18 7DT
Tel: 01612 239915
Category: SLD (11-19)

North Ridge High School
Higher Blackley Education
Village, Alworth Road,
MANCHESTER M9 0RP
Tel: 01615 079700
Category: MLD (11-19)

Piper Hill High School
Firbank Road, Newall
Green, Wythenshawe,
MANCHESTER M23 2YS
Tel: 01614 363009
Category: SLD (11-19)

Rodney House School
Albert Grove, Longsight,
MANCHESTER M12 4WF
Tel: 0161 230 6854
Category: ASD (2-7)

Southern Cross School
Barlow Hall Road, Chorlton,
MANCHESTER M21 7JJ
Tel: 01618 812695
Category: SEBD (11-16)

**The Birches Specialist
Support School**
Newholme Road, West Didsbury,
MANCHESTER M20 2XZ
Tel: 01614 488895
Category: SLD (5-11)

Greater Manchester

OLDHAM
Council

Oldham SENDIASS, Chadderton Court, 451 Middleton Road, Chadderton Oldham, Greater Manchester, OL9 9LB
Tel: 0161 503 1540 Email: iass@pointoldham.co.uk Website: www.oldham.gov.uk

OLDHAM

Bright Futures School
Oberlin Cottage, Oberlin
Street, Greenacres, OLDHAM,
Greater Manchester OL4 3HS
Tel: 01457 878738
Category: AUT ASD (5-16)

**Elland House
School Royton**
Roman Road, Royton, OLDHAM,
Greater Manchester OL2 5PJ
Tel: 7841 615 159
Category: BESD (11-18)

Hathershaw College
Bellfield Avenue, OLDHAM,
Greater Manchester OL8 3EP
Tel: 0161 770 8560
Category: Deaf HI (11-16)

New Bridge Horizons
1 Medtia Square, Phoenix
Street, OLDHAM, Greater
Manchester OL1 1AN
Tel: 0161 883 2403
Category: (19-25)

**New Bridge
Learning Centre**
St Martin's Road, Fitton
Hill, OLDHAM, Greater
Manchester OL8 2PZ
Tel: 01618 832402
Category: (Coed 16-19)

New Bridge School
Roman Road, Hollinwood,
OLDHAM, Greater
Manchester OL8 3PH
Tel: 01618 832401
Category: PMLD SLD MLD
ASD PD (Coed 11-19)

**The Kingfisher Community
Special School**
Foxdenton Lane, Chadderton,
OLDHAM, Greater
Manchester OL9 9QR
Tel: 01617 705910
Category: PMLD SLD
ASD (Coed 4-11)

Greater Manchester

ROCHDALE
Metropolitan Borough Council

Rochdale SEN Assessment Team, Number One Riverside, Smith Street, Rochdale, OL16 1XU
Tel: 01706 925140 Email: sen@rochdale.gov.uk Website: www.rochdale.gov.uk

MIDDLETON

Newlands School
Waverley Road,
MIDDLETON M24 6JG
Tel: 01616 550220
Category: Generic Primary
Special School (Coed 3-11)

ROCHDALE

Brownhill School
Heights Lane, ROCHDALE OL12 0PZ
Tel: 03003 038384
Category: EBD (Coed 7-16)

Redwood School
Hudson's Walk, ROCHDALE OL11 5EF
Tel: 01706 750815
Category: Generic Secondary
Special School (Coed 11-19)

Springside School
Albert Royds Street,
ROCHDALE OL16 2SU
Tel: 01706 764451
Category: Generic Primary
Special School (Coed 3-11)

Greater Manchester

SALFORD
City Council

Salford SIASS, Salford Civic Centre, Chorley Road, Swinton Salford, M27 5AW
Tel: 0161 778 0343 Email: siass@salford.gov.uk Website: www.salford.gov.uk

ECCLES

Chatsworth High School
Chatsworth Road, Ellesmere
Park, ECCLES M30 9DY
Tel: 01619 211405
Category: SLD PMLD
ASD (Coed 11-19)

SWINTON

**Springwood
Primary School**
Barton Road, SWINTON M27 5LP
Tel: 01617 780022
Category: ASD MLD SLD
PMLD (Coed 2-11)

Greater Manchester

STOCKPORT
Metropolitan Borough Council

Stockport SEN Team, Town Hall, Edward Street, Stockport, SK1 3XE

Tel: 0161 474 2525 Email: specialeducation@stockport.gov.uk Website: www.stockport.gov.uk

STOCKPORT

Castle Hill High School
The Fairway, STOCKPORT SK2 5DS
Tel: 01612 853925
Category: EBD GLD
CLD (Coed 11-16)

Heaton School
St James Road, Heaton Moor,
STOCKPORT SK4 4RE
Tel: 01614 321931
Category: SLD PMLD (Coed 10-19)

Lisburne School
Half Moon Lane, Offerton,
STOCKPORT SK2 5LB
Tel: 01614 835045
Category: CLD (Coed 4-11)

Oakgrove School
Matlock Road, Heald Green,
STOCKPORT SK8 3BU
Tel: 01614 374956
Category: SEBD (Coed 5-11)

Valley School
Whitehaven Road, Bramhall,
STOCKPORT SK7 1EN
Tel: 01614 397343
Category: PMLD ASD
SLD (Coed 2-11)

Windlehurst School
Windlehurst Road, Hawk Green,
Marple, STOCKPORT SK6 7HZ
Tel: 01614 274788
Category: EBD (Coed 11-16)

Greater Manchester

TAMESIDE
Metropolitan Borough Council

Tameside SENDIASS, Jubilee Gardens, Gardenfold Way, Droylsden, Tameside, M43 7XU

Tel: 0161 342 3383 Email: sendiass@tameside.gov.uk Website: www.tameside.gov.uk

ASHTON-UNDER LYNE

Samuel Laycock School
Broadoak Road, ASHTON-UNDER
LYNE, Tameside OL6 8RF
Tel: 01613 441992
Category: MLD (Secondary)

AUDENSHAW

Hawthorns School
Sunnyside Moss Campus,
Lumb Lane, AUDENSHAW,
Tameside M34 5SF
Tel: 01613 701312
Category: MLD (Primary)

DUKINFIELD

Cromwell School
Yew Tree Lane, DUKINFIELD,
Tameside SK16 5BJ
Tel: 01613 389730
Category: SLD PMLD
MLD (Secondary)

Oakdale School
Cheetham Hill Road, DUKINFIELD,
Tameside SK16 5LD
Tel: 01613 679299
Category: SLD PMLD (Primary)

HYDE

Thomas Ashton School
Bennett Street, HYDE,
Tameside SK14 4SS
Tel: 01613 686208
Category: BESD (Primary)

Greater Manchester

TRAFFORD
Council

Trafford FIS, Town Hall, 1 Waterside Plaza, Sale, Manchester, M33 7ZF

Tel: 01619 121053 Email: fis@trafford.gov.uk Website: www.trafford.gov.uk/localoffer

FLIXTON

Delamere School
Irlam Road, FLIXTON, Greater
Manchester M41 6AP
Tel: 01617 475893
Category: ASD SLD (Coed 2-11)

SALE

**Brentwood High School
& Community College**
Cherry Lane, SALE,
Cheshire M33 4GY
Tel: 01619 052371
Category: ASD SLD (Coed 11-25)

STRETFORD

Longford Park School
74 Cromwell Road, STRETFORD,
Greater Manchester M32 8QJ
Tel: 01619 121895
Category: SEMH MLD
ASD (Coed 5-11)

URMSTON

Egerton High School
Kingsway Park, URMSTON,
Greater Manchester M41 7FF
Tel: 01617 497094
Category: SEMH (Coed 5-16)

Greater Manchester

WIGAN

Council

Wigan SENDIASS, Embrace Wigan and Leigh, 81 Ribble Road, Platt Bridge Wigan, Greater Manchester, WN2 5EG
Tel: 01942 233323 Website: www.wigan.gov.uk

ATHERTON

Rowan Tree Primary School
Green Hall Close, ATHERTON,
Greater Manchester M46 9HP
Tel: 01942 883928
Category: PD CLD AUT (Coed 2-11)

WIGAN

Hope School & College
Kelvin Grove, Winstanley,
WIGAN WN3 6SP
Tel: 01942 824150
Category: ASD SLD
PMLD (Coed 2-19)

Landgate School
Landgate Lane, Bryn,
WIGAN WN4 0EP
Tel: 01942 776688
Category: AUT SP&LD (Coed 4-19)

Newbridge Learning Community
Moss Lane, Platt Bridge,
WIGAN WN2 3TL
Tel: 01942 776020
Category: SEMH (Coed)

Oakfield High School & College
Long Lane, Hindley Green,
WIGAN WN2 4XA
Tel: 01942 776142
Category: MLD SLD PD
SEBD (Coed 11-19)

Willow Grove Primary School
Willow Grove, Ashton-in-
Makerfield, WIGAN WN4 8XF
Tel: 01942 727717
Category: SEBD (Coed 5-11)

MEDWAY

Council

Medway FIS, Gun Wharf, Dock Road, Chatham, ME4 4TR
Tel: 01634 332195 Email: familyinfo@medway.gov.uk Website: www.medway.gov.uk

GILLINGHAM

Danecourt School
Hotel Road, Watling Street,
GILLINGHAM, Kent ME8 6AA
Tel: 01634 232589
Category: ASD SLD (Coed 4-11)

Rivermead School
Forge Lane, GILLINGHAM,
Kent ME7 1UG
Tel: 01634 338348
Category: ASD Complex
emotional needs (Coed 11-19)

STROOD

Abbey Court School
Rede Court Road,
STROOD, Kent ME2 3SP
Tel: 01634 338220
Category: SLD PMLD (Coed 4-19)

Merseyside

KNOWSLEY

Metropolitan Borough Council

Liverpool & Knowsley SENDIASS, Stoneycroft Childrenís Centre, 38 Scotia Road, Liverpool, Merseyside, L13 6QJ
Tel: 0800 012 9066 Email: liverpoolandknowsleysend@wired.me.uk Website: www.liverpoolandknowsleysend.com

HALEWOOD

Yew Tree Community Primary School
The Avenue, Wood Road,
HALEWOOD, Merseyside L26 1UU
Tel: 0151 477 8950
Category: (3-11)

HUYTON

Alt Bridge School
Wellcroft Road, HUYTON,
Merseyside L36 7TA
Tel: 01514 778310
Category: MLD SPLD CLD
ASD SLD PD (Coed 11-16)

Knowsley Central School
Mossbrow Road, HUYTON,
Merseyside L36 7SY
Tel: 01514 778450
Category: CLD SEBD (Coed 4-14)

KIRKBY

Bluebell Park School
Cawthorne Walk, Southdene,
KIRKBY, Merseyside L32 3XP
Tel: 01514 778350
Category: PD PMLD SLD
MLD (Coed 3-19)

Northwood Community Primary School
Roughwood Drive, Northwood,
KIRKBY, Merseyside L33 8XF
Tel: 01514 778630
Category: (0-11)

STOCKBRIDGE VILLAGE

Meadow Park School
Haswell Drive, STOCKBRIDGE
VILLAGE, Merseyside L28 1RX
Tel: 01514 778100
Category: (7-16)

Merseyside

LIVERPOOL
City Council

Liverpool & Knowsley SENDIASS, Stoneycroft Childrenís Centre, 38 Scotia Road, Liverpool, Merseyside, L13 6QJ
Tel: 0800 012 9066 Email: liverpoolandknowsleysend@wired.me.uk Website: www.liverpoolandknowsleysend.com

LIVERPOOL

Abbot's Lea School
Beaconsfield Road, Woolton,
LIVERPOOL, Merseyside L25 6EE
Tel: 01514 281161
Category: AUT (Coed 5-19)

Bank View High School
177 Long Lane, LIVERPOOL,
Merseyside L9 6AD
Tel: 01513 305101
Category: CLD (Coed 11-18)

Childwall Abbey School
Childwall Abbey Rd, LIVERPOOL,
Merseyside L16 5EY
Tel: 01517 221995
Category: CLD ASD

Clifford Holroyde School
Thingwall Lane, LIVERPOOL,
Merseyside L14 7NX
Tel: 01512 289500
Category: EBD (Coed 7-16)

Ernest Cookson School
54 Bankfield Road, West Derby,
LIVERPOOL, Merseyside L13 0BQ
Tel: 015123 51350
Category: EBD (Boys 5-16)

Hope School
251 Hartsbourne Avenue,
Belle Vale, LIVERPOOL,
Merseyside L25 2RY
Tel: 01513 633130
Category: EBD (Boys 5-16)

Millstead School
Iliad St, Everton, LIVERPOOL,
Merseyside L5 3LU
Tel: 01512 074656
Category: SLD (Coed 2-11)

Palmerston School
Minehead Road, Aigburth,
LIVERPOOL, Merseyside L17 6AU
Tel: 01514 282128
Category: SLD (Coed 11-19)

Princes Primary School
Selborne Street, LIVERPOOL,
Merseyside L8 1YQ
Tel: 01517 092602
Category: SLD (Coed 2-11)

Redbridge High School
179 Long Lane, LIVERPOOL,
Merseyside L9 6AD
Tel: 01513 305100
Category: SLD PMLD (Coed 11-19)

Sandfield Park School
South Drive, Sandfield Park,
LIVERPOOL, Merseyside L12 1LH
Tel: 01512 280324
Category: PD HS (Coed 11-19)

Woolton High School
Woolton Hill Road, Woolton,
LIVERPOOL, Merseyside L25 6JA
Tel: 01513 305120
Category: (Coed 11-16)

Merseyside

SEFTON
Council

Sefton SENDIASS, Redgate Annexe, Redgate, Formby, Merseyside, L37 4EW
Tel: 0151 934 3334 Email: seftonsendiass@sefton.gov.uk Website: www.sefton.gov.uk

BOOTLE

Rowan Park School
Sterrix Lane, Litherland,
BOOTLE, Merseyside L21 0DB
Tel: 01512 224894
Category: SLD (Coed 3-18)

CROSBY

Crosby High School
De Villiers Avenue, CROSBY,
Merseyside L23 2TH
Tel: 01519 243671
Category: MLD (Coed 11-16)

Newfield School
Edge Lane, Thornton, CROSBY,
Merseyside L23 4TG
Tel: 01519 342991
Category: BESD (Coed 5-17)

SOUTHPORT

Merefield School
Westminster Drive, SOUTHPORT,
Merseyside PR8 2QZ
Tel: 01704 577163
Category: SLD (Coed 3-16)

**Presfield High School
& Specialist College**
Preston New Road, SOUTHPORT,
Merseyside PR9 8PA
Tel: 01704 227831
Category: ASD (Coed 11-16)

Merseyside

ST HELENS
Council

St Helens SENDIASS, Sutton Children's Centre, Ellamsbridge Road, St Helens, Merseyside, WA10 6RW
Tel: 01744 673428 Website: www.sthelensgateway.info

NEWTON-LE-WILLOWS

Penkford School
Wharf Road, Earlestown, NEWTON-LE-WILLOWS, Merseyside WA12 9XZ
Tel: 01744 678745
Category: SEBD (9-16)

ST HELENS

Lansbury Bridge School
Lansbury Avenue, Parr, ST HELENS, Merseyside WA9 1TB
Tel: 01744 678579
Category: CLD PD MLD
ASD (Coed 3-16)

Mill Green School
Lansbury Avenue, Parr, ST HELENS, Merseyside WA9 1BU
Tel: 01744 678760
Category: SLD CLD PMLD
ASD (Coed 14-19)

Merseyside

WIRRAL
Council

Wirral SEND Partnership, 5 St John Street, Birkenhead Wirral, CH41 6HY
Tel: 0151 522 7990 Email: contact@wired.me.uk Website: www.wired.me.uk

BIRKENHEAD

Kilgarth School
Cavendish Street, BIRKENHEAD, Merseyside CH41 8BA
Tel: 01516 528071
Category: EBD ADHD (Boys 11-16)

PRENTON

The Observatory School
Bidston Village Road, Bidston, PRENTON, Merseyside CH43 7QT
Tel: 01516 527093
Category: SEBD LD (Coed 11-16)

WALLASEY

Elleray Park School
Elleray Park Road, WALLASEY, Merseyside CH45 0LH
Tel: 01516 393594
Category: CLD SLD PD
AUT PMLD (Coed 2-11)

WIRRAL

Clare Mount Specialist Sports College
Fender Lane, Moreton, WIRRAL, Merseyside CH46 9PA
Tel: 01516 069440
Category: MLD (Coed 11-19)

Gilbrook School
Glebe Hey Road, Woodchurch, WIRRAL, Merseyside CH49 8HE
Tel: 01515 223900
Category: EBD DYS (Coed 4-11)

Hayfield School
Manor Drive, Upton, WIRRAL, Merseyside CH49 4LN
Tel: 01516 779303
Category: MLD CLD
ASD (Coed 4-11)

Meadowside School
Pool Lane, Woodchurch, WIRRAL, Merseyside CH49 5LA
Tel: 01516 787711
Category: CLD SLD AUT
ADHD (Coed 11-19)

Orrets Meadow School
Chapelhill Road, Moreton, WIRRAL, Merseyside CH46 9QQ
Tel: 01516 788070
Category: SPLD SP&LD LD
AUT ASD EBD (Coed 5-11)

Stanley School
Greenbank Drive, Pensby, WIRRAL, Merseyside CH61 5UE
Tel: 01513 426741
Category: (2-11)

Wirral Hospitals' School
Joseph Paxton Campus, 157 Park Road North, Claughton, WIRRAL, Merseyside CH41 0EZ
Tel: 01514 887680
Category: HS (Coed 11-17)

WOODCHURCH

Foxfield School
New Hey Road, Moreton, WOODCHURCH, Merseyside CH49 5LF
Tel: 01516 418810
Category: ADHD SLD
ASD PD (Coed 11-19)

Maintained special schools and colleges

MIDDLESBROUGH
Council

Middlesbrough SENDIASS, 16 High Force Road, Riverside Park, Middlesbrough, TS2 1RH
Tel: 01642 608012 Email: main_sendiassmiddlesbrough@iammain.org.uk Website: www.middlesbrough.gov.uk

MIDDLESBROUGH

Beverley School
Saltersgill Avenue,
MIDDLESBROUGH,
Cleveland TS4 3JS
Tel: 01642 811350
Category: AUT (Coed 3-19)

Holmwood School
Saltersgill Avenue, Easterside,
MIDDLESBROUGH,
Cleveland TS4 3PT
Tel: 01642 819157
Category: EBD (Coed 4-11)

**Priory Woods School
& Arts College**
Tothill Avenue, Netherfields,
MIDDLESBROUGH,
Cleveland TS3 0RH
Tel: 01642 770540
Category: SLD PMLD (Coed 4-19)

MILTON KEYNES
Council

Milton Keynes SENDIASS, Civic Offices, 1 Saxon Gate East, Milton Keynes, MK9 3EJ
Tel: 01908 254518 Email: mksendias@milton-keynes.gov.uk Website: www.milton-keynes.gov.uk

MILTON KEYNES

Romans Field School
Shenley Road, Bletchley, MILTON
KEYNES, Buckinghamshire MK3 7AW
Tel: 01908 376011
Category: SEBD (Coed
Day/boarding 5-12)

Slated Row School
Old Wolverton Road,
Wolverton, MILTON KEYNES,
Buckinghamshire MK12 5NJ
Tel: 01908 316017
Category: MLD Complex
needs (Coed Day 4-19)

The Redway School
Farmborough, Netherfield, MILTON
KEYNES, Buckinghamshire MK6 4HG
Tel: 01908 206400
Category: PMLD CLD SCD
AUT (Coed Day 2-19)

The Walnuts School
Admiral Drive, Hazeley, MILTON
KEYNES, Buckinghamshire MK8 0PU
Tel: 01908 563885
Category: ASD SCD (Coed
Day/boarding 4-19)

White Spire School
Rickley Lane, Bletchley, MILTON
KEYNES, Buckinghamshire MK3 6EW
Tel: 01908 373266
Category: MLD (Coed
Day & boarding 5-19)

NORFOLK
County Council

Norfolk SEND Partnership, 148 Woodside Road, Norwich, Norfolk, NR7 9QL
Tel: 01603 704070 Email: sendpartnership.iass@norfolk.gov.uk Website: www.norfolksendpartnershipiass.org.uk

ATTLEBOROUGH

Chapel Green School
Attleborough Road, Old
Buckenham, ATTLEBOROUGH,
Norfolk NR17 1RF
Tel: 01953 453116
Category: Complex
needs (Coed 3-19)

CROMER

Sidestrand Hall School
Cromer Road, Sidestrand,
CROMER, Norfolk NR27 0NH
Tel: 01263 578144
Category: Complex
Needs (Coed 7-19)

DEREHAM

Fred Nicholson School
Westfield Road, DEREHAM,
Norfolk NR19 1JB
Tel: 01362 693915
Category: Complex
Needs (Coed 7-16)

GREAT YARMOUTH

John Grant School
St George's Drive, Caister-
on-Sea, GREAT YARMOUTH,
Norfolk NR30 5QW
Tel: 01493 720158
Category: Complex
Needs (Coed 3-19)

NORWICH

Hall School
St Faith's Road, Old Catton,
NORWICH, Norfolk NR6 7AD
Tel: 01603 466467
Category: Complex
Needs (Coed 3-19)

Harford Manor School
43 Ipswich Road, NORWICH,
Norfolk NR2 2LN
Tel: 01603 451809
Category: Complex
Needs (Coed 3-19)

Pathways College
The Base, The Hewett
Academy, Cecil Road,
NORWICH, Norfolk NR1 2JT
Tel: 01603 463320
Category: Complex Needs

The Clare School
South Park Avenue, NORWICH,
Norfolk NR4 7AU
Tel: 01603 454199
Category: MSI Complex
Needs (Coed 3-19)

The Parkside School
College Road, NORWICH,
Norfolk NR2 3JA
Tel: 01603 441126
Category: Complex
Needs (Coed 3-11)

The Wherry School
280 Hall Road, NORWICH,
Norfolk NR1 2GB
Tel: 01603 629440
Category: AUT (Day 4-19)

SHERINGHAM

**Sheringham
Woodfields School**
Holt Road, SHERINGHAM,
Norfolk NR26 8ND
Tel: 01263 820520
Category: Complex
Needs (Coed 3-19)

NORTHAMPTONSHIRE
County Council

Northamptonshire SENDIASS, One Angel Square, Angel Street, Northampton, NN1 1ED
Tel: 01604 364772 Email: contact@iassnorthants.co.uk Website: www.iassnorthants.co.uk

CORBY

Red Kite Academy
Purbeck Drive, CORBY,
Northamptonshire NN17 2UJ
Tel: 01536 216489
Category: SLD PMLD AUT (3-19)

KETTERING

**Isebrook SEN Cognition
& Learning College**
Eastleigh Road, KETTERING,
Northamptonshire NN15 6PT
Tel: 01536 500030
Category: MLD ASD SLD
SP&LD PH (11-19)

**Wren Spinney Community
Special School**
Westover Road, KETTERING,
Northamptonshire NN15 7LB
Tel: 01536 481939
Category: SLD PMLD ASD MSI (11 19)

NORTHAMPTON

Fairfields School
Trinity Avenue, NORTHAMPTON,
Northamptonshire NN2 6JN
Tel: 01604 714777
Category: PMLD PH
MSI SLD ASD (3-11)

**Greenfields Specialist
School for Communication**
Prentice Court, Lings Way,
Goldings, NORTHAMPTON,
Northamptonshire NN3 8XS
Tel: 01604 741960
Category: PMLD SLD ASD MSI (11-19)

Kings Meadow School
Manning Road, Moulton
Leys, NORTHAMPTON,
Northamptonshire NN3 7AR
Tel: 01604 673730
Category: BESD (3-11)

**Northgate School
Arts College**
Queens Park Parade,
NORTHAMPTON,
Northamptonshire NN2 6LR
Tel: 01604 714098
Category: MLD SLD ASD (11-19)

TIFFIELD

The Gateway School
St Johns Road, TIFFIELD,
Northamptonshire NN12 8AA
Tel: 01604 878977
Category: BESD (11-19)

WELLINGBOROUGH

**Rowan Gate
Primary School**
Finedon Road, WELLINGBOROUGH,
Northamptonshire NN8 4NS
Tel: 01933 304970
Category: PMLD ASD (3-11)

NORTHUMBERLAND
County Council

Northumberland SENDIASS, County Hall, Morpeth, Northumberland, NE61 2EF
Tel: 01670 623555 Email: alison.bravey@northumberland.gov.uk Website: www.northumberland.gov.uk

ALNWICK

Barndale House School
Howling Lane, ALNWICK,
Northumberland NE66 1DQ
Tel: 01665 602541
Category: SLD

BERWICK UPON
TWEED

The Grove Special School
Grove Gardens, Tweedmouth,
BERWICK UPON TWEED,
Northumberland TD15 2EN
Tel: 01289 306390
Category: SLD

BLYTH

The Dales School
Cowpen Road, BLYTH,
Northumberland NE24 4RE
Tel: 01670 352556
Category: MLD CLD PH EBD

CHOPPINGTON

Cleaswell Hill School
School Avenue, Guide
Post, CHOPPINGTON,
Northumberland NE62 5DJ
Tel: 01670 823182
Category: MLD

CRAMLINGTON

Atkinson House School
North Terrace, Seghill,
CRAMLINGTON,
Northumberland NE23 7EB
Tel: 0191 2980838
Category: EBD

**Cramlington
Hillcrest School**
East View Avenue, CRAMLINGTON,
Northumberland NE23 1DY
Tel: 01670 713632
Category: MLD

HEXHAM

Hexham Priory School
Corbridge Road, HEXHAM,
Northumberland NE46 1UY
Tel: 01434 605021
Category: SLD

MORPETH

**Collingwood School &
Media Arts College**
Stobhillgate, MORPETH,
Northumberland NE61 2HA
Tel: 01670 516374
Category: MLD CLD AUT
SP&LD PH Emotionally fragile
Specific medical conditions

NOTTINGHAM
City Council

Nottingham SEN Team, Glenbrook Management Centre, Wigman Road, Bilborough Nottingham, NG8 4PD
Tel: 01158 764300 Email: special.needs@nottinghamcity.gov.uk Website: www.nottinghamcity.gov.uk

NOTTINGHAM

**Oak Field School &
Sports College**
Wigman Road, Bilborough,
NOTTINGHAM NG8 3HW
Tel: 01159 153265
Category: SCD ASD SPLI
(Coed Day 3-19)

Rosehill Special School
St Matthias Road, St Ann's,
NOTTINGHAM NG3 2FE
Tel: 01159 155815
Category: AUT (Coed Day 4-19)

NOTTINGHAMSHIRE
County Council

Nottinghamshire SEN Team, Ask Us, Futures, 57 Maid Marian Way, Nottingham, Nottinghamshire, NG1 6GE
Tel: 0800 121 7772 Email: enquiries@askusnotts.org.uk Website: www.nottshelpyourself.org.uk

ASHFIELD

Bracken Hill School
Chartwell Road, ASHFIELD,
Nottinghamshire NG17 7HZ
Tel: 01623 477268
Category: (Coed 4-18)

GEDLING

Carlton Digby School
61 Digby Avenue, Mapperley,
GEDLING, Nottingham NG3 6DS
Tel: 01159 568289
Category: SCLD (Coed 3-18)

Derrymount School
Churchmoor Lane, Arnold,
GEDLING, Nottingham NG5 8HN
Tel: 01159 534015
Category: (Coed 3-19)

MANSFIELD

Fountaindale School
Nottingham Road, MANSFIELD,
Nottinghamshire NG18 5BA
Tel: 01623 792671
Category: PhysD MSI (Coed 3-18)

Yeoman Park School
Park Hall Road, Mansfield
Woodhouse, MANSFIELD,
Nottinghamshire NG19 8PS
Tel: 01623 459540
Category: CLD (Coed 3-18)

NEWARK

**The Newark Orchard
School (London Rd Site)**
London Road, Balderton, NEWARK,
Nottinghamshire NG24 3AL
Tel: 01636 682256
Category: (Coed 14-18)

**The Newark Orchard
School (Town Site)**
Appleton Gate, NEWARK,
Nottinghamshire NG24 1JR
Tel: 01636 682255
Category: (Coed 3-14)

RETFORD

St Giles School
Babworth Road, RETFORD,
Nottinghamshire DN22 7NJ
Tel: 01777 703683
Category: PMLD AUT (Coed 3-18)

RUSHCLIFFE

Ash Lea School
Owthorpe Road,
Cotgrave, RUSHCLIFFE,
Nottinghamshire NG12 3PA
Tel: 01159 892744
Category: CLD (Coed 3-18)

OXFORDSHIRE
County Council

Oxfordshire SENDIASS, Freepost SCE11489, Oxford, OX1 1ZS
Tel: 01865 810516 Website: www.oxfordshire.gov.uk/localoffer

BANBURY

Frank Wise School
Hornbeam Close, BANBURY,
Oxfordshire OX16 9RL
Tel: 01295 263520
Category: SLD PMLD (Coed 2-19)

BICESTER

Bardwell School
Hendon Place, Sunderland Drive,
BICESTER, Oxfordshire OX26 4RZ
Tel: 01869 242182
Category: SLD PMLD (Coed 2-19)

OXFORD

John Watson School
Littleworth Road, Wheatley,
OXFORD OX33 1NN
Tel: 01865 452725
Category: SLD PMLD (Coed 2-19)

Mabel Prichard School
Cuddesdon Way, OXFORD OX4 6SB
Tel: 01865 777878
Category: Complex
Needs (Coed 2-19)

Northfield School
Knights Road, Blackbird
Leys, OXFORD OX4 6DQ
Tel: 01865 771703
Category: BESD (Boys 11-18)

**Oxfordshire
Hospital School**
c/o St Nicholasi Primary
School, Raymund Road, Old
Marston, OXFORD OX3 0PJ
Tel: 01865 957480
Category: HS (Coed 3-18)

Woodeaton Manor School
Woodeaton, OXFORD OX3 9TS
Tel: 01865 558722
Category: SEMH (Coed 7-18 Day/
residential weekday boarding)

SONNING COMMON

Bishopswood School
Grove Road, SONNING COMMON,
Oxtordshire RG4 9RH
Tel: 01189 724311
Category: SCLD ASD Complex
Needs (Coed 2-16)

WITNEY

Springfield School
The Bronze Barrow, Cedar
Drive, Madley Park, WITNEY,
Oxfordshire OX28 1AR
Tel: 01993 703963
Category: SLD (Coed 2-16)

PETERBOROUGH
City Council

Peterborough SEND Partnership, Sand Martin House, Bittern Way, Fletton Quays Peterborough, PE2 8TY
Tel: 01733 863979 Email: pps@peterborough.gov.uk Website: www.peterborough.gov.uk

PETERBOROUGH

Heltwate School
Heltwate, Bretton, PETERBOROUGH,
Cambridgeshire PE3 8RL
Tel: 01733 262878
Category: MLD SLD AUT
PD SCD (Coed 4-16)

Marshfields School
Eastern Close, Dogsthorpe,
PETERBOROUGH,
Cambridgeshire PE1 4PP
Tel: 01733 568058
Category: MLD SCD SEBD
SLD (Coed 11-19)

NeneGate School
Park Lane, Eastfield,
PETERBOROUGH,
Cambridgeshire PE1 5GZ
Tel: 01733 349438
Category: EBD (Coed 11-16)

Phoenix School
Clayton, Orton Goldhay,
PETERBOROUGH,
Cambridgeshire PE2 5SD
Tel: 01733 391666
Category: SLD PMLD PD SCN
ASD MSI (Coed 2-19)

PLYMOUTH
City Council

Plymouth SENDIASS, Jan Cutting Healthy Living Centre, Scott Business Park, Beacon Park Rd Plymouth, Devon, PL2 2PQ
Tel: 01752 258933 Email: pias@plymouth.gov.uk Website: www.plymouthias.org.uk

PLYMOUTH

**Brook Green Centre
for Learning**
Bodmin Road, Whitleigh,
PLYMOUTH, Devon PL5 4DZ
Tel: 01752 773875
Category: MLD BESD (11-16)

Cann Bridge School
Miller Way, Estover, PLYMOUTH,
Devon PL6 8UN
Tel: 01752 207909
Category: SLD (3-19)

Courtlands School
Widey Lane, Crownhill,
PLYMOUTH, Devon PL6 5JS
Tel: 01752 776848
Category: MLD BESD (4-11)

**Longcause Community
Special School**
Longcause, Plympton,
PLYMOUTH, Devon PL7 1JB
Tel: 01752 336881
Category: MLD (5-17)

**Mill Ford Community
Special School**
Rochford Crescent, Ernesettle,
PLYMOUTH, Devon PL5 2PY
Tel: 01752 300270
Category: SLD PMLD (3-19)

Mount Tamar School
Row Lane, Higher St Budeaux,
PLYMOUTH, Devon PL5 2EF
Tel: 01752 365128
Category: BESD (5-16)

Woodlands School
Picklecombe Drive, Off
Tamerton Foliot Road, Whitleigh,
PLYMOUTH, Devon PL6 5ES
Tel: 01752 300101
Category: PD PMLD MSI (2-19)

BOROUGH OF POOLE
Borough Council

Poole SENDIASS, Quay Advice Centre, 18 Hill Street, Poole, Dorset, BH15 1NR
Tel: 01202 261933 Email: sendiass@poole.gov.uk Website: www.poolefamilyinformationdirectory.com

POOLE

Winchelsea School
Guernsey Road, Parkstone,
POOLE, Dorset BH12 4LL
Tel: 01202 746240
Category: ADHD ASD
ASP MLD (3-16)

PORTSMOUTH
City Council

Portsmouth SENDIASS, Frank Sorrell Centre, Prince Albert Road, Portsmouth, Hampshire, PO4 9HR
Tel: 0300 303 2000 Email: portsmouthiass@roseroad.org.uk Website: www.portsmouthsendiass.info

PORTSMOUTH

Mary Rose School
Gisors Road, Southsea,
PORTSMOUTH, Hampshire PO4 8GT
Tel: 02392 852330
Category: SCN ASD
PMLD (Coed 2-19)

Redwood Park School
Wembley Grove, Cosham,
PORTSMOUTH, Hampshire PO6 2RY
Tel: 02392 377500
Category: CLD ASD (Coed 11-16)

The Harbour School
151 Locksway Road, Milton,
PORTSMOUTH, Hampshire PO4 8LD
Tel: 023 92818547
Category: BESD

READING
Borough Council

Reading SENDIASS, Whitley Health and Social Services Centre, 268
Northumberland Avenue, Reading, Berkshire, RG2 7PJ
Tel: 0118 937 3421 Email: iass@reading.gov.uk Website: www.readingiass.org

READING

Phoenix College
40 Christchurch Road,
READING, Berkshire RG2 7AY
Tel: 01189 375524
Category: SEMH BESD (Coed 11-16)

The Holy Brook School
145 Ashampstead Road,
Southcote, READING,
Berkshire RG30 3LJ
Tel: 01189 375489
Category: BESD (Coed 5-11)

REDCAR & CLEVELAND
Borough Council

Redcar & Cleveland SENDIASS, Redcar & Cleveland House, Kirkleatham Street, Redcar, Middlesborough, TS10 1RT
Tel: 01642 444527 Email: sendiass@redcar-cleveland.gov.uk Website: www.peoplesinfonet.org.uk

MIDDLESBROUGH

Pathways School
Tennyson Avenue, Grangetown,
MIDDLESBROUGH TS6 7NP
Tel: 01642 779292
Category: SEBD (Coed Day 7-15)

REDCAR

Kirkleatham Hall School
Kirkleatham Village, REDCAR,
Cleveland TS10 4QR
Tel: 01642 483009
Category: SLD PMLD SLCN ASC
PD CLDD (Coed Day 4-19)

RUTLAND
County Council

Rutland SENDIASS, Voluntary Action Leicester, 9 Newarke Street, Leicester, LE1 5SN
Tel: 07977 015 674 Email: info@sendiassrutland.org.uk Website: www.sendiassleicester.org.uk

OAKHAM

**The Parks at Oakham
CE Primary School**
Burley Road, OAKHAM,
Rutland LE15 6GY
Tel: 01572 722404
Category: AUT MLD PMLD
SP&LD VIS SEBD (Coed 2-6)

SHROPSHIRE
Council

Shropshire IASS, Louise House, Roman Road, Shrewsbury, Shropshire, SY3 9JN
Tel: 01743 280019 Email: iass@cabshropshire.org.uk Website: shropshiredisability.net

SHREWSBURY

Woodlands School
The Woodlands Centre, Tilley
Green, Wem, SHREWSBURY,
Shropshire SY4 5PJ
Tel: 01939 232372
Category: SEMH (Coed 11-16)

SLOUGH
Borough Council

Slough SENDIASS, St Martins Place, 51 Bath Road, Slough, Berkshire, SL1 3UF
Tel: 01753 787693 Email: sendiass@slough.gov.uk Website: www.slough.gov.uk

SLOUGH

Arbour Vale School
Farnham Road, SLOUGH,
Berkshire SL2 3AE
Tel: 01753 515560
Category: SLD ASD
MLD (Coed 2-19)

Littledown School
Queen's Road, SLOUGH,
Berkshire SL1 3QW
Tel: 01753 521734
Category: BESD (Coed 5-11)

Millside School
112 Burnham Lane, SLOUGH,
Berkshire SL1 6LZ
Tel: 01628 696061
Category: BESD (Coed 11-16)

SOMERSET

County Council

Somerset SENDIAS, County Hall, Taunton, Somerset, TA1 4DY
Tel: 01823 355578 Email: somersetsendias@somerset.gov.uk Website: www.somersetsend.org.uk

BRIDGWATER

Elmwood School
Hamp Avenue, BRIDGWATER,
Somerset TA6 6AW
Tel: 01278 456243
Category: SLD MLD ASD
EBD (Coed Day 11-16)

Penrose School
Albert Street, Willow Brook,
BRIDGWATER, Somerset TA6 7ET
Tel: 01278 411222
Category: CLD ASD SLD
(4-10 and Post-16)

FROME

Critchill School
Nunney Road, FROME,
Somerset BA11 4LB
Tel: 01373 464148
Category: SLD MLD CLD
(Coed Day 4-16)

STREET

Avalon Special School
Brooks Road, STREET,
Somerset BA16 0PS
Tel: 01458 443081
Category: SLD MLD PMLD
ASD (Coed Day 3-16)

TAUNTON

Selworthy School
Selworthy Road, TAUNTON,
Somerset TA2 8HD
Tel: 01823 284970
Category: SLD PMLD MLD
ASD BESD (Coed Day 4-19)

Sky College
Pickeridge Close, TAUNTON,
Somerset TA2 7HW
Tel: 01823 275569
Category: EBD (Boys
Boarding 11-16)

YEOVIL

Fairmead School
Mudford Road, YEOVIL,
Somerset BA21 4NZ
Tel: 01935 421295
Category: MLD SEBD AUT
SLD (Coed Day 4-16)

Fiveways Special School
Victoria Road, YEOVIL,
Somerset BA21 5AZ
Tel: 01935 476227
Category: SLD PMLD ASD
(Coed Day 4-19)

NORTH SOMERSET

Council

North Somerset SEN Team, Town Hall, Walliscote Grove Road, Weston-Super-Mare, North Somerset, BS23 1UJ
Tel: 01275 884 423 Email: sen.team@n-somerset.gov.uk Website: www.n-somerset.gov.uk

NAILSEA

Ravenswood School
Pound Lane, NAILSEA, North
Somerset BS48 2NN
Tel: 01275 854134
Category: CLD SLD (3-19)

WESTON-SUPER-MARE

Baytree School
The Campus, Highlands
Lane, WESTON-SUPER-MARE,
North Somerset BS24 7DX
Tel: 01934 427555
Category: SLD (3-19)

Westhaven School
Ellesmere Road, Uphill,
WESTON-SUPER-MARE,
North Somerset BS23 4UT
Tel: 01934 632171
Category: CLD (7-16)

SOUTHAMPTON

City Council

Southampton SENDIASS, Civic Centre (North Block), Southampton, Hampshire, SO14 7LY
Tel: 0300 303 2677 Email: southamptoniass@roseroad.org.uk Website: www.southamptonsendiass.info

SOUTHAMPTON

Great Oaks School
Vermont Close, off Winchester
Rd, SOUTHAMPTON,
Hampshire SO16 7LT
Tel: 02380 767660
Category: MLD AUT ASP SLD (11-16)

Springwell School
Hinkler Road, Thornhill,
SOUTHAMPTON,
Hampshire SO19 6DH
Tel: 02380 445981
Category: CLD SP&LD AUT SLD
Challenging behaviour (4-11)

The Cedar School
Redbridge Lane,
Nursling, SOUTHAMPTON,
Hampshire SO16 0XN
Tel: 02380 734205
Category: PD (2-16)

The Polygon School
Handel Terrace, SOUTHAMPTON,
Hampshire SO15 2FH
Tel: 02380 636776
Category: EBD (Boys 11-16)

Vermont School
Vermont Close, Off Winchester
Rd, SOUTHAMPTON,
Hampshire SO16 7LT
Tel: 02380 767988
Category: EBD (Boys 5-11)

STAFFORDSHIRE
County Council

Staffordshire SENDIASS, 79/79a Eastgate Street, Stafford, Staffordshire, ST16 2NG
Tel: 01785 356921 Email: sfps@staffordshire.gov.uk Website: www.staffs-iass.org

BURNTWOOD

Chasetown Community School
Church Street, Chasetown, BURNTWOOD, Staffordshire WS7 3QL
Tel: 01543 686315
Category: SEBD (Coed Day 7-13)

CANNOCK

Hednesford Valley High School
Stanley Road, Hednesford, CANNOCK, Staffordshire WS12 4JS
Tel: 01543 423714
Category: Generic (Coed Day 11-19)

Sherbrook Primary School
Grainger Court, CANNOCK, Staffordshire WS11 5SA
Tel: 01543 227230
Category: Generic (Coed Day 2-11)

LEEK

Horton Lodge Community Special School
Reacliffe Road, Rudyard, LEEK, Staffordshire ST13 8RB
Tel: 01538 306214
Category: PD MSI SP&LD (Coed Day/Boarding 2-11)

LICHFIELD

Queen's Croft High School
Birmingham Road, LICHFIELD, Staffordshire WS13 6PJ
Tel: 01543 227245
Category: Generic (Coed Day11-19)

STAFFORD

Greenhall Nursery
Second Avenue, Holmcroft, STAFFORD, Staffordshire ST16 1PS
Tel: 01785 246159
Category: PD (Coed Day 2-5)

Marshlands Special School
Second Avenue, STAFFORD, Staffordshire ST16 1PS
Tel: 01785 336293
Category: Generic (Coed Day 2-11)

TAMWORTH

Two Rivers High School
Silver Link Road, Glascote, TAMWORTH, Staffordshire B77 2HJ
Tel: 01827 426124
Category: Generic (Coed Day 11-19)

Two Rivers Primary School
Quince, Amington Heath, TAMWORTH, Staffordshire B77 4EN
Tel: 01827 426123
Category: Generic (Coed Day 2-11)

STOKE-ON-TRENT
City Council

Stoke-on-Trent SENDIASS, The Crescent Children's Centre, Pinewood Crescent, Meir Stoke-on-Trent, Staffordshire, ST3 6HZ
Tel: 01782 234701 Email: iass@stoke.gov.uk Website: www.sendiass-stoke.co.uk

BLURTON

Kemball Special School
Beconsfield Drive, BLURTON, Stoke-on-Trent ST3 3JD
Tel: 01782 883120
Category: PMLD SLD ASD CLD (Coed Day 2-19)

BLYTHE BRIDGE

Portland School and Specialist College
Uttoxeter Road, BLYTHE BRIDGE, Staffordshire ST11 9JG
Tel: 01782 882020
Category: MLD SEBD (Coed Day 3-16)

STOKE-ON-TRENT

Abbey Hill School and Performing Arts College
Box Lane, Meir, STOKE-ON-TRENT, Staffordshire ST3 5PP
Tel: 01782 882882
Category: MLD AUT (Coed Day 2-18)

TUNSTALL

Watermill Special School
Turnhurst Road, Packmoor, TUNSTALL, Stoke-on-Trent ST6 6JZ
Tel: 01782 883737
Category: MLD (Coed Day 5-16)

SUFFOLK
County Council

Suffolk SENDIASS, Endeavour House, 8 Russell Road, Ipswich, Suffolk, IP1 2BX
Tel: 01473 265210 Email: enquiries@suffolksendiass.co.uk Website: www.suffolksendiass.co.uk

BURY ST EDMUNDS

Riverwalk School
Mayfield Road, BURY ST EDMUNDS, Suffolk IP33 2PB
Tel: 01284 764280
Category: SLD (Coed Day 3-19)

IPSWICH

The Bridge School (Primary Campus)
Sprites Lane, IPSWICH, Suffolk IP8 3ND
Tel: 01473 556200
Category: SLD PMLD (Coed Day 3-11)

The Bridge School (Secondary Campus)
Sprites Lane, IPSWICH, Suffolk IP8 3ND
Tel: 01473 556200
Category: SLD PMLD (Coed Day 11-16)

LOWESTOFT

Warren School
Clarkes Lane, Oulton Broad, LOWESTOFT, Suffolk NR33 8HT
Tel: 01502 561893
Category: SLD PMLD (Coed Day 3-19)

SUDBURY

Hillside School
Hitchcock Place, SUDBURY,
Suffolk CO10 1NN
Tel: 01787 372808
Category: SLD PMLD
(Coed day 3-19)

SURREY

County Council

Surrey SENDIASS, Third Floor, Consort House, 5-7 Queensway, Redhill, Surrey, RH1 1BY
Tel: 01737 737300 Email: ssiass@surreycc.gov.uk **Website:** sendadvicesurrey.org.uk

ADDLESTONE

Philip Southcote School
Addlestone Moor, Weybridge,
ADDLESTONE, Surrey KT15 2QH
Tel: 01932 562326
Category: HI LD (11-19)

CAMBERLEY

Portesbery School
Newfoundland Road, Deepcut,
CAMBERLEY, Surrey GU16 6TA
Tel: 01252 832100
Category: SLD (2-19)

CATERHAM

Clifton Hill School
Chaldon Road, CATERHAM,
Surrey CR3 5PH
Tel: 01883 347740
Category: SLD (11-19)

Sunnydown School
Portley House, 152 Whyteleafe
Road, CATERHAM, Surrey CR3 5ED
Tel: 01883 342281
Category: ASD SLCN
(Boarding & day 11-16)

FARNHAM

The Abbey School
Menin Way, FARNHAM,
Surrey GU9 8DY
Tel: 01252 725059
Category: LD (11-16)

GUILDFORD

Gosden House School
Horsham Road, Bramley,
GUILDFORD, Surrey GU5 0AH
Tel: 01483 892008
Category: LD (Day 5-16)

Wey House School
Horsham Road, Bramley,
GUILDFORD, Surrey GU5 0BJ
Tel: 01483 898130
Category: BESD (Day 4-11)

OXTED

Limpsfield Grange School
89 Bluehouse Lane, Limpsfield,
OXTED, Surrey RH8 0RZ
Tel: 01883 713928
Category: ELD (Boarding
& day 11-16)

REIGATE

Brooklands School
27 Wray Park Road,
REIGATE, Surrey RH2 0DF
Tel: 01737 249941
Category: SLD (2-11)

SHEPPERTON

Manor Mead School
Laleham Road, SHEPPERTON,
Middlesex TW17 8EL
Tel: 01932 241834
Category: SLD (2-11)

WALTON-ON-THAMES

Walton Leigh School
Queens Road, WALTON-ON-
THAMES, Surrey KT12 5AB
Tel: 01932 223243
Category: SLD (11-19)

WOKING

Freemantles School
Smarts Heath Road, Mayford
Green, WOKING, Surrey GU22 0AN
Tel: 01483 545680
Category: CLD (4-19)

The Park School
Onslow Crescent, WOKING,
Surrey GU22 7AT
Tel: 01483 772057
Category: LD (11-16)

EAST SUSSEX

County Council

East Sussex ISEND, County Hall, St Anne's Crescent, Lewes, East Sussex, BN7 1UE
Email: isend.comms@eastsussex.gov.uk **Website:** www.eastsussex.gov.uk

CROWBOROUGH

Grove Park School
Church Road, CROWBOROUGH,
East Sussex TN6 1BN
Tel: 01892 663018
Category: CLD/ASD (Coed 2-19)

EASTBOURNE

Hazel Court Special School
Larkspur Drive, EASTBOURNE,
East Sussex BN23 8EJ
Tel: 01323 465720
Category: CLD/ASD (Coed 11-19)

WEST SUSSEX

County Council

West Sussex SENDIASS, Early Childhood Service, St James Road, Chichester, West Sussex, PO19 7HA
Tel: 03302 228 555 Email: send.ias@westsussex.gov.uk Website: westsussex.local-offer.org

BURGESS HILL

Woodlands Meed
Chanctonbury Road, BURGESS
HILL, West Sussex RH15 9EY
Tel: 01444 244133
Category: LD (Coed 2-19)

CHICHESTER

Fordwater School
Summersdale Road, CHICHESTER,
West Sussex PO19 6PP
Tel: 01243 782475
Category: SLD (Coed 2-19)

St Anthony's School
Woodlands Lane, CHICHESTER,
West Sussex PO19 5PA
Tel: 01243 785965
Category: MLD (Cocd 4-16)

CRAWLEY

Manor Green College
Lady Margaret Road, Ifield,
CRAWLEY, West Sussex RH11 0DX
Tel: 01293 520351
Category: LD (Coed 11-19)

Manor Green Primary School
Lady Margaret Road, Ifield,
CRAWLEY, West Sussex RH11 0DU
Tel: 01293 526873
Category: LD (Coed 2-11)

HORSHAM

Queen Elizabeth II Silver Jubilee School
Comptons Lane, HORSHAM,
West Sussex RH13 5NW
Tel: 01403 266215
Category: SLD AUT
PMLD (Coed 2-19)

LITTLEHAMPTON

Cornfield School
Cornfield Close, Wick,
LITTLEHAMPTON, West
Sussex BN17 6HY
Tel: 01903 731277
Category: SEBD (Coed 7-16)

SHOREHAM-BY-SEA

Herons Dale Primary School
Hawkins Crescent, SHOREHAM-
BY-SEA, West Sussex BN43 6TN
Tel: 01273 596904
Category: LD (Coed 4-11)

WORTHING

Oak Grove College
The Boulevard, WORTHING,
West Sussex BN13 1JX
Tel: 01903 708870
Category: LD (Coed 11-19)

Palatine Primary School
Palatine Road, Goring-By-Sea,
WORTHING, West Sussex BN12 6JP
Tel: 01903 242835
Category: LD (Coed 3-11)

SWINDON

Borough Council

Swindon SENDIASS, Civic Offices, Euclid Street, Swindon, Wiltshire, SN1 2JH
Email: sendiass@swindon.gov.uk Website: www.swindon.gov.uk

SWINDON

Brimble Hill School
Tadpole Lane, North Swindon
Learning Campus, Redhouse,
SWINDON, Wiltshire SN25 2NB
Tel: 01793 493900
Category: SLD (5-11)

Crowdys Hill School
Jefferies Avenue, Cricklade Road,
SWINDON, Wiltshire SN2 7HJ
Tel: 01793 332400
Category: CLD & other
difficulties (11-16)

Nyland Campus
Nyland Road, Nythe,
SWINDON, Wiltshire SN3 3RD
Tel: 01793 535023
Category: BESD (5-11)

St Luke's School
Cricklade Road, SWINDON,
Wiltshire SN2 7AS
Tel: 01793 705566
Category: BESD (11-16)

The Chalet School
Liden Drive, Liden, SWINDON,
Wiltshire SN3 6EX
Tel: 01793 534537
Category: CLD including ASD (3-11)

Uplands School
The Learning Campus, Tadpole
Lane, Redhouse, SWINDON,
Wiltshire SN25 2NB
Tel: 01793 493910
Category: SLD (11-19)

TELFORD & WREKIN

Council

Telford & Wrekin SENDIASS, The Glebe Centre, Glebe Street, Wellington Telford, TF1 1JP
Tel: 01952 457176 Email: info@iass.org.uk Website: www.telfordsendiass.org.uk

TELFORD

Haughton School
Queen Street, Madeley,
TELFORD, Shropshire TF7 4BW
Tel: 01952 387540
Category: MLD ASD SLD
SP&LD BESD (Coed 5-11)

Queensway North
Queensway, Hadley, TELFORD,
Shropshire TF1 6AJ
Tel: 01952 388555
Category: ASD (11-18)

Queensway South
Hinkshay Road, Dawley,
TELFORD, Shropshire TF4 3PP
Tel: 01952 387670
Category: MLD ASD
ADHD (Coed 9-16)

Southall School
Off Rowan Avenue, Dawley,
TELFORD, Shropshire TF4 3PN
Tel: 01952 387600
Category: MLD ASD
SEBD (Coed 11-16)

The Bridge Special School
Waterloo Road, Hadley,
TELFORD, Shropshire TF1 5NQ
Tel: 01952 387108
Category: (3-16)

TORBAY

Council

Torbay SENDIASS, c/o Torbay Community Development Trust, 4-8 Temperance Street, Torquay, Devon, TQ2 5PU
Tel: 01803 212638 Email: info@sendiasstorbay.org.uk Website: sendiasstorbay.org.uk

TORQUAY

Mayfield School
Moor Lane, Watcombe,
TORQUAY, Devon TQ2 8NH
Tel: 01803 328375
Category: SLD PMLD PH
AUT (3-19) BESD (5-11)

GATESHEAD

Tyne & Wear

Council

Gateshead SEND Team, Civic Centre, Regent Street, Gateshead, Tyne & Wear, NE8 1HH
Tel: 01914 333312 Email: senteam@gateshead.gov.uk Website: www.gateshead.gov.uk

GATESHEAD

**Dryden School Business
& Enterprise College**
Shotley Gardens, Low Fell,
GATESHEAD, Tyne & Wear NE9 5UR
Tel: 01914 203811
Category: SLD (Coed 11-19)

Eslington Primary School
Hazel Road, GATESHEAD,
Tyne & Wear NE8 2EP
Tel: 01914 334131
Category: EBD (Coed 4-11)

Furrowfield School
Whitehill Drive, Felling, GATESHEAD,
Tyne & Wear NE10 9RZ
Tel: 01914 954700
Category: EBD (Boys 11-16)

**Hill Top Specialist
Arts College**
Wealcroft, Leam Lane Estate,
GATESHEAD, Tyne & Wear NE10 8LT
Tel: 01914 692462
Category: MLD AUT (Coed 11-19)

NEWCASTLE
UPON TYNE

Gibside School
Burnthouse Lane, Whickham,
NEWCASTLE UPON TYNE,
Tyne & Wear NE16 5AT
Tel: 01914 410123
Category: SLD MLD AUT
LD (Coed 3-11)

NEWCASTLE UPON TYNE
City Council

Newcastle SEN Team, Civic Centre, Barras Bridge, Newcastle upon Tyne, Tyne & Wear, NE1 8QH
Tel: 01912 115337 Website: www.newcastlechildrenservices.org.uk

NEWCASTLE UPON TYNE

Hadrian School
Bertram Crescent, Pendower,
NEWCASTLE UPON TYNE,
Tyne & Wear NE15 6PY
Tel: 01912 734440
Category: PMLD SLD
(Coed Day 2-11)

Mary Astell Academy
Linhope Road, West Denton,
NEWCASTLE UPON TYNE,
Tyne & Wear NE5 2LW
Tel: 01912 674447
Category: (Coed Day 5-16)

Newcastle Bridges School
Cherry Wood, NEWCASTLE UPON
TYNE, Tyne & Wear NE6 4NW
Tel: 01912 755111
Category: HS (Coed 2-19)

Sir Charles Parson School
Westbourne Avenue, NEWCASTLE
UPON TYNE, Tyne & Wear NE6 4ED
Tel: 01912 952280
Category: SLD PD PMLD
(Coed Day 11-19)

Thomas Bewick School
Linhope Road, West Denton,
NEWCASTLE UPON TYNE,
Tyne & Wear NE5 2LW
Tel: 01912 296020
Category: AUT (Coed
Day/boarding 3-19)

Trinity School
Condercum Road, NEWCASTLE
UPON TYNE, Tyne & Wear NE4 8XJ
Tel: 01912 986950
Category: SEBD (Coed Day 7-16)

Tyne & Wear
SUNDERLAND
City Council

Sunderland SENDIASS, Sandhill Centre, Grindon Lane, Sunderland, Tyne & Wear, SR3 4EN
Tel: 0191 5615643 Email: caroline.comer@sunderland.gov.uk Website: www.sunderland.gov.uk

SUNDERLAND

Sunningdale School
Shaftoe Road, Springwell,
SUNDERLAND, Tyne & Wear SR3 4HA
Tel: 01915 280440
Category: PMLD SLD
(Coed Day 2-11)

WASHINGTON

Columbia Grange School
Oxclose Road, Columbia,
WASHINGTON, Tyne &
Wear NE38 7NY
Tel: 01916 913940
Category: SLD ASD (Coed Day 3-11)

Tyne & Wear
NORTH TYNESIDE
Council

North Tyneside SENDIASS, Quadrant West, Cobalt Business Park, Silverlink North North Tyneside, Tyne & Wear, NE27 0BY
Tel: 01916 438317 Email: sendiass@northtyneside.gov.uk Website: www.northtyneside.gov.uk

LONGBENTON

Benton Dene School
Hailsham Avenue, LONGBENTON,
Tyne & Wear NE12 8FD
Tel: 01916 432730
Category: MLD ASD (Coed 5-11+)

NORTH SHIELDS

Southlands School
Beach Road, Tynemouth, NORTH
SHIELDS, Tyne & Wear NE30 2QR
Tel: 01912 006348
Category: MLD BESD (Coed 11-16+)

WALLSEND

Beacon Hill School
Rising Sun Cottages, High Farm,
WALLSEND, Tyne & Wear NE28 9JW
Tel: 01916 433000
Category: ASD SLD
PMLD (Coed 2-16)

Silverdale School
Langdale Gardens, WALLSEND,
Tyne & Wear NE28 0HG
Tel: 01912 005982
Category: BESD (Coed 7-16)

WHITLEY BAY

Woodlawn School
Drumoyne Gardens, West
Monkseaton, WHITLEY BAY,
Tyne & Wear NE25 9DL
Tel: 01916 432590
Category: PD MSI Medical
needs (Coed 2-18)

Tyne & Wear

SOUTH TYNESIDE
Council

South Tynesdie SENDIASS, Chuter Ede Education Centre, Galsworthy Road, South Shields, Tyne & Wear, NE34 9UG
Tel: 0191 424 6345 Email: sendiass@southtyneside.gov.uk Website: www.southtyneside.info

HEBBURN

Keelman's Way School
Campbell Park Road, HEBBURN,
Tyne & Wear NE31 1QY
Tel: 01914 897480
Category: PMLD SLD
(Coed Day 2-19)

JARROW

**Epinay Business &
Enterprise School**
Clervaux Terrace, JARROW,
Tyne & Wear NE32 5UP
Tel: 01914 898949
Category: MLD EBD (Coed 5-17)

SOUTH SHIELDS

Bamburgh School
Horsley Hill Community
Campus, SOUTH SHIELDS,
Tyne & Wear NE34 7TD
Tel: 01914 274330
Category: PD MED VIS HI
MLD (Coed Day 2-17)

Park View School
Temple Park Road, SOUTH
SHIELDS, Tyne & Wear NE34 0QA
Tel: 01914 541568
Category: BESD (Coed Day 11-16)

WARRINGTON
Borough Council

Warrington SENDIASS, New Town House, Buttermarket Street, Warrington, WA1 2NH
Tel: 01925 442978 Website: askollie.warrington.gov.uk

WARRINGTON

Fox Wood School
Holes Lane, Woolston,
WARRINGTON, Cheshire WA1 4LS
Tel: 01925 818534
Category: SLD (Coed Day 4-19)

Green Lane School
Holes Lane, Woolston,
WARRINGTON, Cheshire WA1 4LS
Tel: 01925 811617
Category: MLD CLD
(Coed Day 4-19)

**Sandy Lane Nursery
and Forest School**
Sandy Lane, Orford, WARRINGTON,
Cheshire WA2 9HY
Tel: 01925 623640
Category: (Coed 2-4)

Woolston Brook School
Green Lane, Padgate,
WARRINGTON, Cheshire WA1 4JL
Tel: 01925 818549
Category: BESD (Coed Day 7-16)

WARWICKSHIRE
County Council

Warwickshire SENDIASS, Canterbury House, Exhall Grange Campus,
Easter Way, Ash Green Coventry, Warwickshire, CV7 9HP
Tel: 024 7636 6054 Email: wias@family-action.org.uk Website: www.warwickshire.gov.uk

ASH GREEN

**Exhall Grange
Specialist School**
Easter Way, ASH GREEN,
Warwickshire CV7 9HP
Tel: 02476 364200
Category: VIS PD Med
(Coed Day 2-19)

HENLEY IN ARDEN

Arden Fields
Stratford Road, HENLEY IN
ARDEN, Warwickshire B95 6AD
Tel: 01564 792514
Category: (Boys 6-16)

WARWICK

Ridgeway School
Deansway, WARWICK,
Warwickshire CV34 5DF
Tel: 01926 491987
Category: Generic SLD VIS HI AUT
MSI PD MLD PMLD (Coed Day 2-11)

**Round Oak School
and Support Service**
Brittain Lane, off Myton Road,
WARWICK, Warwickshire CV34 6DX
Tel: 01926 423311
Category: Generic SLD VIS HI AUT
MSI PD MLD PMLD (Coed Day 11-19)

West Midlands

BIRMINGHAM
City Council

Birmingham SENDIASS, Lancaster Circus, PO Box 16289, Birmingham, B2 2XN
Tel: 0121 303 5004 Email: sendiass@birmingham.gov.uk Website: www.birmingham.gov.uk

BROMSGROVE

Hunters Hill College
Spirehouse Lane,
Blackwell, BROMSGROVE,
Worcestershire B60 1QD
Tel: 01214 451320
Category: BESD MLD (Coed 11-16)

EDGBASTON

Baskerville School
Fellows Lane, Harborne,
EDGBASTON, Birmingham B17 9TS
Tel: 01214 273191
Category: ASD (Coed
boarding 11-19)

Uffculme School
2 Yew Tree Road, EDGBASTON,
Birmingham B13 8QG
Tel: 0121 4649634
Category: ASD (Coed day 3-19)

ERDINGTON

Queensbury School
Wood End Road, ERDINGTON,
Birmingham B24 8BL
Tel: 01213 735731
Category: MLD (Coed Day 11-19)

The Pines Special School
Marsh Hill, ERDINGTON,
Birmingham B23 7EY
Tel: 01214 646136
Category: ASD SLCN
(Coed Day 2-12)

HALL GREEN

**Fox Hollies School &
Performing Arts College**
Highbury Community Campus,
Queensbridge Road, Moseley,
HALL GREEN, Birmingham B13 8QB
Tel: 01214 646566
Category: SLD (Coed Day 11-19)

HODGE HILL

Beaufort School
Stechford Road, HODGE
HILL, Birmingham B34 6BJ
Tel: 01216 758500
Category: SLD PMLD ASD
(Coed Day 2-11)

**Braidwood School
for the Deaf**
Bromford Road, HODGE
HILL, Birmingham B36 8AF
Tel: 01214 645558
Category: Deaf HI (Coed Day 11-19)

NORTHFIELD

**Longwill Primary School
for Deaf Children**
Bell Hill, NORTHFIELD,
Birmingham B31 1LD
Tel: 01214 753923
Category: Deaf HI (Coed Day 2-12)

Victoria School
Bell Hill, NORTHFIELD,
Birmingham B31 1LD
Tel: 01214 769478
Category: PD (Coed Day 2-19)

PERRY BARR

Hamilton School
Hamilton Road, Handsworth,
PERRY BARR, Birmingham B21 8AH
Tel: 01214 641676
Category: ASD SLCN
(Coed Day 4-11)

Mayfield School
Heathfield Road, Handsworth,
PERRY BARR, Birmingham B19 1HJ
Tel: 0121 5237321
Category: ASD BESD MLD
PMLD SLD (Coed Day 3-19)

Oscott Manor School
Old Oscott Hill, Kingstanding,
PERRY BARR, Birmingham B44 9SP
Tel: 01213 608222
Category: ASD SLCN
(Coed Day 11-19)

Priestley Smith School
Beeches Road, Great Barr, PERRY
BARR, Birmingham B42 2PY
Tel: 01213 253900
Category: VI (Coed Day 2-19)

REDDITCH

Skilts School
Gorcott Hill, REDDITCH,
Worcestershire B98 9ET
Tel: 01527 853851
Category: BESD (Boys 5-11)

SELLY OAK

Cherry Oak School
60 Frederick Road, SELLY
OAK, Birmingham B29 6PB
Tel: 01214 642037
Category: ASD SLD SLCN
(Coed Day 3-11)

Lindsworth School
Monyhull Hall Road, Kings Norton,
SELLY OAK, Birmingham B30 3QA
Tel: 01216 935363
Category: BESD (Coed
Boarding 9-16)

Selly Oak Trust School
Oak Tree Lane, SELLY OAK,
Birmingham B29 6HZ
Tel: 01214 720876
Category: MLD (Coed Day 11-19)

**The Dame Ellen
Pinsent School**
Ardencote Road, SELLY OAK,
Birmingham B13 0RW
Tel: 01216 752487
Category: ASD BESD HI MLD
SLCN SLD (Coed day 5-11)

SOLIHULL

**Springfield House
Community Special School**
Kenilworth Road, Knowle,
SOLIHULL, West Midlands B93 0AJ
Tel: 01564 772772
Category: BESD (Coed
Boarding 4-11)

SUTTON COLDFIELD

Langley School
Trinity Road, SUTTON COLDFIELD,
West Midlands B75 6TJ
Tel: 01216 752929
Category: MLD (Coed Day 3-11)

West Midlands

COVENTRY
City Council

Coventry SENDIASS, Limbrick Wood Centre, Thomas Naul Croft, Tile Hill Coventry, West Midlands, CV4 9QX
Tel: 024 7669 4307 Email: iass@coventry.gov.uk Website: www.coventry.gov.uk

COVENTRY

Baginton Fields Secondary School
Sedgemoor Road, COVENTRY, West Midlands CV3 4EA
Tel: 02476 303854
Category: SLD (Coed Day 11-19)

Castle Wood
Deedmore Road, COVENTRY, West Midlands CV2 1FN
Tel: 02476 709060
Category: Broad Spectrum (Coed Day 3-11)

Corley Centre
Church Lane, Corley, COVENTRY, West Midlands CV7 8AZ
Tel: 01676 540218
Category: Complex SCD (Coed 11-19)

Sherbourne Fields Primary & Secondary School
Rowington Close, Off Kingsbury Road, COVENTRY, West Midlands CV6 1PS
Tel: 02476 591501
Category: PD (Coed Day 2-19)

Tiverton Primary
Rowington Close, Off Kingsbury Road, COVENTRY, West Midlands CV6 1PS
Tel: 02476 594954
Category: SLD (Coed Day 3-11)

Woodfield School, Primary Site
Stoneleigh Road, COVENTRY, West Midlands CV4 7AB
Tel: 02476 418755
Category: ESBD (Coed Day 5-11)

Woodfield School, Secondary Site
Hawthorn Lane, COVENTRY, West Midlands CV4 9PB
Tel: 02476 462335
Category: EBD (Boys Day 11-16)

West Midlands

DUDLEY
Council

Dudley SENDIASS, Saltwells Education Centre, Bowling Green Road, Netherton Dudley, West Midlands, DY2 9LY
Tel: 01384 817373 Website: www.dudley.gov.uk

DUDLEY

Rosewood School
Bell Street, Coseley, Bilston, DUDLEY, West Midlands WV14 8XJ
Tel: 01384 816800
Category: EBD (11-16)

The Brier School
Bromley Lane, Kingswinford, DUDLEY, West Midlands DY6 8QN
Tel: 01384 816000
Category: MLD (4-16)

The Old Park School
Thorns Road, Quarry Bank, Brierley Hill, DUDLEY, West Midlands DY5 2JY
Tel: 01384 818905
Category: SLD (4-19)

The Sutton School & Specialist College
Scotts Green Close, DUDLEY, West Midlands DY1 2DU
Tel: 01384 818670
Category: MLD (11-16)

The Woodsetton School
Tipton Road, Sedgley, DUDLEY, West Midlands DY3 1BY
Tel: 01384 818265
Category: MLD (4-11)

HALESOWEN

Halesbury School
Feldon Lane, HALESOWEN, West Midlands B62 9DR
Tel: 01384 818630
Category: MLD (4-16)

STOURBRIDGE

Pens Meadow School
Ridge Hill, Brierley Hill Road, Wordsley, STOURBRIDGE, West Midlands DY8 5ST
Tel: 01384 818945
Category: SLD (3-19)

West Midlands

SANDWELL
Council

Sandwell FIS, 160 Beeches Road, West Bromwich, West Midlands, B70 6HQ
Tel: 0121 569 4914 Email: family_information@sandwell.gov.uk Website: fis.sandwell.gov.uk

LICHFIELD

Shenstone Lodge School
Birmingham Road, Shenstone, LICHFIELD, Staffordshire WS14 0LB
Tel: 01543 480369
Category: EBD (Coed Day 4-16)

OLDBURY

The Meadows School
Dudley Road East, OLDBURY, West Midlands B69 3BU
Tel: 01215 697080
Category: PMLD (Coed Day 11-19)

The Orchard School
Causeway Green Road, OLDBURY, West Midlands B68 8LD
Tel: 01215 697040
Category: PMLD (Coed Day 2-11)

ROWLEY REGIS

The Westminster School
Curral Road, ROWLEY REGIS, West Midlands B65 9AN
Tel: 01215 616884
Category: MLD (Coed Day 11-19)

West Midlands

SOLIHULL
Metropolitan Borough Council

Solihull SENDIASS, Sans Souci, Tanworth Lane, Shirley Solihull, West Midlands, B90 4DD
Tel: 0121 516 5173 Email: solihullsendias@family-action.org.uk Website: socialsolihull.org.uk

BIRMINGHAM

Forest Oak School
Windward Way, Smith's
Wood, BIRMINGHAM, West
Midlands B36 0UE
Tel: 01217 170088
Category: MLD (Coed Day 4-18)

Merstone School
Windward Way, Smith's
Wood, BIRMINGHAM, West
Midlands B36 0UE
Tel: 01217 171040
Category: SLD (Coed Day 2-19)

SOLIHULL

Hazel Oak School
Hazel Oak Road, Shirley, SOLIHULL,
West Midlands B90 2AZ
Tel: 01217 444162
Category: MLD (Coed Day 4-18)

Reynalds Cross School
Kineton Green Road, SOLIHULL,
West Midlands B92 7ER
Tel: 01217 073012
Category: SLD (Coed Day 2-19)

West Midlands

WALSALL
Council

Walsall SENDIASS, Blakenall Village Centre, Thames Road, Blakenhall Walsall, West Midlands, WS3 1LZ
Tel: 01922 650330 Email: iasssend@walsall.gov.uk Website: www.walsallparentpartnership.org.uk

WALSALL

**Castle Business &
Enterprise College**
Odell Road, Leamore, WALSALL,
West Midlands WS3 2ED
Tel: 01922 710129
Category: MLD, Additional
Needs (Coed Day 7-19)

Elmwood School
King George Crescent, Rushall,
WALSALL, West Midlands WS4 1EG
Tel: 01922 721081
Category: EBD (Coed Day 11-16)

Mary Elliot Special School
Leamore Lane, WALSALL,
West Midlands WS2 7NR
Tel: 01922 490190
Category: SLD PMLD AUT
(Coed day 11-19)

Oakwood School
Druids Walk, Walsall Wood,
WALSALL, West Midlands WS9 9JS
Tel: 01543 452040
Category: SLD CLD PMLD
ASD Challenging behaviour
(Coed Day 3-11)

Old Hall School
Bentley Lane, WALSALL,
West Midlands WS2 7LU
Tel: 01902 368045
Category: SLD PMLD AUT
(Coed day 3-11)

The Jane Lane School
Churchill Road, Bentley, WALSALL,
West Midlands WS2 0JH
Tel: 01922 721161
Category: MLD, Additional
Needs (Coed Day 7-19)

West Midlands

WOLVERHAMPTON
City Council

Wolverhampton IASS, The Gem Centre, Neachells Lane, Wolverhampton, West Midlands, WV11 3PG
Tel: 01902 556945 Email: ias.service@wolverhampton.gov.uk Website: www.wolverhampton.gov.uk

WOLVERHAMPTON

Green Park School
The Willows, Green Park Avenue,
Bilston, WOLVERHAMPTON,
West Midlands WV14 6EH
Tel: 01902 556429
Category: PMLD SLD
(Coed Day 4-19)

Penn Fields School
Boundary Way, Penn,
WOLVERHAMPTON, West
Midlands WV4 4NT
Tel: 01902 558640
Category: MLD SLD ASD
(Coed Day 4-19)

Penn Hall School
Vicarage Road, Penn,
WOLVERHAMPTON, West
Midlands WV4 5HP
Tel: 01902 558355
Category: PD SLD MLD
(Coed Day 3-19)

Tettenhall Wood School
Regis Road, Tettenhall,
WOLVERHAMPTON, West
Midlands WV6 8XF
Tel: 01902 556519
Category: ASD (Coed Day 5-19)

**Wolverhampton
Vocational Training
Centre (WVTC)**
Millfield Road, Ettingshall,
WOLVERHAMPTON, West
Midlands WV4 6JP
Tel: 01902 552274
Category: MLD SLD ASD
ADHD (Coed Day 16-18)

WILTSHIRE
Council

Wiltshire FIS, ask, Elmsgate, Edington Road, Steeple Ashton Trowbridge, Wiltshire, BA14 6HP
Tel: 01380 871200 Email: info@askwiltshire.org Website: www.askwiltshire.org

CHIPPENHAM

St Nicholas School
Malmesbury Road, CHIPPENHAM,
Wiltshire SN15 1QF
Tel: 01249 650435
Category: SLD PMLD
(Coed Day 4-19)

DEVIZES

Downland School
Downlands Road, DEVIZES,
Wiltshire SN10 5EF
Tel: 01380 724193
Category: BESD SPLD
(Boys Boarding 11-16)

Rowdeford School
Rowde, DEVIZES, Wiltshire SN10 2QQ
Tel: 01380 850309
Category: MLD (Coed
Boarding 11-16)

TROWBRIDGE

Larkrise School
Ashton Street, TROWBRIDGE,
Wiltshire BA14 7EB
Tel: 01225 761434
Category: SLD MLD
(Coed Day 4-19)

WINDSOR & MAIDENHEAD
Borough Council

Windsor & Maidenhead SENDIASS, Riverside Children's Centre, West Dean, Maidenhead, Berkshire, SL6 7JB
Tel: 01628 683182 Email: ias@rbwm.gov.uk Website: ias-rbwm.co.uk

MAIDENHEAD

Manor Green School
Cannon Road, MAIDENHEAD,
Berkshire SL6 3LE
Tel: 01628 513800
Category: SLD PMLD ASD
MLD (Coed 2-19)

WOKINGHAM
Borough Council

Wokingham SENDIASS, Wokingham Youth Centre, 35 Reading Road, Wokingham, Berkshire, RG41 1EG
Tel: 0118 908 8233 Email: sendiass@wokingham.gov.uk Website: www.wokingham.gov.uk

WOKINGHAM

Addington School
Woodlands Avenue, Woodley,
WOKINGHAM, Berkshire RG5 3EU
Tel: 01189 669073
Category: SLD PMLD ASD
MLD (Coed 4-18)

Northern House School
Gipsy Lane, WOKINGHAM,
Berkshire RG40 2HR
Tel: 01189 771293
Category: BESD (Coed 7-16)

WORCESTERSHIRE
County Council

Worcestershire SENDIASS, Tolladine Road, Worcester, WR4 9NB
Tel: 01905 768153 Email: sendiass@worcestershire.gov.uk Website: www.worcestershire.gov.uk

BROMSGROVE

Chadsgrove School & Specialist Sports College
Meadow Road,
Catshill, BROMSGROVE,
Worcestershire B61 0JL
Tel: 01527 871511
Category: PD PMLD MSI LD (2-19)

Rigby Hall School
19 Rigby Lane, Astonfields,
BROMSGROVE,
Worcestershire B60 2EP
Tel: 01527 875475
Category: SLD MLD ASD (3-19)

EVESHAM

Vale of Evesham School
Four Pools Lane, EVESHAM,
Worcestershire WR11 1BN
Tel: 01386 443367
Category: SLD MLD PMLD ASD (4-19)

KIDDERMINSTER

Wyre Forest School
Habberley Road, KIDDERMINSTER,
Worcestershire DY11 6FA
Tel: 01562 827785
Category: MLD SLD ASD
BESD (Coed 7-16)

REDDITCH

Kingfisher School
Clifton Close, Matchborough,
REDDITCH, Worcestershire B98 0HF
Tel: 01527 502486
Category: BESD (Coed 7-16)

Pitcheroak School
Willow Way, Brockhill, REDDITCH,
Worcestershire B97 6PQ
Tel: 01527 65576
Category: SLD MLD AUT (2-19)

WORCESTER

Fort Royal Community Primary School
Wylds Lane, WORCESTER WR5 1DR
Tel: 01905 355525
Category: MLD PD SLD (2-11)

Regency High School
Carnforth Drive,
WORCESTER WR4 9JL
Tel: 01905 454828
Category: PD MLD SLD (11-19)

Riversides School
Thorneloe Road,
WORCESTER WR1 3HZ
Tel: 01905 21261
Category: BESD (Coed 7-16)

CITY OF YORK
Council

York SENDIASS, West Offices, Station Rise, York, YO1 6GA
Tel: 01904 554319 Email: yorksendiass@york.gov.uk Website: www.york.gov.uk

YORK

Applefields School
Bad Bargain Lane, YORK YO31 0LW
Tel: 01904 553900
Category: MLD AUT
SLD PMLD (11-19)

Danesgate School
Fulford Cross, YORK YO10 4PB
Tel: 01904 642611
Category: (5-16)

Hob Moor Oaks School
Green Lane, Acomb,
YORK YO24 4PS
Tel: 01904 555000
Category: MLD AUT SLD PMLD (3-11)

EAST RIDING OF YORKSHIRE
Council

E Riding of Yorkshire SENDIASS, Families Information Service Hub (FISH),
County Hall, Beverley, East Riding of Yorkshire, HU17 9BA
Tel: 01482 396469 Email: fish@eastriding.gov.uk Website: www.eastridinglocaloffer.org.uk

BROUGH

St Anne's School & Sixth Form College
St Helen's Drive, Welton, BROUGH,
East Riding of Yorkshire HU15 1NR
Tel: 01482 667379
Category: SLD

DRIFFIELD

Kings Mill School & Nursery
Victoria Road, DRIFFIELD, East
Riding of Yorkshire YO25 6UG
Tel: 01377 253375
Category: SLD

GOOLE

Riverside Special School
Ainsty Street, GOOLE, East
Riding of Yorkshire DN14 5JS
Tel: 01405 763925
Category: MLD and other
complex needs

NORTH YORKSHIRE
County Council

North Yorkshire SENDIASS, County Hall, Racecourse Lane, Northallerton, North Yorkshire, DL7 8AD
Tel: 01609 536923 Email: info@sendiassnorthyorks.org Website: www.northyorks.gov.uk

BEDALE

Mowbray School
Masham Road, BEDALE,
North Yorkshire DL8 2SD
Tel: 01677 422446
Category: MLD SP&LD (2-16)

HARROGATE

Forest Moor School
Menwith Hill Road, Darley,
HARROGATE, North
Yorkshire HG3 2RA
Tel: 01423 779232
Category: BESD (Boys 11-16)

Springwater School
High Street, Starbeck, HARROGATE,
North Yorkshire HG2 7LW
Tel: 01423 883214
Category: SLD PMLD (2-19)

KIRKBYMOORSIDE

Welburn Hall School
KIRKBYMOORSIDE, North
Yorkshire YO62 7HQ
Tel: 01751 431218
Category: PHLD (8-18)

KNARESBOROUGH

The Forest School
Park Lane, KNARESBOROUGH,
North Yorkshire HG5 0DG
Tel: 01423 864583
Category: MLD (2-16)

NORTHALLERTON

The Dales School
Morton-on-Swale,
NORTHALLERTON, North
Yorkshire DL7 9QW
Tel: 01609 772932
Category: SLD PMLD (2-19)

SCARBOROUGH

Brompton Hall School
High Street, Brompton-by-
Sawdon, SCARBOROUGH,
North Yorkshire YO13 9DB
Tel: 01723 859121
Category: BESD (Boys 8-16)

Springhead School
Barry's Lane, Seamer Road,
SCARBOROUGH, North
Yorkshire YO12 4HA
Tel: 01723 367829
Category: SLD PMLD (2-19)

SKIPTON

Brooklands School
Burnside Avenue, SKIPTON,
North Yorkshire BD23 2DB
Tel: 01756 794028
Category: MLD SLD PMLD (2-19)

South Yorkshire

BARNSLEY
Council

Barnsley SENDIASS, PO Box 634, Barnsley, South Yorkshire, S70 9GG
Tel: 01226 787234 Email: parentpartners@barnsley.gov.uk Website: www.barnsley.gov.uk

BARNSLEY

Greenacre School
Keresforth Hill Road, BARNSLEY,
South Yorkshire S70 6RG
Tel: 01226 287165
Category: SLD CLD PMLD
MSI AUT (Coed Day 2-19)

Springwell Learning Community
St Helen's Boulevard, Carlton Road,
BARNSLEY, South Yorkshire S71 2AY
Tel: 01226 291133

South Yorkshire

DONCASTER
Council

Doncaster SEN Team, Civic Office, Waterdale, Doncaster, DN1 3BU
Tel: 01302 737209 Email: sen@doncaster.gov.uk Website: www.doncaster.gov.uk

DONCASTER

Coppice School
Ash Hill Road, Hatfield,
DONCASTER, South
Yorkshire DN7 6JH
Tel: 01302 844883
Category: SLD ASD BESD
(Coed Day 3-19)

Heatherwood School
Leger Way, DONCASTER,
South Yorkshire DN2 6HQ
Tel: 01302 322044
Category: SLD PD (Coed Day 3-19)

**North Bridge
Enterprise College**
Marshgate, Elwis Street,
DONCASTER, South
Yorkshire DN5 8AF
Tel: 01302 343935
Category: (Coed 11-17)

**North Ridge
Community School**
Tenter Balk Lane, Adwick-
le-Street, DONCASTER,
South Yorkshire DN6 7EF
Tel: 01302 720790
Category: SLD (Coed Day 3-19)

Stone Hill School
Barnsley Road, Scawsby,
DONCASTER, South
Yorkshire DN5 7UB
Tel: 01302 800090
Category: MLD (Coed 5-16)

South Yorkshire

ROTHERHAM
Metropolitan Borough Council

Rotherham SENDIASS, Riverside House, 1st Floor, Wing C, Rotherham, South Yorkshire, S65 1AE
Tel: 01709 823627 Website: www.rotherhamsendiass.org.uk

MEXBOROUGH

Milton School
Storey Street, Swinton,
MEXBOROUGH, South
Yorkshire S64 8QG
Tel: 01709 570246
Category: MLD (5-16) ASD (5-11)

ROTHERHAM

Abbey School
Little Common Lane,
Kimberworth, ROTHERHAM,
South Yorkshire S61 2RA
Tel: 01709 740074
Category: MLD

Kelford School
Oakdale Road, Kimberworth,
ROTHERHAM, South
Yorkshire S61 2NU
Tel: 01709 512088
Category: SLD

Maltby Hilltop School
Larch Road, Maltby, ROTHERHAM,
South Yorkshire S66 8AZ
Tel: 01709 813386
Category: SLD

Newman School
East Bawtry Road, Whiston,
ROTHERHAM, South
Yorkshire S60 3LX
Tel: 01709 828262
Category: PH Medical needs

The Willows School
Locksley Drive, Thurcroft,
ROTHERHAM, South
Yorkshire S66 9NT
Tel: 01709 542539
Category: MLD

South Yorkshire

SHEFFIELD
City Council

Sheffield SENDIASS, Floor 6, North Wing, Moorfoot Building, Sheffield, S1 4PL
Tel: 0114 273 6009 Email: ed-parent.partnership@sheffield.gov.uk Website: www.sheffield.gov.uk

SHEFFIELD

**Aldine House Secure
Childrenís Centre**
75 Limb Lane, Dore, SHEFFIELD,
South Yorkshire S17 3ES
Tel: 01142 621160
Category: (Coed 10-17)

Bents Green School
Ringinglow Road, SHEFFIELD,
South Yorkshire S11 7TB
Tel: 01142 363545
Category: AUT ASD
SCD (Coed 11-19)

**Heritage Park
Foundation School**
Norfolk Park Road, SHEFFIELD,
South Yorkshire S2 2RU
Tel: 01142 796850
Category: BESD (KS 2/3/4)

**Holgate Meadows
Foundation School**
Lindsay Road, SHEFFIELD,
South Yorkshire S5 7WE
Tel: 01142 456305
Category: BESD (KS 2/3/4)

Mossbrook School
Bochum Parkway, SHEFFIELD,
South Yorkshire S8 8JR
Tel: 01142 372768
Category: AUT SCD (Coed 4-11)

Norfolk Park School
Archdale Road, SHEFFIELD,
South Yorkshire S2 1PL
Tel: 01142 726165
Category: LD Complex
Needs (Coed 3-11)

Rowan School
4 Durvale Court, Dore, SHEFFIELD,
South Yorkshire S17 3PT
Tel: 01142 350479
Category: AUT SCD (Primary)

Seven Hills School
Granville Road, SHEFFIELD,
South Yorkshire S2 2RJ
Tel: 01142 743560
Category: LD Complex Needs

Talbot Specialist School
Lees Hall Road, SHEFFIELD,
South Yorkshire S8 9JP
Tel: 01142 507394
Category: LD Complex
Needs (Coed 11-19)

Woolley Wood School
Chaucer Road, SHEFFIELD,
South Yorkshire S5 9QN
Tel: 01142 327160
Category: LD Complex Needs

West Yorkshire

CALDERDALE
Council

Calderdale IASS, Empire Building, 3rd Floor, Dewsbury, WF12 8DJ
Tel: 01422 266141 Email: joanne.grenfell@calderdale.gov.uk Website: www.calderdalesendiass.org.uk

BRIGHOUSE

Highbury School
Lower Edge Road, Rastrick,
BRIGHOUSE, West Yorkshire HD6 3LD
Tel: 01484 716319
Category: All (3-11)

HALIFAX

**Ravenscliffe High School
& Sports College**
Skircoat Green, HALIFAX,
West Yorkshire HX3 0RZ
Tel: 01422 358621
Category: All (11-18)

Wood Bank School
Dene View, Luddendenfoot,
HALIFAX, West Yorkshire HX2 6PB
Tel: 01422 884170
Category: All (4-11)

West Yorkshire

KIRKLEES
Council

Kirklees IASS, Empire Building, 3rd Floor, Dewsbury, WF12 8DJ
Tel: 0300 330 1504 Email: kias@kias.org.uk Website: www.kias.org.uk

BATLEY

Fairfield School
White Lee Road, BATLEY,
West Yorkshire WF17 8AS
Tel: 01924 326103
Category: SLD (Coed Day 3-19)

DEWSBURY

Ravenshall School
Ravensthorpe Road, Thornhill Lees,
DEWSBURY, West Yorkshire WF12 9EE
Tel: 01924 456811
Category: MLD (Coed Day 5-16)

HUDDERSFIELD

Castle Hill School
Newsome Road South,
Newsome, HUDDERSFIELD,
West Yorkshire HD4 6JL
Tel: 01484 544558
Category: SLD AUT PMLD
(Coed Day 3-19)

Southgate School
Southfield Road, Almondbury,
HUDDERSFIELD, West
Yorkshire HD5 8TG
Tel: 01484 504544
Category: Complex Needs
(Coed Day 4-16)

Woodley School & College
Dog Kennel Bank, HUDDERSFIELD,
West Yorkshire HD5 8JE
Tel: 01484 223937
Category: MLD AUT SEMH
(Coed Day 5-16)

West Yorkshire

LEEDS
City Council

Leeds SENDIASS, 9 Harrogate Road, Chapel Allerton, Leeds, West Yorkshire, LS7 3NB
Tel: 0113 378 5020 Email: sendiass@leeds.gov.uk Website: www.educationleeds.co.uk

LEEDS

Broomfield (South SILC)
Broom Place, Belle Isle, LEEDS, West Yorkshire LS10 3JP
Tel: 01132 771603
Category: Complex physical, learning and care needs (Coed 2-19)

John Jamieson School (East SILC)
Hollin Hill Drive, Oakwood, LEEDS, West Yorkshire LS8 2PW
Tel: 01132 930236
Category: Complex physical, learning and care needs (Coed 3-19)

Milestone (West SILC)
4 Town Street, Stanningley, LEEDS, West Yorkshire LS28 6HL
Tel: 0113 3862450
Category: Complex physical, learning and care needs (Coed 2-19)

Penny Field School (North West SILC)
Tongue Lane, Meanwood, LEEDS, West Yorkshire LS6 4QD
Tel: 01133 368270
Category: Complex physical, learning and care needs (Coed 4-19)

Springwell Leeds North
Woodnook Drive, Tinshill, LEEDS, West Yorkshire LS16 6NE
Tel: 0113 4870555
Category: SEMH

West Oaks SEN Specialist School & College (North East SILC)
Westwood Way, Boston Spa, Wetherby, LEEDS, West Yorkshire LS23 6DX
Tel: 01937 844772
Category: Complex physical, learning and care needs (Coed 2-19)

West Yorkshire

WAKEFIELD
Council

Wakefield SEND Development Team, Room 230 County Hall, Bond Street, Wakefield, WF1 2QW
Tel: 01924 302410 Email: send@wakefield.gov.uk Website: www.wakefield.gov.uk

CASTLEFORD

Kingsland School Castleford
Poplar Avenue, Townville, CASTLEFORD, West Yorkshire WF10 3QJ
Tel: 01977 513769
Category: SLD MLD (Coed 4-11)

OSSETT

Highfield School
Gawthorpe Lane, Gawthorpe, OSSETT, West Yorkshire WF5 9BS
Tel: 01977 513769
Category: MLD (Coed 11-16)

PONTEFRACT

High Well School
Rookhill Road, PONTEFRACT, West Yorkshire WF8 2DD
Tel: 01924 572100
Category: EBD (Coed 11-16)

Oakfield Park School
Barnsley Road, Ackworth, PONTEFRACT, West Yorkshire WF7 7DT
Tel: 01977 613423
Category: SLD PMLD (Coed 11-19)

WAKEFIELD

Kingsland School Stanley
Aberford Road, Stanley, WAKEFIELD, West Yorkshire WF3 4BA
Tel: 01924 828990
Category: SLD PMLD (Coed 2-11)

CHANNEL ISLANDS

GUERNSEY

Council

Guernsey Standards & Learning Effectiveness, Sir Charles Frossard House, La Charroterie, St Peter Port, Guernsey, GY1 1FH
Tel: 01481 733000 Website: www.gov.gg

FOREST

Le Rondin School & Centre
Rue des Landes, FOREST,
Guernsey GY8 0DP
Tel: 01481 268300
Category: MLD SLD PMLD (3-11)

ST SAMPSON'S

Le Murier School
Rue de Dol, ST SAMPSON'S,
Guernsey GY2 4DA
Tel: 01481 246660
Category: MLD PMLD
SLD (Coed 11-16)

ST. PETER PORT

Les Voies School
Collings Road, ST. PETER
PORT, Guernsey GY1 1FW
Tel: 01481 710721
Category: SEBD (Coed 4-16)

JERSEY

Council

Jersey Inclusion & Early Intervention Section, PO Box 142, Highlands Campus, St. Saviour, Jersey, JE4 8QJ
Tel: 01534 445504 Email: inclusion@gov.je Website: www.gov.je

ST HELIER

Mont a l'Abbe School
La Grande Route de St
Jean, La Pouquelaye, ST
HELIER, Jersey JE2 3FN
Tel: 01534 875801
Category: LD (3-19)

ST SAVIOUR

La Sente School
St Saviour's Hill, ST SAVIOUR,
Jersey JE2 7LF
Tel: 01534 618042
Category: SEMH (Coed 6-16)

NORTHERN IRELAND

BELFAST

City Council

Education Authority, SEN Team, Belfast Office, 40 Academy Street, Belfast, Northern Ireland, BT1 2NQ
Tel: +44 (0)28 9056 4000 Email: info@eani.org.uk Website: www.eani.org.uk

BELFAST

Belfast Hospital School
Royal Belfast Hospital School
for Sick Children, Falls Road,
BELFAST, Co Antrim BT12 6BE
Tel: 02890 633498
Category: HS (Coed 4-19)

Cedar Lodge School
24 Lansdowne Park North,
BELFAST, Co Antrim BT15 4AE
Tel: 02890 777292
Category: EPI ASD ADHD
Medical needs (Coed 4-16)

Clarawood School
Clarawood Park, BELFAST,
Co Antrim BT5 6FR
Tel: 02890 472736
Category: SEBD (Coed 8-12)

Fleming Fulton School
Upper Malone Road, BELFAST,
Co Antrim BT9 6TY
Tel: 02890 613877
Category: PH MLD (Coed 3-19)

Glenveagh School
Harberton Park, BELFAST,
Co Antrim BT9 6TX
Tel: 02890 669907
Category: SLD (Coed 8-19)

**Greenwood House
Assessment Centre**
Greenwood Avenue, Upper
Newtownards Road, BELFAST,
Co Antrim BT4 3JJ
Tel: 02890 471000
Category: SP&LD MLD EBD SLD
Medical needs (Coed 4-7)

Harberton Special School
Haberton Park, BELFAST,
Co Antrim BT9 6TX
Tel: 02890 381525
Category: AUT ASP SP&LD EBD
Medical needs (Coed 4-11)

**Loughshore Educational
Resource Centre**
889 Shore Road, BELFAST,
Co Antrim BT36 7DH
Tel: 02890 773062
Category: ADHD ASD

Mitchell House School
Marmont Park, Holywood Road,
BELFAST, Co Antrim BT4 2GT
Tel: 02890 768407
Category: PD MSI (Coed 3-18)

Oakwood School & Assessment Centre
Harberton Park, BELFAST,
Co Antrim BT9 6TX
Tel: 02890 605116
Category: SLD PMLD ASD (Coed 3-8)

Park School & Educational Resource Centre
145 Ravenhill Road, BELFAST,
Co Antrim BT6 8GH
Tel: 02890 450513
Category: MLD (Coed 11-16)

St Gerard's School & Support Services
Blacks Road, BELFAST,
Co Antrim BT10 0NB
Tel: 02890 600330
Category: MLD (Coed 4-16)

St Teresa's Speech, Language & Communication Centre
St Teresaís Primary School, Glen Road, BELFAST, Co Antrim BT11 8BL
Tel: 02890 611943

St Vincent's Centre
6 Willowfield Drive, BELFAST,
Co Antrim BT6 8HN
Tel: 02890 461444

NORTH EASTERN

Councils

Education Authority, SEN Team, Antrim Office, County Hall, 182 Galgorm Rd Ballymena, Northern Ireland, BT42 1HN
Tel: +44 (0)28 2565 3333 **Email:** info@eani.org.uk **Website:** www.eani.org.uk

ANTRIM

Riverside School
Fennel Road, ANTRIM,
Co Antrim BT41 4PB
Tel: 02894 428946
Category: SLD

BALLYMENA

Castle Tower School
50 Larne Road Link, BALLYMENA,
Co Antrim BT42 3GA
Tel: 02825 633400
Category: MLD SLD PD SEBD

MAGHERAFELT

Kilronan School
46 Ballyronan Road, MAGHERAFELT,
Co Londonderry BT45 6EN
Tel: 02879 632168
Category: SLD

NEWTOWNABBEY

Hill Croft School
3 Manse Way, NEWTOWNABBEY,
Co Antrim BT36 5UW
Tel: 02890 837488
Category: SLD

Jordanstown School
85 Jordanstown Road,
NEWTOWNABBEY, Co Antrim BT37 0QE
Tel: 02890 863541
Category: HI VIS (Coed 4-19)

Rosstulla Special School
2 Jordanstown Road,
NEWTOWNABBEY, Co Antrim BT37 0QS
Tel: 02890 862743
Category: MLD (Coed 5-16)

SOUTH EASTERN

Councils

Education Authority, SEN Team, Dundonald Office, Grahamsbridge Road, Dundonald, Northern Ireland, BT16 2HS
Tel: +44 (0)28 9056 6200 **Email:** info@eani.org.uk **Website:** www.eani.org.uk

BANGOR

Clifton Special School
292a Old Belfast Road,
BANGOR, Co Down BT19 1RH
Tel: 02891 270210
Category: SLD

BELFAST

Longstone Special School
Millars Lane, Dundonald,
BELFAST, Co Down BT16 2DA
Tel: 02890 480071
Category: MLD

Tor Bank School
5 Dunlady Road, Dundonald,
BELFAST, Co Down BT16 1TT
Tel: 02890 484147
Category: SLD

CRAIGAVON

Brookfield School
65 Halfpenny Gate Road, Moira,
CRAIGAVON, Co Armagh BT67 0HP
Tel: 02892 622978
Category: MLD (Coed 5-11)

DONAGHADEE

Killard House School
Cannyreagh Road, DONAGHADEE,
Co Down BT21 0AU
Tel: 02891 882361
Category: MLD

DOWNPATRICK

Ardmore House School
95a Saul Street, DOWNPATRICK,
Co Down BT30 6NJ
Tel: 02844 614881
Category: EBD

Knockevin Special School
33 Racecourse Hill, DOWNPATRICK,
Co Down BT30 6PU
Tel: 02844 612167
Category: SLD

HILLSBOROUGH

Beechlawn School
3 Dromore Road, HILLSBOROUGH,
Co Down BT26 6PA
Tel: 02892 682302
Category: MLD

LISBURN

Parkview Special School
2 Brokerstown Road, LISBURN,
Co Antrim BT28 2FF
Tel: 02892 601197
Category: SLD

Maintained special schools and colleges

SOUTHERN

Councils

Education Authority, SEN Team, Armagh Office, 3 Charlemont Place, The Mall Armagh, Northern Ireland, BT61 9AX
Tel: +44 (0)28 3751 2200 Email: info@eani.org.uk Website: www.eani.org.uk

ARMAGH

Lisanally Special School
85 Lisanally Lane, ARMAGH,
Co Armagh BT61 7HF
Tel: 02837 523563
Category: SLD (Coed)

BANBRIDGE

Donard School
22a Castlewellan Road,
BANBRIDGE, Co Down BT32 4XY
Tel: 02840 662357
Category: SLD (Coed)

CRAIGAVON

Ceara School
Sloan Street, Lurgan, CRAIGAVON,
Co Armagh BT66 8NY
Tel: 02838 323312
Category: SLD (Coed)

NEWRY

Rathore School
23 Martin's Lane, Carnagat,
NEWRY, Co Down BT35 8PJ
Tel: 02830 261617
Category: SLD (Coed)

WESTERN

Councils

Education Authority, SEN Team, Omagh Office, 1 Hospital Road, Omagh, Northern Ireland, BT79 0AW
Tel: +44 (0)28 8241 1411 Email: info@eani.org.uk Website: www.eani.org.uk

ENNISKILLEN

Willowbridge School
8 Lough Shore Road,
Drumlyon, ENNISKILLEN, Co
Fermanagh BT74 7EY
Tel: 02866 329947
Category: SLD MLD (Coed)

LONDONDERRY

**Ardnashee School
& College**
15-17 Racecourse Road,
LONDONDERRY, Co
Londonderry BT48 7RE
Tel: 02871 263270
Category: SLD (Coed)

OMAGH

**Arvalee School &
Resource Centre**
Strule Campus, Gortin Road,
OMAGH, Co Tyrone BT79 7DH
Tel: 02882 255710
Category: MLD SLD (Coed)

STRABANE

**Knockavoe School &
Resource Centre**
10a Melmount Gardens,
STRABANE, Co Tyrone BT82 9EB
Tel: 02871 883319
Category: SLD MLD (Coed)

LIMAVADY

Rossmar School
2 Ballyquin Road, LIMAVADY,
Co Londonderry BT49 9ET
Tel: 02877 762351
Category: MLD (Coed)

SCOTLAND

ABERDEEN

Council

Enquire, Children in Scotland, Rosebery House, 9 Haymarket Terrace Edinburgh, EH12 5EZ
Tel: 0345 123 2303 Email: info@enquire.org.uk Website: www.enquire.org.uk

ABERDEEN

**Aberdeen School
for the Deaf**
c/o Sunnybank School, Sunnybank
Road, ABERDEEN AB24 3NJ
Tel: 01224 261722
Category: HI

Orchard Brae School
Howes Road, ABERDEEN AB16 7RW
Tel: 01224 788950
Category: SCLD

ABERDEENSHIRE
Council

Enquire, Children in Scotland, Rosebery House, 9 Haymarket Terrace Edinburgh, EH12 5EZ
Tel: 0345 123 2303 Email: info@enquire.org.uk Website: www.enquire.org.uk

FRASERBURGH
Westfield School
Argyll Road, FRASERBURGH,
Aberdeenshire AB43 9BL
Tel: 01346 518699
Category: PMLD SCLD
(Coed 5-18, 0-3 Nursery)

INVERURIE
St Andrew's School
St Andrew's Garden, INVERURIE,
Aberdeenshire AB51 3XT
Tel: 01467 536940
Category: PMLD SCLD (Coed 3-18)

PETERHEAD
Anna Ritchie School
Grange Gardens, PETERHEAD,
Aberdeenshire AB42 2AP
Tel: 01779 403670
Category: PMLD SCLD (Coed 3-18)

STONEHAVEN
Carronhill School
Mill of Forest Road, STONEHAVEN,
Kincardineshire AB39 2GZ
Tel: 01569 763886
Category: PMLD SCLD (Coed 3-18)

EAST AYRSHIRE
Council

Enquire, Children in Scotland, Rosebery House, 9 Haymarket Terrace Edinburgh, EH12 5EZ
Tel: 0345 123 2303 Email: info@enquire.org.uk Website: www.enquire.org.uk

CUMNOCK
Hillside School
Dalgleish Avenue, Drumbrochan,
CUMNOCK, East Ayrshire KA18 1QQ
Tel: 01290 423239
Category: SLD PMLD (Coed 6-17)

KILMARNOCK
Park School
Beech Avenue, Grange,
KILMARNOCK, East
Ayrshire KA1 2EW
Tel: 01563 549988
Category: LD PD (Coed 5-18)

Willowbank School
Grassyards Road, New Farm Loch,
KILMARNOCK, East Ayrshire KA3 7BB
Tel: 01563 526115
Category: SLD PMLD

SOUTH AYRSHIRE
Council

Enquire, Children in Scotland, Rosebery House, 9 Haymarket Terrace Edinburgh, EH12 5EZ
Tel: 0345 123 2303 Email: info@enquire.org.uk Website: www.enquire.org.uk

AYR
Southcraig Campus
Belmont Avenue, AYR,
South Ayrshire KA7 2ND
Tel: 01292 612146
Category: SLD CLD (Coed 1-5)

GIRVAN
Invergarven School
Coalpots Road, GIRVAN,
South Ayrshire KA26 0FX
Tel: 01465 716808
Category: SLD CLD PD
MSI (Coed 3-16)

Maintained special schools and colleges

CLACKMANNANSHIRE
Council

Enquire, Children in Scotland, Rosebery House, 9 Haymarket Terrace Edinburgh, EH12 5EZ
Tel: 0345 123 2303 Email: info@enquire.org.uk Website: www.enquire.org.uk

ALLOA
**Primary Schools'
Support Service**
East Castle Street, ALLOA,
Clackmannanshire FK10 1BB
Tel: 01259 212151

**Secondary Schools'
Support Service**
Bedford Place, ALLOA,
Clackmannanshire FK10 1LJ
Tel: 01259 724345

SAUCHIE
Lochies School
Gartmorn Road, SAUCHIE,
Clackmannanshire FK10 3PB
Tel: 01259 452312
Category: CLD SLD (Coed 5-11)

COMHAIRLE NAN EILEAN SIAR
Council

Enquire, Children in Scotland, Rosebery House, 9 Haymarket Terrace Edinburgh, EH12 5EZ
Tel: 0345 123 2303 Email: info@enquire.org.uk Website: www.enquire.org.uk

STORNOWAY
Stornoway Primary School
Jamieson Drive, STORNOWAY,
Isle of Lewis HS1 2LF
Tel: 01851 703418

EAST DUNBARTONSHIRE
Council

Enquire, Children in Scotland, Rosebery House, 9 Haymarket Terrace Edinburgh, EH12 5EZ
Tel: 0345 123 2303 Email: info@enquire.org.uk Website: www.enquire.org.uk

KIRKINTILLOCH
Merkland School
Langmuir Road, KIRKINTILLOCH,
East Dunbartonshire G66 2QF
Tel: 01419 552336
Category: MLD PH

LENZIE
Campsie View School
Boghead Road, LENZIE, East
Dunbartonshire G66 4DP
Tel: 01419 552339
Category: SCLD

WEST DUNBARTONSHIRE
Council

Enquire, Children in Scotland, Rosebery House, 9 Haymarket Terrace Edinburgh, EH12 5EZ
Tel: 0345 123 2303 Email: info@enquire.org.uk Website: www.enquire.org.uk

CLYDEBANK
Cunard School
Cochno Street, Whitecrook,
CLYDEBANK, West
Dunbartonshire G81 1RQ
Tel: 01419 521621
Category: SEBD (Primary)

Kilpatrick School
Mountblow Road,
Dalmuir, CLYDEBANK, West
Dunbartonshire G81 4SW
Tel: 01389 804430
Category: SCLD (Primary/
Secondary)

CITY OF EDINBURGH
Council

Enquire, Children in Scotland, Rosebery House, 9 Haymarket Terrace Edinburgh, EH12 5EZ
Tel: 0345 123 2303 Email: info@enquire.org.uk Website: www.enquire.org.uk

EDINBURGH

Braidburn Special School
107 Oxgangs Road North,
EDINBURGH EH14 1ED
Tel: 01313 122320
Category: EPI PH (Coed 2-18)

Edinburgh Secure Services (Howdenhall)
39 Howdenhall Road,
EDINBURGH EH16 6PG
Tel: 01316 648488

Gorgie Mills Special School
97 Gorgie Park Road,
EDINBURGH EH11 2QL
Tel: 01313 133848

Kaimes School
140 Lasswade Road,
EDINBURGH EH16 6RT
Tel: 01316 648241
Category: SP&LD ASD (Coed 5-18)

Oaklands School
750 Ferry Road,
EDINBURGH EH4 4PQ
Tel: 01313 158100
Category: SLD CLD PD MSI

Pilrig Park Special School
12 Balfour Place,
EDINBURGH EH6 5DW
Tel: 01314 677960
Category: MLD SLD (Coed 11-16)

Prospect Bank Special School
81 Restalrig Road,
EDINBURGH EH6 8BQ
Tel: 01315 532239
Category: LD SP&LD (Coed 5-12)

Redhall Special School
3c Redhall Grove,
EDINBURGH EH14 2DU
Tel: 01314 431256
Category: LD (Cocd 4-11)

Rowanfield Special School
67c Groathill Road North,
EDINBURGH EH4 2SA
Tel: 01313 436116
Category: EBD

St Crispin's Special School
19 Watertoun Road,
EDINBURGH EH9 3HZ
Tel: 01316 674831
Category: SLD AUT (Coed 5-16)

Woodlands Special School
36 Dolphin Avenue,
EDINBURGH EH14 5RD
Tel: 01314 493447

FALKIRK
Council

Enquire, Children in Scotland, Rosebery House, 9 Haymarket Terrace Edinburgh, EH12 5EZ
Tel: 0345 123 2303 Email: info@enquire.org.uk Website: www.enquire.org.uk

FALKIRK

Mariner Support Service
Laurieston Campus, Bog
Road, FALKIRK FK2 9PB
Tel: 01324 501090
Category: SEBD (Secondary)

Windsor Park School
Bantaskine Road, FALKIRK FK1 5HT
Tel: 01324 508640
Category: Deaf (Coed 3-16)

GRANGEMOUTH

Carrongrange School
Oxgang Road,
GRANGEMOUTH FK3 9HP
Tel: 01324 492592
Category: CLD MLD (Secondary)

Oxgang School
c/o Moray Primary School, Moray
Place, GRANGEMOUTH FK3 9DL
Tel: 01324 501311
Category: BESD (5-11)

FIFE
Council

Enquire, Children in Scotland, Rosebery House, 9 Haymarket Terrace Edinburgh, EH12 5EZ
Tel: 0345 123 2303 Email: info@enquire.org.uk Website: www.enquire.org.uk

CUPAR

Kilmaron School
Balgarvie Road, CUPAR,
Fife KY15 4PE
Tel: 01334 659480
Category: CLD PD (Coed 3-18)

DUNFERMLINE

Calaiswood School
Nightingale Place,
DUNFERMLINE, Fife KY11 8LW
Tel: 01383 602481
Category: CLD (Coed 3-18)

Woodmill High School ASN
Shields Road, DUNFERMLINE,
Fife KY11 4ER
Tel: 01383 602406
Category: SEBD

GLENROTHES

John Fergus School
Erskine Place, GLENROTHES,
Fife KY7 4JB
Tel: 01592 583489
Category: CD PD (Coed Day 3-18)

KIRKCALDY

Rosslyn School
Windmill Community
Campus, Windmill Road,
KIRKCALDY, Fife KY1 3AL
Tel: 01592 583482
Category: SLD PMLD PD (Coed 3-19)

LEVEN

Hyndhead School
Barncraig Street, Buckhaven,
LEVEN, Fife KY8 1JE
Tel: 01592 583480
Category: SLD ASD (Coed 5-18)

GLASGOW

City Council

Enquire, Children in Scotland, Rosebery House, 9 Haymarket Terrace Edinburgh, EH12 5EZ
Tel: 0345 123 2303 Email: info@enquire.org.uk Website: www.enquire.org.uk

GLASGOW

Abercorn Secondary School
195 Garscube Road,
GLASGOW G4 9QH
Tel: 01413 326212
Category: MLD

Ashton Secondary School
100 Avenue End Road,
GLASGOW G33 3SW
Tel: 01417 743428
Category: PH VIS CLD

Broomlea Primary School
Keppoch Campus, 65 Stonyhurst
Street, GLASGOW G22 5AX
Tel: 01413 368428
Category: CLD

Cardinal Winning Secondary School
30 Fullarton Avenue,
GLASGOW G32 8NJ
Tel: 01417 783714
Category: MLD

Cartvale Secondary School
3 Burndyke Court,
GLASGOW G51 2BG
Tel: 01414 451767
Category: SEBN

Croftcroighn Primary School
290 Mossvale Road,
GLASGOW G33 5NY
Tel: 01417 743760
Category: CLD

Drummore Primary School
129 Drummore Road,
GLASGOW G15 7NH
Tel: 01419 441323
Category: MLD

Eastmuir Primary School
211 Hallhill Road,
GLASGOW G33 4QL
Tel: 01417 713464
Category: MLD

Greenview Learning Centre
384 Drakemire Drive,
GLASGOW G45 9SR
Tel: 01416 341551
Category: SEBN

Hampden Primary School
18 Logan Gardens,
GLASGOW G5 0LJ
Tel: 01414 296095
Category: CLD

Hazelwood School
50 Dumbreck Court,
GLASGOW G41 5DQ
Tel: 01414 279334
Category: HI VIS CLD (2-19)

Howford Primary School
487 Crookston Road,
GLASGOW G53 7TX
Tel: 01418 822605
Category: CLD

John Paul II Primary School
29 Dunagoil Road,
GLASGOW G45 9UR
Tel: 01416 345219

Kelbourne Park Primary School
109 Hotspur Street,
GLASGOW G20 8LH
Tel: 01419 461405
Category: PH CLD

Kirkriggs Primary School
500 Croftfoot Road,
GLASGOW G45 0NJ
Tel: 01416 347158
Category: MLD

Langlands Primary School
Glenside Avenue,
GLASGOW G53 5FD
Tel: 01418 920952
Category: CLD

Lourdes Primary School
150 Berryknowes Road,
GLASGOW G52 2DE
Tel: 01418 822305

Middlefield School
80 Ardnahoe Avenue,
GLASGOW G42 0DL
Tel: 01416 431399
Category: ASD (Day)

Newhills Secondary School
42 Newhills Road,
GLASGOW G33 4HJ
Tel: 01417 731296
Category: CLD

Parkhill Secondary School
375 Cumbernauld Road,
GLASGOW G31 3LP
Tel: 01415 542765
Category: MLD

St Albert's Primary School
36 Maxwell Drive,
GLASGOW G41 5DU
Tel: 01414 291983

St Kevin's Primary School
25 Fountainwell Road,
GLASGOW G21 1TN
Tel: 01415 573722
Category: MLD

St Oswald's Secondary School
9 Birgidale Road,
GLASGOW G45 9NJ
Tel: 01416 373952
Category: MLD

Westmuir High School
255 Rigby Street,
GLASGOW G32 6DJ
Tel: 01415 566276
Category: SEBN

HIGHLAND

Council

Enquire, Children in Scotland, Rosebery House, 9 Haymarket Terrace Edinburgh, EH12 5EZ
Tel: 0345 123 2303 Email: info@enquire.org.uk Website: www.enquire.org.uk

INVERNESS

Drummond School
Drummond Road, INVERNESS,
Highland IV2 4NZ
Tel: 01463 701050
Category: SLD PMLD
CLD (Coed 3-16)

The Bridge
14 Seafield Road, INVERNESS,
Highland IV1 1SG
Tel: 01463 256600

ROSS-SHIRE

St Clement's School
Tulloch Street, Dingwall, ROSS-
SHIRE, Highland IV15 9JZ
Tel: 01349 863284
Category: SP&LD VIS
HI PD (Coed 5-11)

St Duthus School
Academy Street, Tain, ROSS-
SHIRE, Highland IV19 1ED
Tel: 01862 894407
Category: SLD PLD CLD (Coed 3-18)

INVERCLYDE

Council

Enquire, Children in Scotland, Rosebery House, 9 Haymarket Terrace Edinburgh, EH12 5EZ
Tel: 0345 123 2303 Email: info@enquire.org.uk Website: www.enquire.org.uk

GOUROCK

Garvel Deaf Centre
c/o Moorfoot Primary School,
GOUROCK, Inverclyde PA19 1ES
Tel: 01475 715642
Category: Deaf

PORT GLASGOW

Craigmarloch School
New Port Glasgow Community
Campus, Kilmacolm Road, PORT
GLASGOW, Inverclyde PA14 6PP
Tel: 01475 715345
Category: (Coed Day 6-18)

NORTH LANARKSHIRE

Council

Enquire, Children in Scotland, Rosebery House, 9 Haymarket Terrace Edinburgh, EH12 5EZ
Tel: 0345 123 2303 Email: info@enquire.org.uk Website: www.enquire.org.uk

AIRDRIE

**Mavisbank School
and Nursery**
Mitchell Street, AIRDRIE, North
Lanarkshire ML6 0EB
Tel: 01236 632108
Category: PMLD (Coed 3-18)

COATBRIDGE

Buchanan High School
67 Townhead Road, COATBRIDGE,
North Lanarkshire ML5 2HT
Tel: 01236 632052
Category: (Coed Day 12-18)

Drumpark School
Albert Street, COATBRIDGE,
North Lanarkshire ML5 3ET
Tel: 01236 794884
Category: MLD PH SP&LD (3-18)

Pentland School
Tay Street, COATBRIDGE,
North Lanarkshire ML5 2NA
Tel: 01236 794833
Category: SEBD (Coed 5-11)

Portland High School
31-33 Kildonan Street, COATBRIDGE,
North Lanarkshire ML5 3LG
Tel: 01236 632060
Category: SEBD (Coed 11-16)

Willowbank School
299 Bank Street, COATBRIDGE,
North Lanarkshire ML5 1EG
Tel: 01236 632078
Category: SEBD (Coed 11-18)

CUMBERNAULD

Glencryan School
Greenfaulds Road, CUMBERNAULD,
North Lanarkshire G67 2XJ
Tel: 01236 794866
Category: MLD PH ASD (Coed 5-18)

**Redburn School
and Nursery**
Kildrum Ring Road, CUMBERNAULD,
North Lanarkshire G67 2EL
Tel: 01236 736904
Category: SLD CLD PH (Coed 2-18)

MOTHERWELL

Bothwellpark High School
Annan Street, MOTHERWELL,
North Lanarkshire ML1 2DL
Tel: 01698 274939
Category: SLD (Coed 11-18)

**Clydeview School
and Nursery**
Magna Street, MOTHERWELL,
North Lanarkshire ML1 3QZ
Tel: 01698 264843
Category: SLD (Coed 5-11)

Firpark Primary School
177 Milton Street, MOTHERWELL,
North Lanarkshire ML1 1DL
Tel: 01698 274933
Category: (Coed Day 3-10)

Firpark Secondary School
Firpark Street, MOTHERWELL,
North Lanarkshire ML1 2PR
Tel: 01698 251313
Category: MLD PH (Coed 11-18)

UDDINGSTON

Fallside Secondary School
Sanderson Avenue,
Viewpark, UDDINGSTON,
North Lanarkshire G71 6JZ
Tel: 01698 274986
Category: EBD (Coed 11-16)

Maintained special schools and colleges

SOUTH LANARKSHIRE
Council

Enquire, Children in Scotland, Rosebery House, 9 Haymarket Terrace Edinburgh, EH12 5EZ
Tel: 0345 123 2303 Email: info@enquire.org.uk Website: www.enquire.org.uk

BLANTYRE

KEAR Campus School
Bardykes Road, BLANTYRE,
South Lanarkshire G72 9UJ
Tel: 01698 722120
Category: SEBD

CAMBUSLANG

Rutherglen High School
Langlea Road, CAMBUSLANG,
South Lanarkshire G72 8ES
Tel: 01416 433480

CARLUKE

Victoria Park School
Market Road, CARLUKE,
South Lanarkshire ML8 4BE
Tel: 01555 750591
Category: PMLD SLD

EAST KILBRIDE

Greenburn School
Calderwood Road, EAST KILBRIDE,
South Lanarkshire G74 3DP
Tel: 01355 237278
Category: PMLD

Sanderson High School
High Common Road, EAST
KILBRIDE, South Lanarkshire G74 2LP
Tel: 01355 588625

West Mains School
Logie Park, EAST KILBRIDE,
South Lanarkshire G74 4BU
Tel: 01355 249938
Category: SLD

HAMILTON

**Hamilton School
for the Deaf**
Anderson Street, HAMILTON,
South Lanarkshire ML3 0QL
Tel: 01698 823377
Category: Deaf

MIDLOTHIAN
Council

Enquire, Children in Scotland, Rosebery House, 9 Haymarket Terrace Edinburgh, EH12 5EZ
Tel: 0345 123 2303 Email: info@enquire.org.uk Website: www.enquire.org.uk

DALKEITH

Saltersgate School
3 Cousland Road, DALKEITH,
Midlothian EH22 2PS
Tel: 01316 544703
Category: GLD (Coed)

WEST LOTHIAN
Council

Enquire, Children in Scotland, Rosebery House, 9 Haymarket Terrace Edinburgh, EH12 5EZ
Tel: 0345 123 2303 Email: info@enquire.org.uk Website: www.enquire.org.uk

BLACKBURN

Connolly School Campus
Hopefield Road, BLACKBURN,
West Lothian EH47 7HZ
Tel: 01506 283888
Category: SEBN (Primary)

Pinewood Special School
Elm Grove, BLACKBURN,
West Lothian EH47 7QX
Tel: 01506 656374
Category: SCLD (Primary/
Secondary)

LIVINGSTON

Beatlie School Campus
The Mall, Craigshill, LIVINGSTON,
West Lothian EH54 5EJ
Tel: 01506 777598
Category: SCLD MSI PD
(Nursery – Secondary)

Cedarbank School
Cedarbank, Ladywell East,
LIVINGSTON, West Lothian EH54 6DR
Tel: 01506 442172
Category: ASD LD (Secondary)

Ogilvie School Campus
Ogilvie Way, Knightsridge,
LIVINGSTON, West Lothian EH54 8HL
Tel: 01506 441430
Category: SCLD (Primary)

PERTH & KINROSS
Council

Enquire, Children in Scotland, Rosebery House, 9 Haymarket Terrace Edinburgh, EH12 5EZ
Tel: 0345 123 2303 Email: info@enquire.org.uk Website: www.enquire.org.uk

PERTH

Fairview School
Oakbank Crescent, PERTH,
Perthshire & Kinross PH1 1DF
Tel: 01738 473050
Category: SLD CLD (Coed 2-18)

RENFREWSHIRE
Council

Enquire, Children in Scotland, Rosebery House, 9 Haymarket Terrace Edinburgh, EH12 5EZ
Tel: 0345 123 2303 Email: info@enquire.org.uk Website: www.enquire.org.uk

LINWOOD

Riverbrae School
2 Middleton Road, LINWOOD,
Renfrewshire PA3 3DP
Tel: 0300 300 1372

PAISLEY

Mary Russell School
Hawkhead Road, PAISLEY,
Renfrewshire PA2 7BE
Tel: 01418 897628
Category: MLD (Coed 5-18)

EAST RENFREWSHIRE
Council

Enquire, Children in Scotland, Rosebery House, 9 Haymarket Terrace Edinburgh, EH12 5EZ
Tel: 0345 123 2303 Email: info@enquire.org.uk Website: www.enquire.org.uk

NEWTON MEARNS

The Isobel Mair School
58 Stewarton Road, NEWTON
MEARNS, East Renfrewshire G77 6NB
Tel: 0141 577 7600
Category: CLD (Coed 5-18)

STIRLING
Council

Enquire, Children in Scotland, Rosebery House, 9 Haymarket Terrace Edinburgh, EH12 5EZ
Tel: 0345 123 2303 Email: info@enquire.org.uk Website: www.enquire.org.uk

STIRLING

Castleview School
Raploch Community Campus,
Drip Road, STIRLING FK8 1SD
Tel: 01786 272326
Category: PD PMLD

Ochil House
c/o Wallace High School, Airthrey
Road, STIRLING FK9 5HW
Tel: 01786 462166
Category: SCLD (Coed 11-18)

WALES

BLAENAU GWENT
County Borough Council

SNAP Cymru, Head Office, 10 Coopers Yard, Curran Road Cardiff, CF10 5NB
Tel: 0845 1203730 Email: gwent@snapcymru.org Website: www.snapcymru.org

EBBW VALE

Pen-y-Cwm Special School
Ebbw Fawr Learning Community,
Strand Annealing Lane, EBBW
VALE, Blaenau Gwent NP23 5QD
Tel: 01495 304031
Category: SLD PMLD

BRIDGEND
County Borough Council

SNAP Cymru, Head Office, 10 Coopers Yard, Curran Road Cardiff, CF10 5NB
Tel: 0808 801 0608 Email: enquiries@snapcymru.org Website: www.snapcymru.org

BRIDGEND

Heronsbridge School
Ewenny Road, BRIDGEND CF31 3HT
Tel: 01656 815725
Category: PMLD VIS AUT (Coed
Day & boarding 3-18)

Ysgol Bryn Castell
Abergarw Road, Brynmenyn,
BRIDGEND CF32 9NZ
Tel: 01656 815595
Category: EBD LD HI ASD MLD
SLD SP&LD (Coed 3-19)

CAERPHILLY
County Borough Council

SNAP Cymru, Head Office, 10 Coopers Yard, Curran Road Cardiff, CF10 5NB
Tel: 0808 801 0608 Email: enquiries@snapcymru.org Website: www.snapcymru.org

CAERPHILLY

**Trinity Fields
Special School**
Caerphilly Road, Ystrad Mynach,
CAERPHILLY CF82 7XW
Tel: 01443 866000
Category: SLD VIS HI CLD
SP&LD (Coed 3-19)

CARDIFF
Council

SNAP Cymru, Head Office, 10 Coopers Yard, Curran Road Cardiff, CF10 5NB
Tel: 0808 801 0608 Email: enquiries@snapcymru.org Website: www.cardiff.gov.uk

CARDIFF

Greenhill School
Heol Brynglas, Rhiwbina,
CARDIFF CF14 6UJ
Tel: 02920 693786
Category: SEBD (Coed 11-16)

Meadowbank School
Colwill Road, Gabalfa,
CARDIFF CF14 2QQ
Tel: 02920 616018
Category: SLCD (Coed 4-11)

Riverbank School
Vincent Road, Caerau,
CARDIFF CF5 5AQ
Tel: 02920 563860
Category: MLD SLD (Coed 4-11)

The Court School
Station Road, Llanishen,
CARDIFF CF14 5UX
Tel: 02920 752713
Category: SEBD (Coed 4-11)

The Hollies School
Brynheulog, Pentwyn,
CARDIFF CF23 7XG
Tel: 02920 734411
Category: ASD PMED (Coed 4-11)

Ty Gwyn School
Vincent Road, Caerau,
CARDIFF CF5 5AQ
Tel: 02920 838560
Category: PMLD ASD (Coed 4-19)

Woodlands High School
Vincent Road, Caerau,
CARDIFF CF5 5AQ
Tel: 02920 561279
Category: MLD SLD (Coed 11-19)

CARMARTHENSHIRE
County Council

SNAP Cymru, Head Office, 10 Coopers Yard, Curran Road Cardiff, CF10 5NB
Tel: 0808 801 0608 Email: enquiries@snapcymru.org Website: www.snapcymru.org

CARMARTHEN

Rhydygors School
Rhyd-y-gors, Johnstown,
CARMARTHEN,
Carmarthenshire SA31 3NQ
Tel: 01267 231171
Category: EBD

LLANELLI

Ysgol Heol Goffa
Heol Goffa, LLANELLI,
Carmarthenshire SA15 3LS
Tel: 01554 759465
Category: SLD PMLD

CONWY
County Borough Council

SNAP Cymru, Head Office, 10 Coopers Yard, Curran Road Cardiff, CF10 5NB
Tel: 0808 801 0608 Email: enquiries@snapcymru.org Website: www.snapcymru.org

LLANDUDNO

Ysgol Y Gogarth
Ffordd Nant y Gamar, Craig y Don,
LLANDUDNO, Conwy LL30 1YE
Tel: 01492 860077
Category: General SEN (2-19)

DENBIGHSHIRE

County Council

SNAP Cymru, Head Office, 10 Coopers Yard, Curran Road Cardiff, CF10 5NB
Tel: 0808 801 0608 Email: enquiries@snapcymru.org Website: www.snapcymru.org

DENBIGH

Ysgol Plas Brondyffryn
Park Street, DENBIGH,
Denbighshire LL16 3DR
Tel: 01745 813914
Category: AUT SLD (Coed 4-19)

RHYL

Ysgol Tir Morfa
Derwen Road, RHYL,
Denbighshire LL18 2RN
Tel: 01745 350388
Category: MLD SLD (Coed 4-19)

FLINTSHIRE

County Council

SNAP Cymru, Head Office, 10 Coopers Yard, Curran Road Cardiff, CF10 5NB
Tel: 0808 801 0608 Email: enquiries@snapcymru.org Website: www.snapcymru.org

FLINT

Ysgol Maes Hyfryd
Fifth Avenue, FLINT,
Flintshire CH6 5QL
Tel: 01352 792720
Category: (Coed 11-16)

Ysgol Pen Coch
Prince of Wales Avenue,
FLINT, Flintshire CH6 5NF
Tel: 01352 792730
Category: (Coed 5-11)

GWYNEDD

Council

SNAP Cymru, Head Office, 10 Coopers Yard, Curran Road Cardiff, CF10 5NB
Tel: 0808 801 0608 Email: enquiries@snapcymru.org Website: www.snapcymru.org

CAERNARFON

Ysgol Pendalar
Ffordd Bethel, CAERNARFON,
Gwynedd LL55 1DU
Tel: 01248 672141
Category: SLD (3-18)

PENRHYNDEUDRAETH

Ysgol Hafod Lon
Parc Busnes Eryri,
PENRHYNDEUDRAETH,
Gwynedd LL48 6LD
Tel: 01766 772140
Category: SLD (3-18)

MERTHYR TYDFIL
County Borough Council

SNAP Cymru, Head Office, 10 Coopers Yard, Curran Road Cardiff, CF10 5NB
Tel: 0808 801 0608 Email: enquiries@snapcymru.org Website: www.snapcymru.org

MERTHYR TYDFIL

Greenfield Special School
Duffryn Road, Pentrebach,
MERTHYR TYDFIL CF48 4BJ
Tel: 01443 690468
Category: SLD MLD PMLD ASD
EBD MSI SP&LD (Coed 3-19)

MONMOUTHSHIRE
County Council

SNAP Cymru, Head Office, 10 Coopers Yard, Curran Road Cardiff, CF10 5NB
Tel: 0808 801 0608 Email: enquiries@snapcymru.org Website: www.snapcymru.org

CHEPSTOW

Mounton House School
Pwyllmeyric, CHEPSTOW,
Monmouthshire NP16 6LA
Tel: 01291 635050
Category: BESD (Boys
Day/Boarding 11-16)

NEATH PORT TALBOT
County Borough Council

SNAP Cymru, Head Office, 10 Coopers Yard, Curran Road Cardiff, CF10 5NB
Tel: 0808 801 0608 Email: enquiries@snapcymru.org Website: www.snapcymru.org

NEATH

Ysgol Hendrefelin
Heol Hendre, Bryncoch,
NEATH SA10 7TY
Tel: 01639 642786
Category: GLD (Coed 3-16)

Ysgol Maes Y Coed
Heol Hendre, Bryncoch,
NEATH SA10 7TY
Tel: 01639 643648
Category: GLD (Coed 2-19)

NEWPORT
City Council

SNAP Cymru, Head Office, 10 Coopers Yard, Curran Road Cardiff, CF10 5NB
Tel: 0808 801 0608 Email: enquiries@snapcymru.org Website: www.snapcymru.org

NEWPORT

Maes Ebbw School
Maesglas Road, Maesglas,
NEWPORT, Newport NP20 3DG
Tel: 01633 815480
Category: SLD PMLD AUT PH

PEMBROKESHIRE
County Council

SNAP Cymru, Head Office, 10 Coopers Yard, Curran Road Cardiff, CF10 5NB
Tel: 0808 801 0608 Email: enquiries@snapcymru.org Website: www.snapcymru.org

HAVERFORDWEST

Portfield School
Off Portfield, HAVERFORDWEST,
Pembrokeshire SA61 1BS
Tel: 01437 762701
Category: SLD PMLD CLD
ASC (Coed 4-18+)

POWYS
County Council

SNAP Cymru, Head Office, 10 Coopers Yard, Curran Road Cardiff, CF10 5NB
Tel: 0808 801 0608 Email: enquiries@snapcymru.org Website: www.snapcymru.org

BRECON

Ysgol Penmaes
Canal Road, BRECON,
Powys LD3 7HL
Tel: 01874 623508
Category: SLD ASD PMLD
(Coed Day/Residential 3-19)

NEWTOWN

Brynllywarch Hall School
Kerry, NEWTOWN, Powys SY16 4PB
Tel: 01686 670276
Category: MLD EBD

Ysgol Cedewain
Maesyrhandir, NEWTOWN,
Powys SY16 1LH
Tel: 01686 627454
Category: SLD ASD PMLD
(Coed Day 3-19)

RHONDDA CYNON TAFF
County Borough Council

SNAP Cymru, Head Office, 10 Coopers Yard, Curran Road Cardiff, CF10 5NB
Tel: 0808 801 0608 Email: enquiries@snapcymru.org Website: www.snapcymru.org

ABERDARE

Maesgwyn Special School
Cwmdare Road, Cwmdare,
ABERDARE, Rhondda
Cynon Taf CF44 8RE
Tel: 01685 873933
Category: MLD (Coed 11-18)

Park Lane Special School
Park Lane, Trecynon, ABERDARE,
Rhondda Cynon Taf CF44 8HN
Tel: 01685 874489
Category: SLD (3-19)

PENTRE

Ysgol Hen Felin
Gelligaled Park, Ystrad, PENTRE,
Rhondda Cynon Taf CF41 7SZ
Tel: 01443 431571
Category: SLD (3-19)

PONTYPRIDD

Ysgol Ty Coch
Lansdale Drive, Tonteg,
PONTYPRIDD, Rhondda
Cynon Taf CF38 1PG
Tel: 01443 203471
Category: SLD (3-19)

**Ysgol Ty Coch
– Buarth y Capel**
Ynysybwl, PONTYPRIDD,
Rhondda Cynon Taf CF37 3PA
Tel: 01443 791424
Category: AUT ASD (14-19)

City and County of
SWANSEA
Council

SNAP Cymru, Head Office, 10 Coopers Yard, Curran Road Cardiff, CF10 5NB
Tel: 0808 801 0608 Email: enquiries@snapcymru.org Website: www.snapcymru.org

SWANSEA

Pen-y-Bryn Lower
Mynydd Garnllwyd Road,
Morriston, SWANSEA SA6 7QG
Tel: 01792 799064
Category: MLD SLD AUT

Ysgol Crug Glas
Croft Street, SWANSEA SA1 1QA
Tel: 01792 652388
Category: SLD PMLD

Ysgol Pen-y-Bryn
Glasbury Road, Morriston,
SWANSEA SA6 7PA
Tel: 01792 799064
Category: MLD SLD AUT

TORFAEN
County Borough Council

SNAP Cymru, Head Office, 10 Coopers Yard, Curran Road Cardiff, CF10 5NB
Tel: 0808 801 0608 Email: enquiries@snapcymru.org Website: www.snapcymru.org

CWMBRAN

Crownbridge School
Turnpike Road, Croesyceiliog,
CWMBRAN, Torfaen NP44 2BJ
Tel: 01633 624201
Category: SLD (2-19)

VALE OF GLAMORGAN
Council

SNAP Cymru, Head Office, 10 Coopers Yard, Curran Road Cardiff, CF10 5NB
Tel: 0808 801 0608 Email: enquiries@snapcymru.org Website: www.snapcymru.org

PENARTH

Ysgol Y Deri
Sully Road, PENARTH, Vale
of Glamorgan CF64 2TP
Tel: 02920 352280
Category: AUT PMLD MLD SLD
(Coed 5 Day/Residential 3-19)

WREXHAM
County Borough Council

SNAP Cymru, Head Office, 10 Coopers Yard, Curran Road Cardiff, CF10 5NB
Tel: 0808 801 0608 Email: enquiries@snapcymru.org Website: www.snapcymru.org

WREXHAM

St Christopher's School
Stockwell Grove,
WREXHAM LL13 7BW
Tel: 01978 346910
Category: MLD SLD
PMLD (Coed 6-19)

Maintained academies

ENGLAND

BATH & NORTH EAST SOMERSET

Bath

Aspire Academy
Frome Road, Odd Down,
BATH BA2 5RF
Tel: 01225 832212
Category: EBD (Coed 4-16)

Fosse Way School
Longfellow Road, Midsomer
Norton, BATH BA3 3AL
Tel: 01761 412198
Category: PH SLD SPLD ASD
MLD MSI CLD (Coed 3-19)

Three Ways School
Frome Road, Odd Down,
BATH BA2 5RF
Tel: 01225 838070
Category: PH SLD SPLD ASD
MLD MSI CLD (Coed 2-19)

BEDFORD

Grange Academy
Halsey Road, Kempston, BEDFORD,
Bedfordshire MK42 8AU
Tel: 01234 407100
Category: MLD ASD (Coed 5-18)

CENTRAL BEDFORDSHIRE

Dunstable

Weatherfield Academy
Brewers Hill Road, DUNSTABLE,
Bedfordshire LU6 1AF
Tel: 01582 605632
Category: MLD (7-19)

BLACKPOOL

Park Community Academy
158 Whitegate Drive, BLACKPOOL,
Lancashire FY3 9HF
Tel: 01253 764130
Category: MLD CLD
SEBD (Coed 4-16)

BRADFORD

Hazelbeck School
Wagon Lane, Bingley, BRADFORD,
West Yorkshire BD16 1EE
Tel: 01274 777107
Category: SLD PMLD
ASD (Secondary)

High Park School
Thorn lane, BRADFORD,
West Yorkshire BD9 6RY
Tel: 01274 614092
Category: ASD (Primary
& Secondary)

Southfield School
Haycliffe Lane, BRADFORD,
West Yorkshire BD5 9ET
Tel: 01274 779662
Category: SLD PMLD
ASD (Secondary)

KEIGHLEY

Beckfood Phoenix Primary Special School
Braithwaite Avenue, KEIGHLEY,
West Yorkshire BD22 6HZ
Tel: 01535 607038
Category: ASD, HI, PMLD,
SLD, SP&LD, VIS (Primary)

CAMBRIDGESHIRE

Huntingdon

Spring Common Academy
American Lane, HUNTINGDON,
Cambridgeshire PE29 1TQ
Tel: 01480 377403
Category: ASD EBD MLD
PMLD SLD (Coed 2-19)

CHESHIRE EAST

CREWE

Adelaide School
Adelaide Street, CREWE,
Cheshire CW1 3DT
Tel: 01270 685151
Category: AUT ADHD BESD
DYSL (Coed 9-18)

KNUTSFORD

Booths Mere Academy
Longridge, KNUTSFORD,
Cheshire WA16 8PA
Tel: 01625 383045
Category: BESD (Coed Day 11-16)

CORNWALL

TRURO

Pencalenick School
St Clement, TRURO, Cornwall TR1 1TE
Tel: 01872 520385
Category: SCLD (Coed 9-16)

CUMBRIA

Barrow In Furness

George Hastwell School
Moor Tarn Lane, Walney, BARROW
IN FURNESS, Cumbria LA14 3LW
Tel: 01229 475253
Category: ASC PMLD SLD (2-19)

CARLISLE

James Rennie School
California Road, Kingstown,
CARLISLE, Cumbria CA3 0BU
Tel: 01228 554280
Category: MSI PMLD
SLD (3-19 Coed)

DORSET

Weymouth

Wyvern Academy
Dorchester Road, WEYMOUTH,
Dorset DT3 5AL
Tel: 01305 817917
Category: ASD PMLD
SLD Complex (2-19)

DURHAM

Peterlee

Hopewood Academy (Ascent Trust)
Crawlaw Road, Easington Colliery,
PETERLEE, Durham SR8 3LP
Tel: 03339 991454
Category: ASD HI MLD
PMLD SLD (2-19)

HALTON

Runcorn

Cavendish High Academy
Lincoln Close, RUNCORN,
Cheshire WA7 4YX
Tel: 01928 561706
Category: SLD (11-19)

HAMPSHIRE

Basingstoke

Coppice Spring School
Pack Lane, BASINGSTOKE,
Hampshire RG22 5TH
Tel: 01256 336601
Category: BESD (Coed 11-16)

Dove House School
Sutton Road, BASINGSTOKE,
Hampshire RG21 5SU
Tel: 01256 351555
Category: MLD ASD (Coed 11-16)

HARTLEPOOL

Catcote Academy
Catcote Road,
HARTLEPOOL TS25 4EZ
Tel: 01429 264036
Category: MLD SLD PMLD
ASD BESD (Coed 11-25)

HEREFORDSHIRE

Hereford

Barrs Court School
Barrs Court Road,
HEREFORD HR1 1EQ
Tel: 01432 265035
Category: CLD PMLD MSI PD ADHD
ASD OCD SP&LD SLD (Coed 11-19)

The Brookfield School & Specialist College
Grandstand Road,
HEREFORD HR4 9NG
Tel: 01432 265153
Category: BESD MLD ASD
ADHD (Coed 7-16)

HERTFORDSHIRE

Hertford

Hailey Hall School
Hailey Lane, HERTFORD,
Hertfordshire SG13 7PB
Tel: 01992 465208
Category: EBD (Boys 11-16)

Letchworth Garden City

Woolgrove School Special Needs Academy
Pryor Way, LETCHWORTH GARDEN CITY, Hertfordshire SG6 2PT
Tel: 01462 622422
Category: MLD AUT
(Coed Day 5-11)

Stevenage

Larwood School
Webb Rise, STEVENAGE, Hertfordshire SG1 5QU
Tel: 01438 236333
Category: EBD (Coed Day & boarding 5-11)

Ware

Pinewood School
Hoe Lane, WARE, Hertfordshire SG12 9PB
Tel: 01920 412211
Category: MLD (Coed Residential 11-16)

Welwyn Garden City

Knightsfield School
Knightsfield, WELWYN GARDEN CITY, Hertfordshire AL8 7LW
Tel: 01707 376874
Category: HI (Coed Day & boarding 10-19)

KENT

Dartford

Milestone Academy
Ash Road, New Ash Green, DARTFORD, Kent DA3 8JZ
Tel: 01474 709420
Category: PMLD SLD AUT MLD PSCN (Coed 2-19)

LEICESTER CITY

Leicester

Ash Field Academy
Broad Avenue, LEICESTER LE5 4PY
Tel: 0116 273 7151
Category: PhysD (4-19)

LEICESTERSHIRE

Coalville

Forest Way School
Warren Hills Road, COALVILLE, Leicestershire LE67 4UU
Tel: 01530 831899
Category: SLD PMLD (3-19)

Hinckley

Dorothy Goodman School Hinckley
Stoke Road, HINCKLEY, Leicestershire LE10 0EA
Tel: 01455 634582
Category: PMLD SLD MLD ASD AUT (3-19)

LINCOLNSHIRE

Boston

John Fielding School
Ashlawn Drive, BOSTON, Lincolnshire PE21 9PX
Tel: 01205 363395
Category: SLD (2-19)

Gainsborough

Warren Wood Community School
Middlefield Lane, GAINSBOROUGH, Lincolnshire DN21 1PU
Tel: 01427 615498
Category: SLD

Gosberton

Gosberton House School
11 Westhorpe Road, GOSBERTON, Lincolnshire PE11 4EW
Tel: 01775 840250
Category: MLD (3-11)

Grantham

Ambergate Sports College
Dysart Road, GRANTHAM, Lincolnshire NG31 7LP
Tel: 01476 564957
Category: MLD (5-16)

Sandon School
Sandon Close, GRANTHAM, Lincolnshire NG31 9AX
Tel: 01476 564994
Category: SLD (2-19)

Horncastle

St Lawrence School
Bowl Alley Lane, HORNCASTLE, Lincolnshire LN9 5EJ
Tel: 01507 522563
Category: MLD (5-16)

Lincoln

Athena School
South Park Avenue, LINCOLN, Lincolnshire LN5 8EL
Tel: 01522 534559
Category: EBD, SEMH

Fortuna School
Kingsdown Road, Doddington Park, LINCOLN, Lincolnshire LN6 0FB
Tel: 01522 705561
Category: EBD (4-11)

St Francis School
Wickenby Crescent, Ermine Estate, LINCOLN, Lincolnshire LN1 3TJ
Tel: 01522 526498
Category: PD Sensory (2-19)

The Pilgrim School
Carrington Drive, LINCOLN, Lincolnshire LN6 0DE
Tel: 01522 682319
Category: HS (4-16)

Louth

St Bernard's School
Wood Lane, LOUTH, Lincolnshire LN11 8RS
Tel: 01507 603776
Category: SLD (2-19)

Spalding

The Garth School
Pinchbeck Road, SPALDING, Lincolnshire PE11 1QF
Tel: 01775 725566
Category: SLD (2-19)

The Priory School
Neville Avenue, SPALDING, Lincolnshire PE11 2EH
Tel: 01775 724080
Category: MLD (11-16)

Spilsby

The Eresby School
Eresby Avenue, SPILSBY, Lincolnshire PE23 5HU
Tel: 01790 752441
Category: SLD MLD ASD PMLD (2-19)

Woodlands Academy
Partney Road, SPILSBY, Lincolnshire PE23 5EJ
Tel: 01790 753902
Category: EBD

NORTH EAST LINCOLNSHIRE

Grimsby

Humberston Park Special School
St Thomas Close, GRIMSBY, N E Lincolnshire DN36 4HS
Tel: 01472 590645
Category: SLD PMLD PD CLD MSI (Coed 3-19)

The Cambridge Park Academy
Cambridge Road, GRIMSBY, N E Lincolnshire DN34 5EB
Tel: 01472 230110
Category: ASD SLCN MLD SLD (Coed 3-19)

LONDON – BROMLEY

Bromley Beacon Academy (Bromley Campus)
Old Homesdale Road, BROMLEY, Kent BR2 9LJ
Tel: 020 3319 0503
Category: SEMH (Coed 7-18)

Orpington

Bromley Beacon Academy (Orpington Campus)
Avalon Road, ORPINGTON, Kent BR6 9BD
Tel: 01689 821205
Category: SEMH (Coed 7-14)

LONDON – ROYAL BOROUGH OF GREENWICH

Charlton Park Academy
Charlton Park Road, LONDON SE7 8HX
Tel: 02082 496844
Category: SCLD SCD PMLD PD ASD (Coed 11-19)

LONDON – HILLINGDON

Hayes

The Willows School Academy Trust
Stipularis Drive, HAYES,
Middlesex UB4 9QB
Tel: 02088 417176
Category: SEBD ASD ADHD
Challenging behaviour (Coed 3-11)

Uxbridge

Moorcroft (Eden Academy)
Bramble Close, Hillingdon,
UXBRIDGE, Middlesex UB8 3BF
Tel: 01895 437799
Category: SLD PMLD
AUT (Coed 11-19)

West Drayton

Young People's Academy
Falling Lane, Yiewsley, WEST
DRAYTON, Middlesex UB7 8AB
Tel: 01895 446747
Category: BESD AUT
ADHD (Coed 11-16)

LONDON – SOUTHWARK

Peckham

Newlands Academy
Stuart Road, PECKHAM SE15 3AZ
Tel: 02076 392541
Category: SEBD (Boys 11-16)

LONDON – SUTTON

Carshalton

Wandle Valley School
Welbeck Road, CARSHALTON,
Surrey SM5 1LW
Tel: 02086 481365
Category: SEBD (Coed 5-16)

Wallington

Carew Academy
Church Road, WALLINGTON,
Surrey SM6 7NH
Tel: 02086 478349
Category: MLD BESD
ASD PD (Coed 7-18)

LONDON – WALTHAM FOREST

Walthamstow

Hornbeam Academy - William Morris Campus
Folly Lane, WALTHAMSTOW,
London E17 5NT
Tel: 02085 032225
Category: MLD SLD
PMLD (Coed 11-16)

Whitefield School
Macdonald Road, WALTHAMSTOW,
London E17 4AZ
Tel: 02085 313426
Category: LD MSI SP&LD
(Coed 3-19)

Woodford Green

Hornbeam Academy - Brookfield House Campus
Alders Avenue, WOODFORD
GREEN, Essex IG8 9PY
Tel: 02085 272464
Category: HI PD Complex
medical needs (Coed 2-16)

GREATER MANCHESTER – BOLTON

Horwich

Lever Park School
48 Stocks Park Drive,
HORWICH BL6 6DE
Tel: 01204 332666
Category: SEBD (Coed 11-16)

GREATER MANCHESTER – OLDHAM

Hollinwood Academy
Roman Road, Hollinwood,
OLDHAM, Greater
Manchester OL8 3PT
Tel: 0161 883 2404
Category: ASD SCD (4-19)

Spring Brook Academy - Lower School
Heron Street, OLDHAM, Greater
Manchester OL8 4JD
Tel: 0161 883 2431
Category: BESD (Coed 5-11)

Spring Brook Academy - Upper School
Dean Street, Failsworth, OLDHAM,
Greater Manchester M35 0DQ
Tel: 0161 883 3431
Category: BESD (11-16)

GREATER MANCHESTER – SALFORD

Eccles

New Park High Acadmey
Waterslea, Off Green Lane,
ECCLES M30 0RW
Tel: 01619 212000
Category: SEBD LD (Coed 8-16)

Oakwood Academy
Chatsworth Road, Ellesmere
Park, ECCLES M30 9DY
Tel: 01619 212880
Category: MLD HI VIS SEBD
Complex needs (Coed 10-19)

GREATER MANCHESTER – TRAFFORD

Altrincham

Pictor Academy
Grove Lane, Timperley,
ALTRINCHAM, Cheshire WA15 6PH
Tel: 01619 123082
Category: SLCN SPLD ASD
PD MLD (Coed 2-11)

Sale

Manor Academy
Manor Avenue, SALE,
Cheshire M33 5JX
Tel: 01619 761553
Category: ASD SEMH
MLD (Coed 11-18)

MEDWAY

Chatham

Bradfields Academy
Churchill Avenue, Wayfield,
CHATHAM, Kent ME5 0LB
Tel: 01634 683990
Category: MLD SLD
ASD (Coed 11-19)

MERSEYSIDE – KNOWSLEY

Halewood

Finch Woods Academy
Baileys Lane, HALEWOOD,
Merseyside L26 0TY
Tel: 01512 888930
Category: SEBD (Coed 11-16)

MILTON KEYNES

Stephenson Academy
Crosslands, Stantonbury,
MILTON KEYNES,
Buckinghamshire MK14 6AX
Tel: 01908 889400
Category: EBD (Boys Day/
boarding 12-16)

NORFOLK

King's lynn

Churchill Park Academy
Winston Churchill Drive, Fairstead,
KING'S LYNN, Norfolk PE30 4RP
Tel: 01553 763679
Category: Complex
Needs (Day 2-19)

Fen Rivers Academy
School House, Kilhams Way,
KING'S LYNN, Norfolk PE30 2HU
Tel: 01553 887330
Category: SEBD (4-16)

Norwich

Eaton Hall Specialist Academy
Pettus Road, Eaton, NORWICH,
Norfolk NR4 7BU
Tel: 01603 45/480
Category: SEBD (3-11)

NORTHAMPTONSHIRE

Corby

Maplefields School
Tower Hill Road, CORBY,
Northamptonshire NN18 0TH
Tel: 01536 424090
Category: BESD (3-19)

Kettering

Kingsley Special Academy
Churchill Way, KETTERING,
Northamptonshire NN15 5DP
Tel: 01536 316880
Category: PMLD SLD ASD (3-11)

Northampton

Billing Brook School
Penistone Road, NORTHAMPTON,
Northamptonshire NN3 8EZ
Tel: 01604 773910
Category: MLD ASD
SLD SPLD PH (3-19)

Purple Oaks Academy
Whiston Road, NORTHAMPTON,
Northamptonshire NN2 7RR
Tel: 01604 434471
Category: AUT SLD (3-19)

Wellingborough

Friars Academy
Friar's Close, WELLINGBOROUGH,
Northamptonshire NN8 2LA
Tel: 01933 304950
Category: MLD SLD ASD (11-19)

NOTTINGHAM

Nethergate Academy
Swansdowne Drive, Clifton,
NOTTINGHAM NG11 8HX
Tel: 01159 152959

Westbury Academy
Chingford Road, Bilborough,
NOTTINGHAM NG8 3BT
Tel: 01159 155858
Category: EBD (Coed Day 7-16)

Woodlands Academy
Beechdale Road, Aspley,
NOTTINGHAM NG8 3EZ
Tel: 01159 155734
Category: MLD (Coed Day 3-16)

NOTTINGHAMSHIRE

Broxtowe

Foxwood Academy
Derby Road, Bramcote
Hills, Beeston, BROXTOWE,
Nottingham NG9 3GF
Tel: 01159 177202
Category: (Coed 3-18)

Mansfield

Redgate School
Somersall Street, MANSFIELD,
Nottinghamshire NG19 6EL
Tel: 01623 455944
Category: MLD SLD
ASD (Coed 3-11)

The Beech Academy
Fairholme Drive, MANSFIELD,
Nottinghamshire NG19 6DX
Tel: 01623 626008
Category: (Coed 11-18)

OXFORDSHIRE

Abingdon

Kingfisher School
Radley Road, ABINGDON,
Oxfordshire OX14 3RR
Tel: 01235 555512
Category: SLD PMLD (Coed 2-19)

Oxford

Endeavour Academy
Waynflete Road, Headington,
OXFORD OX3 8DD
Tel: 01865 767766
Category: AUT SLD (Coed
Day/residential 9-19)

Iffley Academy
Iffley Turn, OXFORD OX4 4DU
Tel: 01865 747606
Category: MLD CLD
BESD (Coed 5-18)

Northern House School
South Parade, Summertown,
OXFORD OX2 7JN
Tel: 01865 557 004
Category: BESD (Coed 5-11)

Wantage

Fitzwaryn School
Denchworth Road, WANTAGE,
Oxfordshire OX12 9ET
Tel: 01235 764504
Category: MLD CLD
PMLD (Coed 3-19)

PETERBOROUGH

Medeshamstede Academy
Reeves Way, PETERBOROUGH,
Cambridgeshire PE1 5LQ
Tel: 01733 821403
Category: ASD ASP (Coed 4-18)

BOROUGH OF POOLE

Longspee Academy
Learoyd Road, Canford Heath,
POOLE, Dorset BH17 8PJ
Tel: 01202 380266
Category: BESD (5-14)

Montacute School
3 Canford Heath Road,
POOLE, Dorset BH17 9NG
Tel: 01202 693239
Category: PMLD SLD CLD
PH Medical needs (3-19)

PORTSMOUTH

Cliffdale Primary Academy
Battenburg Avenue, North End,
PORTSMOUTH, Hampshire PO2 0SN
Tel: 02392 662601
Category: CLD ASD (Coed 4-11)

READING

The Avenue School
Conwy Close, Tilehurst,
READING, Berkshire RG30 4BZ
Tel: 01189 375554
Category: AUT Complex
Needs (Coed 2-19)

REDCAR & CLEVELAND

Saltburn-by-sea

KTS Academy
Marshall Drive, Brotton, SALTBURN-
BY-SEA, Cleveland TS12 2UW
Tel: 01287 677265
Category: SLD PMLD SLCN ASC
PD CLDD (Coed day 2-19)

SHROPSHIRE

Oswestry

Kettlemere Centre, Lakelands Academy
Oswestry Road, Ellesmere,
OSWESTRY, Shropshire SY12 0EA
Tel: 01691 622543
Category: SCD

Shrewsbury

Severndale Specialist Academy
Monkmoor Campus, Woodcote
Way, Monkmoor, SHREWSBURY,
Shropshire SY2 5SH
Tel: 01743 563333
Category: PMLD SLD MLD
CLDD (Coed Day 2-19)

SOUTHEND-ON-SEA

Kingsdown School
Snakes Lane, SOUTHEND-
ON-SEA, Essex SS2 6XT
Tel: 01702 527486
Category: SLD PMLD PNI
PD (Coed Day 3-14)

St Nicholas School
Philpott Avenue, SOUTHEND-
ON-SEA, Essex SS2 4RL
Tel: 01702 462322
Category: MLD AUT SEMH
(Coed Day 11-16)

Westcliff-on-sea

Lancaster School
Prittlewell Chase, WESTCLIFF-
ON-SEA, Essex SS0 0RT
Tel: 01702 342543
Category: SLD PMLD PNI
PD (Coed Day 14-19)

STAFFORDSHIRE

Burton upon trent

The Fountains High School
Bitham Lane, Stretton, BURTON
UPON TRENT, Staffordshire DE13 0HB
Tel: 01283 247580
Category: Generic
(Coed Day 11-18)

The Fountains Primary School
Bitham Lane, Stretton, BURTON
UPON TRENT, Staffordshire DE13 0HB
Tel: 01283 247600
Category: Generic (Coed Day 2-11)

Leek

Springfield School
Springfield Road, LEEK,
Staffordshire ST13 6LQ
Tel: 01538 383558
Category: Generic (Coed Day 3-11)

**The Meadows
Special School**
Springfield Road, LEEK,
Staffordshire ST13 6EU
Tel: 01538 225050
Category: Generic
(Coed Day 11-19)

Lichfield

Rocklands School
Purcell Avenue, LICHFIELD,
Staffordshire WS13 7PH
Tel: 01543 548700
Category: ASD MLD PMLD
SLD (Coed Day 2-11)

Saxon Hill
Kings Hill Road, LICHFIELD,
Staffordshire WS14 9DE
Tel: 01543 414892
Category: Generic (Coed
Day/Boarding 2-19)

Newcastle Under Lyme

Blackfriars Academy
Priory Road, NEWCASTLE UNDER
LYME, Staffordshire ST5 2TF
Tel: 01782 987150
Category: Generic
(Coed Day 11-19)

Coppice Academy
Abbots Way, Westlands,
NEWCASTLE UNDER LYME,
Staffordshire ST5 2EY
Tel: 01782 973500
Category: Generic
(Coed Day 11-16)

Merryfields Special School
Hoon Avenue, NEWCASTLE UNDER
LYME, Staffordshire ST5 9NY
Tel: 01782 914219
Category: Generic (Coed Day 2-11)

Stafford

Walton Hall Academy
Stafford Road, Eccleshall,
STAFFORD, Staffordshire ST21 6JR
Tel: 01785 850420
Category: Generic (Coed
Day/Boarding 11-19)

Stoke On Trent

**Cicely Haughton
Community Special School**
Westwood Manor, Wetley
Rocks, STOKE ON TRENT,
Staffordshire ST9 0BX
Tel: 01782 550202
Category: SEBD (Coed
Boarding 4-11)

UTTOXETER

Loxley Hall School
Stafford Road, Loxley, UTTOXETER,
Staffordshire ST14 8RS
Tel: 01889 723050
Category: SEBD (Coed
Boarding 11-16)

STOCKTON-ON-TEES

Billingham

Ash Trees Academy
Bowes Road, BILLINGHAM,
Stockton-on-Tees TS23 2BU
Tel: 01642 563712
Category: SLD PMLD
AUT (Coed 4-11)

Stockton-On-Tees

**Abbey Hill Academy
& Sixth Form**
Ketton Road, Hardwick Green,
STOCKTON-ON-TEES TS19 8BU
Tel: 01642 677113
Category: SLD PMLD
AUT (Coed 11-19)

Green Gates Academy
Melton Road, Elmtree,
STOCKTON-ON-TEES TS19 0JD
Tel: 01642 570104
Category: BESD (Coed
Residential 5-11)

Thornaby-On-Tees

Westlands Academy
Eltham Crescent, THORNABY-
ON-TEES TS17 9RA
Tel: 01642 883030
Category: BESD (Coed
Residential 11-16)

SUFFOLK

Bury St Edmunds

Priory School
Mount Road, BURY ST
EDMUNDS, Suffolk IP32 7BH
Tel: 01284 761934
Category: MLD (Coed
Day & boarding 8-16)

Ipswich

Stone Lodge Academy
Stone Lodge Lane West,
IPSWICH, Suffolk IP2 9HW
Tel: 01473 601175
Category: MLD ASD
(Coed Day 5-11)

**Thomas Wolsey
Ormiston Academy**
Defoe Road, IPSWICH,
Suffolk IP1 6SG
Tel: 01473 467600
Category: PD/Comunication
(Coed Day 3-16)

Lowestoft

**The Ashley School
Academy Trust**
Ashley Downs, LOWESTOFT,
Suffolk NR32 4EU
Tel: 01502 565439
Category: MLD (Coed
Day & boarding 7-16)

SURREY

Camberley

**Carwarden House
Community School**
118 Upper Chobham Road,
CAMBERLEY, Surrey GU15 1EJ
Tel: 01276 709080
Category: LD (11-19)

Chobham

Wishmore Cross School
Alpha Road, CHOBHAM,
Surrey GU24 8NE
Tel: 01276 857555
Category: BESD (Boarding
& day 11-16)

Farnham

The Ridgeway School
Frensham Road, FARNHAM,
Surrey GU9 8HB
Tel: 01252 724562
Category: SLD (2-19)

Guildford

Pond Meadow School
Larch Avenue, GUILDFORD,
Surrey GU1 1DR
Tel: 01483 532239
Category: SLD (2-19)

Leatherhead

West Hill School
Kingston Road, LEATHERHEAD,
Surrey KT22 7PW
Tel: 01372 814714
Category: LD (11-16)

Reigate

**Chart Wood School
(Merstham Campus)**
Taynton Drive, Merstham,
REIGATE, Surrey RH1 3PU
Tel: 01737 215488
Category: BESD (Boys 9-16)

**Chart Wood School
(Reigate Campus)**
Alexander Road, REIGATE,
Surrey RH2 8EA
Category: BESD (Boys 9-16)

Worcester Park

Linden Bridge School
Grafton Road, WORCESTER
PARK, Surrey KT4 7JW
Tel: 02083 303009
Category: ASD (Residential
& day 4-19)

EAST SUSSEX

Bexhill-On-Sea

**Glyne Gap
Academy School**
Hastings Road, BEXHILL-ON-
SEA, East Sussex TN40 2PU
Tel: 01424 217720
Category: CLD/ASD (Coed 2-19)

Eastbourne

The Lindfield School
Lindfield Road, EASTBOURNE,
East Sussex BN22 0BQ
Tel: 01323 502988
Category: ACLD (Coed 11-16)

The South Downs Academy
(West Site), Beechy Avenue,
EASTBOURNE, East Sussex BN20 8NU
Tel: 01323 730302
Category: ACLD CLD (Coed 3-11)

Hastings

Torfield School
Croft Road, HASTINGS,
East Sussex TN34 3JT
Tel: 01424 428228
Category: ACLD (Coed 3-11)

Heathfield

St Mary's School
Maynards Green, Horam,
HEATHFIELD, East Sussex TN21 0BT
Tel: 01435 812278
Category: SEBD (Boys 9-16)

Seaford

Cuckmere House School
Eastbourne Road, SEAFORD,
East Sussex BN25 4BA
Tel: 01323 893319
Category: SEBD (Coed 6-16)

St Leonards-On-Sea

New Horizons School
Beauchamp Road, ST LEONARDS-
ON-SEA, East Sussex TN38 9JU
Tel: 01424 858020
Category: SEBD (Coed 7-16)

Saxon Mount School
Edinburgh Road, ST LEONARDS-
ON-SEA, East Sussex TN38 8HH
Tel: 01424 426303
Category: ACLD (Coed 11-16)

WEST SUSSEX

Chichester

Littlegreen Academy
Compton, CHICHESTER,
West Sussex PO18 9NW
Tel: 02392 631259
Category: SEBD (Boys 7-16)

THURROCK

Grays

**Beacon Hill Academy
(Post 16 Provision)**
Buxton Road, GRAYS,
Essex RM16 2WU
Tel: 01375 898656
Category: SCLD (Coed 16-19)

Treetops School
Buxton Road, GRAYS,
Essex RM16 2WU
Tel: 01375 372723
Category: MLD ASD (Coed 3-19)

South Ockendon

**Beacon Hill Academy
(Main Site)**
Erriff Drive, SOUTH OCKENDON,
Essex RM15 5AY
Tel: 01708 852006
Category: SCLD (Coed 2-16)

TORBAY

Paignton

The Brunel Academy
170b Torquay Road, Preston,
PAIGNTON, Devon TQ3 2AL
Tel: 01803 665522
Category: BESD (11-16)

Torquay

Combe Pafford School
Steps Lane, Watcombe,
TORQUAY, Devon TQ2 8NL
Tel: 01803 327902
Category: MLD PD ASC
Complex Needs (8-19)

The Burton Academy
South Parks Road, TORQUAY,
Devon TQ2 8JE
Tel: 01803 326330
Category: BESD (11-16)

TYNE & WEAR – GATESHEAD

Cedars Academy
Ivy Lane, Low Fell, GATESHEAD,
Tyne & Wear NE9 6QD
Tel: 01914 874595
Category: PD (Coed 2-16)

TYNE & WEAR – SUNDERLAND

**Barbara Priestman
Academy**
Meadowside, SUNDERLAND,
Tyne & Wear SR2 7QN
Tel: 03339 991453
Category: ASD CLD
(Coed Day 11-19)

North View Academy
St Lukes Road, South Hylton,
SUNDERLAND, Tyne & Wear SR4 0HB
Tel: 01917 070122
Category: SEMH ASD (4-11)

Portland Academy
Weymouth Road,
Chapelgarth, SUNDERLAND,
Tyne & Wear SR3 2NQ
Tel: 03339 991455
Category: SLD (Coed Day 11-19)

The New Bridge Academy
Craigshaw Road, Hylton Castle,
SUNDERLAND, Tyne & Wear SR5 3NF
Tel: 01919 171700
Category: SEBD (Coed Day 11-19)

WARWICKSHIRE

Coleshill

Woodlands School
Packington Lane, COLESHILL,
West Midlands B46 3JE
Tel: 01675 463590
Category: Generic SLD VIS HI AUT
MSI PD MLD PMLD (Coed Day 2-19)

Nuneaton

Discovery Academy
Vernons Lane, NUNEATON,
Warwickshire CV11 5SS
Tel: 07494 457314
Category: (Coed 9-19)

Oak Wood Primary School
Morris Drive, NUNEATON,
Warwickshire CV11 4QH
Tel: 02476 740907
Category: Generic SLD MLD VIS HI
AUT MSI PD PMLD (Coed Day 2-11)

**Oak Wood Secondary
School**
Morris Drive, NUNEATON,
Warwickshire CV11 4QH
Tel: 02476 740901
Category: Generic SLD MLD VIS HI
AUT MSI PD PMLD (Coed Day 11-19)

Quest Academy
St Davids Way, Bermuda Park,
NUNEATON, Warwickshire CV10 7SD
Tel: 01788 593112
Category: (Coed 9-19)

Rugby

Brooke School
Overslade Lane, RUGBY,
Warwickshire CV22 6DY
Tel: 01788 812324
Category: Generic SLD VIS HI AUT
MSI PD MLD PMLD (Coed Day 2-19)

Stratford-Upon-Avon

Welcombe Hills School
Blue Cap Road, STRATFORD-UPON-
AVON, Warwickshire CV37 6TQ
Tel: 01789 266845
Category: Generic SLD VIS HI AUT
MSI PD MLD PMLD (Coed Day 2-19)

WEST MIDLANDS – BIRMINGHAM

Erdington

Wilson Stuart School
Perry Common Road, ERDINGTON,
Birmingham B23 7AT
Tel: 01213 734475
Category: PD (Coed Day 2-19)

Kitts Green

Hallmoor School
Scholars Gate, KITTS GREEN,
Birmingham B33 0DL
Tel: 01217 833972
Category: MLD (Coed Day 4-19)

Ladywood

**Calthorpe Teaching
Academy**
Darwin Street, Highgate,
LADYWOOD, Birmingham B12 0TP
Tel: 01217 734637
Category: SLD (Coed Day 2-19)

James Brindley School
Bell Barn Road, Edgbaston,
LADYWOOD, Birmingham B15 2AF
Tel: 01216 666409
Category: Hospital School
(Coed Day 2-19)

Sutton Coldfield

The Bridge School
Coppice View Road, SUTTON
COLDFIELD, Birmingham B73 6UE
Tel: 01214 648265
Category: ASD PMLD
SLD (Coed 2-11)

Yardley

Brays School
Brays Road, Sheldon, YARDLEY,
Birmingham B26 1NS
Tel: 01217 435730
Category: ASD HI PD PMLD
SLD VI (Coed 2-11)

WEST MIDLANDS – COVENTRY

River Bank Academy
Princethorpe Way, COVENTRY,
West Midlands CV3 2QD
Tel: 02476 303776
Category: Broad Spectrum
(Coed Day 11-19)

**RNIB Three Spires
Academy**
Kingsbury Road, COVENTRY,
West Midlands CV6 1PJ
Tel: 02476 594952
Category: MLD (Coed Day 3-11)

WEST MIDLANDS – SOLIHULL

BIRMINGHAM

Northern House School
Lanchester Way, Castle Bromwich, BIRMINGHAM, West Midlands B36 9LF
Tel: 01217 489760
Category: SEMH (Coed Day 11-16)

WEST MIDLANDS – WALSALL

Phoenix Academy
Odell Road, Leamore, WALSALL, West Midlands WS3 2ED
Tel: 01922 712834
Category: EBD (Coed Day 4-11)

WEST MIDLANDS – WOLVERHAMPTON

Broadmeadow Special School
Lansdowne Road, WOLVERHAMPTON, West Midlands WV1 4AL
Tel: 01902 558330
Category: SLD ASD PMLD (Coed Day 2-6)

Cherry Trees School
Giggetty Lane, Wombourne, WOLVERHAMPTON, West Midlands WV5 0AX
Tel: 01902 894484
Category: Generic (Coed Day 3-11)

Northern House School
Cromer Gardens, Whitmore Reans, WOLVERHAMPTON, West Midlands WV6 0UB
Tel: 01902 551564
Category: BESD ADHD (Coed Day 8-16)

Westcroft School
Greenacres Avenue, Underhill, WOLVERHAMPTON, West Midlands WV10 8NZ
Tel: 01902 558350
Category: CLD (Coed Day 4-16)

Wightwick Hall School
Tinacre Hill, Wightwick, WOLVERHAMPTON, West Midlands WV6 8DA
Tel: 01902 761889
Category: Generic (Coed Day 11-19)

WILTSHIRE

Salisbury

Exeter House Special School
Somerset Road, SALISBURY, Wiltshire SP1 3BL
Tel: 01722 334168
Category: SLD PMLD SPLD Del (Coed Day 2-19)

NORTH YORKSHIRE

Scarborough

The Woodlands Academy
Woodlands Drive, SCARBOROUGH, North Yorkshire YO12 6QN
Tel: 01723 373260
Category: MLD (2-16)

SOUTH YORKSHIRE – DONCASTER

Pennine View School
Old Road, Conisbrough, DONCASTER, South Yorkshire DN12 3LR
Tel: 01709 864978
Category: MLD (Coed Day 7-16)

WEST YORKSHIRE – KIRKLEES

Huddersfield

Joseph Norton Academy
Busker Lane, Scissett, HUDDERSFIELD, West Yorkshire HD8 9JU
Tel: 01484 868218
Category: SEMH (Coed Day 7-16)

WEST YORKSHIRE – LEEDS

Springwell Leeds East
Brooklands View, Seacroft, LEEDS, West Yorkshire LS14 6XR
Tel: 0113 4870555
Category: SEMH

Springwell Leeds Primary
Oakwood Lane, LEEDS, West Yorkshire LS8 3LF
Tel: 0113 4870555
Category: SEMH

Springwell Leeds South
Middleton Road, LEEDS, West Yorkshire LS10 3JA
Tel: 0113 4870555
Category: SFMH

WEST YORKSHIRE – WAKEFIELD

Cheltenham

The Ridge Academy
Clyde Crescent, CHELTENHAM, Gloucestershire GL52 5QH
Tel: 01242 512680
Category: SEBD (Coed 5-11)

Dursley

Greenfield Academy
Drake Lane, DURSLEY, Gloucestershire GL11 5HD
Tel: 01453 542130
Category: SEBD (Coed Day 11-16)

The Peak Academy
Drake Lane, DURSLEY, Gloucestershire GL11 5HD
Tel: 01453 542130
Category: SEBD (Boys Day 11-16)

SCOTLAND

GLASGOW

Hollybrook Academy
135 Hollybrook Street, GLASGOW G42 7HU
Tel: 01414 235937
Category: MLD (Secondary)

John Paul Academy
2 Arrochar Street, GLASGOW G23 5LY
Tel: 01415 820140

Linburn Academy
77 Linburn Road, GLASGOW G52 4EX
Tel: 01418 832082
Category: CLD (Secondary)

Rosshall Academy
131 Crookston Road, GLASGOW G52 3PD
Tel: 01415 820200

INVERCLYDE

Greenock

Lomond View Academy
Ingleston Street, GREENOCK, Inverclyde PA15 4UQ
Tel: 01475 714414

Useful associations and websites

AbilityNet

Freephone & text phone helpline: 0800 269 545
Email: enquiries@abilitynet.org.uk
Website: www.itcanhelp.org.uk
Twitter: @AbilityNet
Facebook: @AbilityNet

Helps people of any age and with any disability to use technology to achieve their goals at home, at work and in education. Provides specialist advice services and free information resources.

Action for Sick Children

10 Ravenoak Road
Cheadle Hulme
Stockport SK8 7DL
Tel: 0161 486 6788
Helpline: 0800 0744 519
Email: enquiries@actionforsickchildren.org
Website: www.actionforsickchildren.org
Twitter: @Action4SickCh
Facebook: @ActionforSickChildren

A charity specially formed to ensure that sick children receive the highest standard of care possible.

Action on Hearing Loss

1-3 Highbury Station Road
London N1 1SE
Tel: 0808 808 0123 (freephone)
Textphone: 0808 808 9000 (freephone)
SMS: 0780 0000 360
Email: information@hearingloss.org.uk
Website: www.actiononhearingloss.org.uk
Twitter: @ActionOnHearing
Facebook: @actiononhearingloss

Action on Hearing Loss, formerly the Royal National Institute for Deaf People, is the largest national charity representing the 11 million confronting deafness and hearing loss in the UK.

Action on Hearing Loss Cymru

Ground Floor
Anchor Court (North)
Keen Road
Cardiff
CF24 5JW
Tel: 02920 333 034
Text: 02920 333 036
Fax: 02920 333 035
Email: wales@hearingloss.org.uk

See main entry above.

Action on Hearing Loss Northern Ireland

Harvester House
4-8 Adelaide Street
Belfast
BT2 8GA
Tel: 028 9023 9619
Fax: 028 9031 2032
Textphone: 028 9024 9462
Email: information.nireland@hearingloss.org.uk
Twitter: @hearinglossNI

See main entry above.

Action on Hearing Loss Scotland

Empire House
131 West Nile Street
Glasgow
G1 2RXJ
Tel: 0141 341 5330
Textphone: 0141 341 5347
Fax: 0141 354 0176
Email: scotland@hearingloss.org.uk

See main entry above.

Activity Alliance

Sport Park, Loughborough University
3 Oakwood Drive
Loughborough
Leicestershire LE11 3QF
Tel: 01509 227750
Fax: 0509 227777
Email: info@efds.co.uk
Website: www.activityalliance.org.uk
Twitter: @AllForActivity
Facebook: @ActivityAlliance

A charity that creates opportunities for disabled people to participate in sporting activities.

ADDISS – National Attention Deficit Disorder Information & Support Service

PO Box 340
Edgware
Middlesex HA8 9HL
Tel: 020 8952 2800
Fax: 020 8952 2909
Email: info@addiss.co.uk
Website: www.addiss.co.uk

ADDISS provides information and assistance for those affected by ADHD.

Advisory Centre for Education – (ACE)

72 Durnsford Road
London
N11 2EJ
Tel: 0300 0115 142
Email: enquiries@ace-ed.org.uk
Website: www.ace-ed.org.uk
Twitter: @ACEducationUK

ACE is an independent national advice centre for parents/carers of children aged 5 to 16. Advice booklets can be downloaded or ordered from the website. Training courses and seminars for LA officers, schools and governors are available. As well as a training package for community groups advising parents on education matters. Has Facebook page and you can follow them on Twitter.

AFASIC – Unlocking Speech and Language

209-211 City Road
London EC1V 1JN
Tel: 020 7490 9410
Fax: 020 7251 2834
Helpline: 0300 666 9410
Website: www.afasic.org.uk
Twitter: @Afasic
Facebook: @Afasic.Charity

Helps children and young people with speech and language impairments. Provides: training/conferences for parents and professionals; a range of publications; support through local groups; and expertise in developing good practice. Has a Facebook page.

Association of Sign Language Interpreters (ASLI)

Fourwinds House
Balderton
Chester
CH4 9LF
Tel: 01244 573644
Textphone: 18001 0871 474 0522
Fax: 08451 70 80 61
Email: office@asli.org.uk
Website: www.asli.org.uk
Twitter: @ASLIuk
Facebook: @ASLIuk

Has a useful online directory of sign language interpreters.

Asthma UK

18 Mansell St
London E1 8AA
Tel: 0300 222 5800
Email: info@asthma.org.uk
Website: www.asthma.org.uk
Twitter: @AsthmaUK
Facebook: @AsthmaUK

Charity dedicated to helping the 5.2 million people in the UK who are affected by asthma.

Ataxia (UK)

12 Broadbent Close
London N6 5JW
Tel: 020 7582 1444
Helpline: 0845 644 0606
Email: office@ataxia.org.uk
Website: www.ataxia.org.uk
Twitter: @AtaxiaUK
Facebook: @ataxiauk

Aims to support all people affected by ataxia. Has a Facebook page and you can follow them on Twitter.

BIBIC (British Institute for Brain Injured Children)

Old Kelways
Somerton Road
Langport
Somerset TA10 9SJ
Tel: 01458 253344
Fax: 01278 685573
Email: info@bibic.org.uk
Website: www.bibic.org.uk
Twitter: @bibic_charity

BIBIC helps children with a disability or learning difficulty caused by conditions such as cerebral palsy, Down's syndrome and other genetic disorders; acquired brain injury caused by trauma or illness; and developmental disorders such as autism, ADHD, Asperger syndrome and dyspraxia.

All children are assessed by a multi-professional team who put together a report and a therapy plan that is taught to the family by the child's key worker. This provides support for the family to learn about their child and how they can make a positive difference to their development. Sections of the plan are designed to be shared with the child's school and social groups to ensure a consistent approach in areas such as communication, behaviour and learning. Families return on a regular basis for reassessments and updated therapy programmes.

Brain and Spine Foundation

Fourth Floor
CAN Mezzanine
7-14 Great Dover Street
London SE1 4YR
Tel: 020 3096 7880
Helpline: 0808 808 1000
Fax: 020 7793 5939
Fax helpline: 020 7793 5939
Email: info@brainandspine.org.uk
Website: www.brainandspine.org.uk
Twitter: @brainspine
Facebook: @brainandspine

A charity founded in 1992 to help those people affected by brain and spine conditions.

British Blind Sport (BBS)

Pure Offices
Plato Close
Tachbrook Park
Leamington Spa
Warwickshire CV34 6WE
Tel: 01926 424247
Fax: 01926 427775
Email: info@britishblindsport.org.uk
Website: www.britishblindsport.org.uk
Twitter: @BritBlindSport
Facebook: @BritishBlindSport

BBS provide sport and recreation for blind and partially sighted people.

British Deaf Association England

356 Holloway Road
London N7 6PA
Tel: 020 7697 4140
Textphone: 07795 410724
Fax: 01772 561610
Email: bda@bda.org.uk
Website: www.bda.org.uk
Twitter: @BDA_Deaf
Facebook: @BritishDeafAssociation

The BDA is a democratic, membership-led national charity campaigning on behalf of deaf sign language users in the UK. It exists to advance and protect the interests of the deaf community, to increase deaf people's access to facilities and lifestyles that most hearing people take for granted and to ensure greater awareness of their rights and responsibilities as members of society. The association has several main service areas, with teams covering education and youth, information, health promotions, video production and community services, offering advice and help. There is a national helpline that provides information and advice on a range of subjects such as welfare rights, the Disability Discrimination Act (DDA) and education.

British Deaf Association Northern Ireland

Unit 5c, Weavers Court
Linfield Road
Belfast BT12 5GH
Tel: 02890 437480
Textphone: 02890 437486
Fax: 02890 437487
Email: northernireland@bda.org
Website: www.bda.org.uk

See main entry under British Deaf Association England.

British Deaf Association Scotland

1st Floor Central Chambers, Suite 58
93 Hope Street
Glasgow G2 6LD
Tel: 0141 248 5565
Fax: 0141 248 5554
Email: scotland@bda.org.uk
Website: www.bda.org.uk

See main entry under British Deaf Association England.

British Deaf Association Wales

163 Newport Road
Cardiff CF24 1AG
Email: bdm.waleseng@bda.org.uk
Website: www.bda.org.uk

See main entry under British Deaf Association England.

British Dyslexia Association

Unit 6a, Bracknell Beeches
Old Bracknell Lane
Bracknell RG12 7BW
Tel: 0333 405 4567 (Helpline) or
0333 405 4555 (Admin)
Fax: 0845 251 9005
Email: helpline@bdadyslexia.org.uk
Website: www.bdadyslexia.org.uk
Twitter: @BDAdyslexia
Facebook: @bdadyslexia

Helpline/information service open between 10am and 4pm (M-F) also open late on Wednesdays 5-7pm. Has a Facebook page.

British Institute of Learning Disabilities (BILD)

Birmingham Research Park
97 Vincent Drive
Edgbaston
Birmingham B15 2SQ
Tel: 0121 415 6960
Fax: 0121 415 6999
Email: enquiries@bild.org.uk
Website: www.bild.org.uk

BILD are committed to improving the quality of life of people with learning disabilities. They do this by advancing education, research and practice and by promoting better ways of working with children and adults with learning disabilities. BILD provides education, training, information, publications, journals, membership services, research and consultancy. Has a Facebook page and you can follow them on Twitter.

British Psychological Society

St Andrews House
48 Princess Road East
Leicester LE1 7DR
Tel: 0116 254 9568
Fax: 0116 227 1314
Email: enquiries@bps.org.uk
Website: www.bps.org.uk
Twitter: @BPSofficial
Facebook: @OfficialBPS

The representative body for psychology and psychologists in the UK. Has search facility for details on psychologists.

Butterfly AVM Charity

Unit C2 Crispin Industrial Centre,
Angel Road Works
Advent Way
London
N18 3AH
Tel: 07811 400633
Fax: 0208 8037600
Email: support@butterflyavmcharity.org.uk
Website: www.butterflyavmcharity.org.uk
Twitter: @Butterfly080666
Facebook: @ButterflyAvmCharity

Offers advice and support to anyone affected by an AVM

CALL Scotland

University of Edinburgh
Paterson's Land
Holyrood Road
Edinburgh
Midlothian EH8 8AQ
Tel: 0131 651 6236
Fax: 0131 651 6234
Email: call.scotland@ed.ac.uk
Website: www.callscotland.org.uk
Twitter: @CallScotland
Facebook: @CallScotland1983

CALL Scotland provides services and carries out research and development projects across Scotland for people, particularly children, with severe communication disabilities, their families and people who work with them in augmentative communication techniques and technology, and specialised computer use.

Cambian Group

Helpline: 0800 138 1418
Email: education@cambiangroup.com
Website: www.cambiangroup.com
Twitter:@Cambian_Group
Facebook: @cambiangroup

Cambian Group is one of the UK's leading providers of specialist services in education, care, mental health and learning disabilities. Works with 140 public authorities.

Capability Scotland (ASCS)

Osborne House
1 Osborne Terrace
Edinburgh EH12 5HG
Tel: 0131 337 9876
Textphone: 0131 346 2529
Fax: 0131 346 7864
Website: www.capability-scotland.org.uk
Twitter: @capability_scot
Facebook: @CapabilityScotland

ASCS is a national disability advice and information service, which provides free confidential advice and information on a range of disability issues including advice on cerebral palsy.

Carers UK

20 Great Dover Street
London SE1 4LX
Tel: 020 7378 4999
Fax: 020 7378 9781
Adviceline: 0808 808 7777 or Email: advice@
carersuk.org
Email: info@carersuk.org
Website: www.carersuk.org
Twitter: @CarersUK
Facebook: @carersuk

For carers run by carers.

Carers Northern Ireland

58 Howard Street
Belfast BT1 6PJ
Tel: 028 9043 9843
Email: info@carersni.org
Website: www.carersuk.org/northern-ireland
Twitter: @CarersNI
Facebook: @carersuk

See main entry under Carers UK.

Carers Scotland

The Cottage
21 Pearce Street
Glasgow G51 3UT
Tel: 0141 445 3070
Email: info@carersscotland.org
Website: www.carersuk.org/scotland
Twitter: @CarersScotland
Facebook: @carersuk

See main entry under Carers UK.

Carers Wales

Unit 5
Ynys Bridge Court
Cardiff
CF15 9SS
Tel: 029 2081 1370
Email: info@carerswales.org
Website: www.carersuk.org/wales
Twitter: @carerswales
Facebook: @carersuk

See main entry under Carers UK.

Centre for Studies on Inclusive Education (CSIE)

The Park
Daventry Road
Knowle
Bristol BS4 1DQ
Tel: 0117 353 3150
Fax: 0117 353 3151
Email: admin@csie.org.uk
Website: www.csie.org.uk
Twitter: @CSIE_UK
Facebook: @csie.uk

Promoting inclusion for all children in restructured mainstream schools.

Challenging Behaviour Foundation

c/o The Old Courthouse
New Road Avenue
Chatham
Kent ME4 6BF
Tel: 01634 838739
Family support line: 0300 666 0126
Email: info@thecbf.org.uk
Website: www.challengingbehaviour.org.uk
Twitter: @CBFdn
Facebook: @thecbf

Supports families, professionals and stakeholders who live/work with people with severe learning disabilities who have challenging behaviour.

Child Brain Injury Trust (CBIT)

Unit 1, The Great Barn
Baynards Green Farm
Bicester
Oxfordshire OX27 7SG
Tel: 01869 341075
Email: office@cbituk.org
Website: www.childbraininjurytrust.org.uk
Twitter: @CBITUK
Facebook: @childbraininjurytrust

Formerly known as the Children's Head Injury Trust (CHIT) this organisation was originally set up in 1991. It offers support to children and families affected by brain injuries that happen after birth. Registered charity nos. 1113326 & SCO39703. Has Facebook page and you can follow them on Twitter.

Communication Matters

3rd Floor, University House
University of Leeds
Leeds LS2 9JT
Tel/Fax: 0113 343 1533
Email: admin@communications.org.uk
Website: www.communicationmatters.org.uk
Twitter: @Comm_Matters
Facebook: @communicationmattersuk

Support for people who find communication difficult.

Contact a Family

209-211 City Road
London EC1V 1JN
Tel: 020 7608 8700
Helpline: 0808 808 3555 Textphone: 0808 808 3556
Fax: 020 7608 8701
Email: helpline@cafamily.org.uk
Website: www.contact.org.uk
Twitter: @ContactAFamily
Facebook: @contactafamily

A charity that provides support, advice and information to families with disabled children. Has a Facebook page and you can follow them on Twitter.

Coram Children's Legal Centre

Riverside Office Centre
Century House North, North Station Road
Colchester,
Essex CO1 1RE
Tel: 01206 714 650
Fax: 01206 714 660
Email: info@coramclc.org.uk
Website: www.childrenslegalcentre.com
Twitter: @CCLCUK
Facebook: @CCLCUK

The Children's Legal Centre is an independent national charity concerned with law and policy affecting children and young people. The centre runs a free and confidential legal advice and information service covering all aspects of law and the service is open to children, young people and anyone with concerns about them. The Education Legal Advocacy unit provides advice and representation to children and/or parents involved in education disputes with a school or a local education authority.

Council for Disabled Children

115 Mare Street
London E8 4RM
Tel: 020 7843 1900
Fax: 020 7843 6313
Email: cdc@ncb.org.uk
Website: www.councilfordisabledchildren.org.uk
Twitter: @CDC_tweets
Facebook: @councilfordisabledchildren

The council promotes collaborative work and partnership between voluntary and non-voluntary agencies, parents and children and provides a national forum for the discussion, development and dissemination of a wide range of policy and practice issues relating to service provision and support for children and young people with disabilities and special educational needs. Has a particular interest in inclusive education, special education needs, parent partnership services, play and leisure and transition.

Council for the Registration of Schools Teaching Dyslexic Pupils (CReSTeD)

C/o Helen Arkell Dyslexia Centre,
Arkell Lane,
Frensham,
Farnham,
Surrey,
GU10 3BL
Email: crested.admin@crested.org.uk
Website: www.crested.org.uk

CReSTeD's aim is to help parents and also those who advise them choose an educational establishment for children with Specific Learning Difficulties (SpLD). It maintains a register of schools and teaching centres which meets its criteria for the teaching of pupils with Specific Learning Difficulties.

All schools and centres included in the Register are visited regularly to ensure they continue to meet the criteria set by CReSTeD. CReSTeD acts as a source of names for educational establishments which parents can use as their first step towards making a placement decision which will be critical to their child's educational future.

CPotential

143 Coppetts Road
London
N10 1JP
Tel: 020 8444 7242
Fax: 020 8444 7241
Email: info@cplondon.org.uk
Website: www.cpotential.org.uk
Twitter: @C_Potential
Facebook: @CPotentialTrust

Provides education for young children with cerebral palsy using the system of Conductive Education.

Cystic Fibrosis Trust

One Aldgate
Second floor
London EC3N 1RE
Tel: 020 3795 1555
Helpline: 0300 373 1000 or 0203 795 2184
Fax: 020 8313 0472
Email: enquiries@cysticfibrosis.org.uk
Website: www.cysticfibrosis.org.uk
Twitter: @CFtrust
Facebook: @cftrust

The Cystic Fibrosis Trust is a national charity established in 1964. It offers information and support to people with cystic fibrosis, their families, their carers and anyone affected by cystic fibrosis. It funds research, offers some financial support to people with cystic fibrosis and campaigns for improved services. It provides a wide range of information including fact sheets, publications and expert concensus documents on treatment and care for people with cystic fibrosis.

Disabled Living Foundation

Unit 1, 34 Chatfield Road
Wandsworth
London SW11 3SE
Tel: 020 7289 6111
Helpline: 0300 999 0004
Email: info@dlf.org.uk
Website: www.dlf.org.uk
Twitter: @DLFUK
Facebook: @dlfuk

This foundation provides free, impartial advice about products for disabled people.

Down's Syndrome Education International

6 Underley Business Centre
Kirkby, Lonsdale
Cumbria LA6 2DY
Tel: 0300 330 0750
Fax: 0300 330 0754
Email: enquiries@downsed.org
Website: www.dseinternational.org
Twitter: @dseint
Facebook: @dseinternational

Down's Syndrome Education International works around the world to improve the development, education and social achievements of many thousands of people living with Down's syndrome. We undertake and support scientific research and disseminate quality information and advice widely through our websites, books, films and training courses.

Our education services support families and professionals to help people with Down's syndrome achieve sustained gains in all areas of their development.

For 30 years, we have disseminated the latest research findings in practical and accessible formats to the widest audiences, from birth to adulthood. Please visit our website for more information. We have a Facebook page and you can follow us on Twitter.

Down's Syndrome Association

Langdon Down Centre
2a Langdon Park
Teddington TW11 9PS
Tel: 0333 1212 300
Email: info@downs-syndrome.org.uk
Website: www.downs-syndrome.org.uk
Twitter: @DSAInfo
Facebook: @downssyndromeassociation

We provide information and support for people with Down's syndrome, their families and carers, and the professionals who work with them. We strive to improve knowledge of the condition. We champion the rights of people with Down's syndrome.

Down's Syndrome Association Northern Ireland

Unit 2, Marlborough House
348 Lisburn Road
Belfast BT9 6GH
Tel: 028 90666 5260
Fax: 028 9066 7674
Email: enquiriesni@downs-syndrome.org.uk

See main entry above.

Down's Syndrome Association Wales

Suite 1, 206 Whitchurch Road
Heath
Cardiff CF14 3NB
Tel: 0333 1212 300
Email: wales@downs-syndrome.org.uk

See main entry above.

.

Dyslexia Scotland

2nd floor – East Suite
Wallace House
17-21 Maxwell Place
Stirling FK8 1JU
Tel: 01786 446 650
Helpline: 0344 800 8484
Fax: 01786 471235
Email: info@dyslexiascotland.org.uk
Website: www.dyslexiascotland.org.uk
Twitter: @DyslexiaScotlan

Scottish association set up to support and campaign on behalf of people affected by dyslexia. They have a useful and easy to use website.

Dyspraxia Foundation

8 West Alley
Hitchin
Hertfordshire SG5 1EG
Tel: 01462 455016
Helpline: 01462 454 986
Fax: 01462 455052
Email: info@dyspraxiafoundation.org.uk
Website: www.dyspraxiafoundation.org.uk
Twitter: @DYSPRAXIAFDTN
Facebook: @dyspraxiafoundation

The foundation exists to support individuals and families affected by dyspraxia; to promote better diagnostic and treatment facilities for those who have dyspraxia; to help professionals in health and education to assist those with dyspraxia; and to promote awareness and understanding of dyspraxia. As well as various publications, the Dyspraxia Foundation organises conferences and talks and supports a network of local groups across the United Kingdom.

Education Scotland

Denholm House
Almondvale Business Park
Almondvale Way
Livingston EH54 6GA
Tel: 0131 244 4330
Textphone: 18001+ 0131 244 4330
Email: enquiries@educationscotland.gov.scot
Website: education.gov.scot
Twitter: @EducationScot
Facebook: @EducationScot

Education Scotland is an executive non-departmental public body sponsored by the Scottish government. It is the main organisation for the development and support of the Scottish curriculum and is at the heart of all major developments in Scottish education, moving education forward with its partners.

ENABLE Scotland

Inspire House
3 Renshaw Place
Eurocentral
Lanarkshire ML1 4UF
Tel: 01698 737 000
Fax: 0844 854 9748
Helpline: 0300 0200 101
Email: enabledirect@enable.org.uk
Website: www.enable.org.uk
Twitter: @ENABLEScotland
Facebook: @enablescotland

Contact the ENABLE Scotland Information Service about any aspect of learning disability. They offer jobs, training, respite breaks, day services, supported living, housing and support for people with learning disabilities in different parts of Scotland. Its legal service can assist families with wills and trusts.

Epilepsy Action

New Anstey House
Gate Way Drive,
Yeadon
Leeds LS19 7XY
Tel: 0113 210 880
Helpline: 0808 800 5050
Fax: 0113 391 0300
Email: epilepsy@epilepsy.org.uk
Website: www.epilepsy.org.uk
Twitter: @epilepsyaction
Facebook: @epilepsyaction

Epilepsy Action is the UK's leading epilepsy organisation and exists to improve the lives of everyone affected by the condition. As a member-led association, it is led by and represent people with epilepsy, their friends, families and healthcare professionals.

Epilepsy Society

Chesham Lane
Chalfont St Peter
Gerrards Cross,
Buckinghamshire SL9 0RJ
Tel: 01494 601300
Helpline: 01494 601400
Fax: 01494 871927
Website: www.epilepsysociety.org.uk
Twitter: @epilepsysociety
Facebook: @EpilepsySociety

The Epilepsy Society provides information and support to those affected by epilepsy.

GIFT

7 Tower Road
Writtle
Chelmsford
Essex CM1 3NR
Tel: 01245 830321
Email: enquiries@giftcourses.co.uk
Website: www.giftcourses.co.uk
Twitter: @giftcourses
Facebook: @giftcourses

GIFT aims to offer a value-for-money education consultancy of quality, which meets the needs of gifted and talented children and those working to support them in the excitement and challenge of achieving their full potential as human beings. Residential and non-residential courses are organised for exceptionally able children aged five to 18 throughout the year (see our website). INSET courses for schools on provision, identification and school policy are provided with a special emphasis on workshops for practical activities.

Haringey Association for Independent Living (HAIL)

Tottenham Town Hall
Town Hall Approach Road
Tottenham
London N15 4RY
Tel: 020 8275 6550
Fax: 020 8275 6559
Email: admin@hailltd.org
Website: www.hailltd.org
Twitter: @HAIL_tweets
Facebook: @HAIL6650

Haringey Association for Independent Living is a support service for adults with learning difficulties moving towards independent living. You can follow them on Twitter.

Headway

Bradbury House
190 Bagnall Road
Old Basford
Nottingham NG6 8SF
Tel: 0115 924 0800
Helpline: 0808 800 2244
Fax: 0115 958 4446
Email: enquiries@headway.org.uk
Website: www.headway.org.uk
Twitter: @HeadwayUK
Facebook: @headwayuk

A charity that supports people with brain injuries and their carers.

Helen Arkell Dyslexia Centre

Arkell Lane
Frensham
Farnham
Surrey GU10 3BL
Tel: 01252 792400
Email: enquiries@helenarkell.org.uk
Website: www.helenarkell.org.uk
Twitter: @ArkellDyslexia

A registered charity providing comprehensive help and care for children with specific learning difficulties, including assessment, specialist tuition, speech and language therapy, summer schools and short courses. Initial consultations can be arranged in order to give advice on options for support. Professional teacher-training programmes and schools' support. Financial help available in cases of need.

Huntington's Disease Association

Suite 24
Liverpool Science Park IC1
131 Mount Pleasant
Liverpool L3 5TF
Tel: 0151 331 5444
Fax: 0151 331 5441
Email: info@hda.org.uk
Website: www.hda.org.uk
Twitter: @HDA_tweeting
Facebook: @hdauk

Registered charity offering support to people affected by Huntington's Disease (HD); which is sometimes referred to as Huntington's Chorea. Has a Facebook page.

Independent Panel for Special Education Advice (IPSEA)

24 Gold Street
Saffron Walden CB10 1EJ
Tel: 01799 582030
Adviceline: 0800 018 4016
Email: info@ipsea.org.uk
Website: www.ipsea.org.uk
Twitter: @IPSEAcharity

IPSEA offers free and independent advice and support to parents of children with special educational needs including: free advice on LAs' legal duties towards children with free accompanied visits where necessary, free support and possible representation for those parents appealing to the Special Educational Needs Tribunal, free second opinions on a child's needs and the provision required to meet those needs.

Institute for Neuro-Physiological Psychology (INPP)

1 Stanley Street
Chester
Cheshire CH1 2LR
Tel: 01244 311414
Fax: 01244 311414
Email: mail@inpp.org.uk
Website: www.inpp.org.uk
Twitter: @INPPLtd
Facebook: @INPPLtd

Established in 1975 to research into the effect central nervous system (CNS) dysfunctions have on children with learning difficulties, to develop appropriate CNS remedial and rehabilitation programmes, and to correct underlying physical dysfunctions in dyslexia, dyspraxia and attention deficit disorder (ADD).

Ivemark Syndrome Association

18 French Road
Poole
Dorset BH17 7HB
Tel: 01202 699824
Email: marcus.fisher@virgin.net

Support group for families with children affected by Ivemark Syndrome (also know as right atrial isomerism).

Jeans for Genes

199 Victoria Street
London SW1E 5NE
Tel: 0800 980 4800
Email: hello@jeanforgenes.com
Website: www.jeansforgenesday.com
Twitter: @JeansforGenes
Facebook: @JeansforGenesUK

The first Friday of every October is Jeans for Genes Day. Their aim is to raise money to fund research into genetic disorders and their target figure is £3million each year.

KIDS

7-9 Elliott's Place
London, N1 8HX
Tel: 020 7359 3635
Website: www.kids.org.uk
Twitter: @KIDScharity
Facebook: @KIDScharity

KIDS was established in 1970 to help disabled children in their development and communication skills. Has a Facebook page and you can follow them on Twitter.

Leonard Cheshire Disability England

66 South Lambeth Road
London SW8 1RL
Tel: 020 3242 0200
Fax: 020 3242 0250
Email: info@leonardcheshire.org
Website: www.leonardcheshire.org
Twitter: @LeonardCheshire
Facebook: @LeonardCheshireDisability

Leonard Cheshire – the UK's largest voluntary-sector provider of support services for disabled people. They also support disabled people in 52 countries around the world.

Leonard Cheshire Disability Northern Ireland

10-12 Derryvolgie Avenue
Belfast BT9 6FL
Tel: 028 9024 6247
Fax: 028 9024 6395
Email: northernirelandoffice@leonardcheshire.org

See main entry – Leonard Cheshire Disability England.

Leonard Cheshire Disability Scotland

Murrayburgh House
17 Corstorphine Road
Edinburgh EH12 6DD
Tel: 0131 346 9040
Fax: 0131 346 9050
Email: scotlandoffice@leonardcheshire.org

See main entry – Leonard Cheshire Disability England.

Leonard Cheshire Disability Wales

Llanhennock Lodge
Llanhennock
Nr Caerleon
NP18 1LT
Tel: 01633 422583
Email: walesoffice@leonardcheshire.org

See main entry – Leonard Cheshire Disability England.

Leukaemia Care UK

1 Birch Court
Blackpole East
Worcester WR3 8SG
Tel: 01905 755977 Careline: 08088 010 444
Fax: 01905 755 166
Email: care@leukaemiacare.org.uk
Website: www.leukaemiacare.org.uk
Twitter: @LeukaemiaCareUK
Facebook: @LeukaemiaCARE

Registered charity that exists to provide care and support to anyone affected by leukaemia.

Leukaemia Care Scotland

Regus Management
Maxim 1, Maxim Office Park
2 Parklands Way, Eurocentral
Motherwell ML1 4WR
Tel: 01698 209073
Email: scotland@leukaemiacare.org.uk

See main entry on Leukaemia Care UK.

Listening Books

12 Lant Street
London SE1 1QH
Tel: 020 7407 9417
Fax: 020 7403 1377
Email: info@listening-books.org.uk
Website: www.listening-books.org.uk
Twitter: @ListeningBooks
Facebook: @ListeningBooks12

A charity that provides a postal and internet based audio library service to anyone who is unable to read in the usual way due to an illness, disability or learning difficulty such as dyslexia.

Has a range of educational audio material to support all aspects of the National Curriculum, as well as thousands of general fiction and non-fiction titles for all ages. There is no limit to the number of titles you may borrow during the year.

Manx Dyslexia Association

Coan Aalin
Greeba Bridge
Greba
Isle of Man IM4 3LD
Tel: 07624 315724
Email: manxdyslexia@gmail.com
Website: www.manxdyslexia.com

Charity (no. IM706) founded in 1993 to help raise the awareness of dyslexia on the Isle of Man.

MENCAP England

123 Golden Lane
London EC1Y 0RT
Tel: 020 7454 0454
Helpline: 0808 808 1111
Fax: 020 7608 3254
Email: information@mencap.org.uk
Website: www.mencap.org.uk
Twitter: @mencap_charity
Facebook: @Mencap

The Royal MENCAP Society is a registered charity that offers services to adults and children with learning disabilities. We offer help and advice in benefits, housing and employment via our helpline.

Helplines are open from Monday to Friday 9.30am-4.30pm; Wednesday – subject to change: (open am-closed pm). Language line is also used. Our office is open Monday Friday 9-5pm.

We also offer help and advice to anyone who has any other issues or we can signpost them in the right direction. We can also provide information and support for leisure, recreational services (Gateway Clubs) residential services and holidays.

MENCAP Northern Ireland

5 School Road
Newtownbreda
Belfast BT8 6BT
Tel: 028 9069 1351
Email: helpline.ni@mencap.org.uk
Twitter: @Mencap_NI

See main entry – MENCAP England.

MENCAP Cymru

31 Lambourne Crescent
Cardiff Business Park
Llanishen, Cardiff CF14 5GF
Helpline: 0808 8000 300
Email: helpline.wales@mencap.org.uk
Twitter: @MencapCymru

See main entry – MENCAP England.

MENSA

British Mensa Ltd
St John's House
St John's Square
Wolverhampton WV2 4AH
Tel: 01902 772771
Fax: 01902 392500
Email: enquiries@mensa.org.uk
Website: www.mensa.org.uk
Twitter: @BritishMensa
Facebook: @BritishMensa

MENSA aims to bring about awareness that giftedness in a child is frequently a specific learning difficulty and should be recognised and treated as such, train teachers to recognise giftedness in a child, train teachers to teach gifted children, establish mutually beneficial relationships with other organisations having similar aims to our own and to devise and implement strategies aimed, at ministerial and senior civil servant levels, at bringing about recognition of the importance of catering for the needs of gifted children.

Mind, the National Association for Mental Health

15-19 Broadway
Stratford
London E15 4BQ
Tel: 020 8519 2122
Fax: 020 8522 1725
Email: supporterrelations@mind.org.uk
Website: www.mind.org.uk
Twitter: @MindCharity
Facebook: @mindforbettermentalhealth

Mind (the National Association for Mental Health) is the leading mental health charity in England and Wales. Mind works for a better life for everyone with experience of mental or emotional stress. It does this by: advancing the views, needs and ambitions of people experiencing mental distress; promoting inclusion and challenging discrimination; influencing policy through effective campaigning and education; providing quality services that meet the expressed needs of people experiencing mental distress and which reflect the requirements of a diverse community; achieving equal legal and civil rights through campaigning and education.

With over 60 years of experience, Mind is a major national network consisting of over 200 local Mind associations, which cover most major towns and rural areas in England and Wales. These are separately registered charities operating under the Mind brand. The Mind network is the largest charitable provider of mental health services in the community. The work of the local associations is strengthened and supported by staff and activities through its many offices in England and Wales. This ensures that, as a national charity, Mind keeps a distinct local perspective to their work.

Mind believes in the individual and equipping them to make informed choices about options open to them. Mind's mental health telephone information service (Mindinfoline) deals with thousands of calls each year. We offer a vital lifeline to people in distress, their relatives and carers, as well as providing mental health information to members of the public, professionals and students.

Mind Cymru

3rd Floor, Quebec House
Castlebridge
5-19 Cowbridge Road East
Cardiff CF11 9AB
Tel: 029 2039 5123
Fax: 029 2034 6585
Email: supporterrelations@mind.org.uk

See main entry above.

Motability

City Gate House
22 Southwark Bridge Road
London SE1 9HB
Tel: 0300 4564566
Minicom/textphone: 0300 037 0100
Fax: 01279 632000
Website: www.motability.co.uk
Facebook: @motability

Motability helps disabled people to use their mobility allowance to obtain new transport.

MS Society

MS National Centre
372 Edgware Road
London NW2 6ND
Tel: 020 8438 0700
Fax: 020 8438 0701
Website: www.mssociety.org.uk
Twitter: @MSSocietyUK
Facebook: @MSSociety

Multiple Sclerosis Society.

MS Society Cymru

Temple Court
Cathedral Road
Cardiff CF11 9HA
Tel: 029 2078 6676
See main entry above.

MS Society Northern Ireland

The Resource Centre
34 Annadale Avenue
Belfast BT7 3JJ
Tel: 02890 802 802

See main entry above.

MS Society Scotland

National Office, Ratho Park
88 Glasgow Road
Ratho Station
Newbridge EH28 8PP
Tel: 0131 335 4050
Fax: 0131 335 4051

See main entry on MS Society.

Muscular Dystrophy Campaign

61A Great Suffolk Street
London SE1 0BU
Tel: 020 7803 4800
Helpline: 0800 652 6352
Email: info@musculardystrophyuk.org
Website: www.musculardystrophyuk.org
Twitter: @MDUK_News
Facebook: @musculardystrophyuk

Provides information and advice for families affected by muscular dystrophy and other neuromuscular conditions.

NAS – The National Autistic Society – England

393 City Road
London EC1V 1NG
Tel: 020 7833 2299
Helpline: 0800 800 4104
Fax: 020 7833 9666
Email: nas@nas.org.uk
Website: www.autism.org.uk
Twitter: @Autism
Facebook: @NationalAutisticSociety

The National Autistic Society is the UK's leading charity for people who are affected by autism. For more than 50 years we have worked to support children and young people with autism (including Asperger syndrome) to reach their goals. A well-rounded education, tailored to the needs of the individual, can help people to reach their full potential.

NAS Cymru

6/7 Village Way,
Greenmeadow Springs Business Park
Tongwynlais
Cardiff CF15 7NE
Tel: 02920 629 312
Fax: 02920 629 317
Email: wales@nas.org.uk

See main entry NAS – England.

NAS Northern Ireland

59 Malone Road
Belfast BT9 6SA
Tel: 02890 687 066
Fax: 02890 688 518
Email: northern.ireland@nas.org.uk

See main entry NAS – England.

NAS Scotland

Central Chambers
1st Floor
109 Hope Street
Glasgow G2 6LL
Tel: 0141 221 8090
Fax: 0141 221 8118
Email: scotland@nas.org.uk

See main entry NAS – England.

Nasen

4/5 Amber Business Village
Amber Close
Amington
Tamworth
Staffordshire B77 4RP
Tel: 01827 311500
Fax: 01827 313005
Email: welcome@nasen.org.uk
Website: www.nasen.org.uk
Twitter: @nasen_org
Facebook: @nasen.org

nasen promotes the interests of children and young people with exceptional learning needs and influences the quality of provision through strong and cohesive policies and strategies for parents and professionals.

Membership offers a number of journals, professional development and publications at a reduced cost, and provides a forum for members to share concerns and disseminate expertise and knowledge.

National Association for Able Children in Education (NACE)

NACE National Office
Horticulture House
Manor Court
Chilton
Didcot
Oxfordshire OX11 0RN
Tel: 01235 425000
Email: info@nace.co.uk
Website: www.nace.co.uk
Twitter: @naceuk

NACE works with teachers to support able children in schools. The organisation also provides, publications, journals, booklets, courses and conferences.

National Association of Independent Schools and Non-Maintained Special Schools (NASS)

PO Box 705
York YO30 6WW
Tel: 01904 624446
Email: krippon@nasschools.org.uk
Website: www.nasschools.org.uk
Twitter: @NASSCHOOLS

NASS is a voluntary organisation that represents the interests of those special schools outside the maintained sector of the education system.

Our commitment is to achieve excellence and to attain the highest professional standards in working with unique children and young people who have physical, sensory and intellectual difficulties. We exist to promote, develop and maintain the highest professional standards for non-maintained and independent special schools. We offer free information and advice on our member schools to families and professionals.

National Federation of the Blind of the UK

St John Wilson House
215 Kirkgate
Wakefield
Yorkshire WF1 1JG
Tel: 01924 291313
Fax: 01924 200244
Email: admin@nfbuk.org
Website: www.nfbuk.org
Twitter: @NFBUK

A charity that was set up to better the understanding between blind and sighted people.

Natspec

Robins Wood House
Robins Wood Road
Aspley
Nottingham NG8 3NH
Tel: 0115 854 1322
Email: info@natspec.org.uk
Website: www.natspec.org.uk
Twitter: @Natspec

Natspec represents independent specialist colleges across England, Wales and Northern Ireland, providing for over 3000 learners with learning difficulties and/or disabilities, often with complex or additional needs. Most colleges offer residential provision. Member colleges support learners in their transition to adult life, participation in the community and where possible, employment.

Natspec acts as a national voice for its member colleges and works in partnership with a range of other providers, agencies and organisations. You can contact colleges directly, via the website, or through your connexions/careers service.

NDCS – The National Deaf Children's Society

Ground Floor South, Castle House
37-45 Paul Street
London
EC2A 4LS
Tel: 020 7490 8656
Minicom: 020 7490 8656
Fax: 020 7251 5020
Email: ndcs@ndcs.org.uk
Website: www.ndcs.org.uk
Twitter: @NDCS_UK
Facebook: @NDCS.UK

Leading provider of information, advice, advocacy and support for deaf children, their parents and professionals on all aspects of childhood deafness. This includes advice and information on education, including further and higher education, and support at Special Educational Needs Tribunals.

NDCS also provides advice on equipment and technology for deaf children at home and at school.

NDCS Cmyru

Ty-Nant Court, Morganstown, Cardiff, South Glamorgan CF15 8LW
Tel: 029 2037 3474
Minicom: 029 20811861
Fax: 029 2081 4900
Email: ndcswales@ndcs.org.uk

See main entry above.

NDCS Northern Ireland

The NICVA Building
61 Duncairn Gardens
Belfast BT15 2GB
Tel: 028 9035 2011
Text: 028 9027 8177
Fax: 028 9027 8205
Email: nioffice@ndcs.org.uk

See main entry above.

NDCS Scotland

Second Floor, Empire House
131 West Nile Street
Glasgow G1 2RX
Tel: 0141 354 7850
Textphone: 0141 332 6133
Fax: 0141 331 2780
Email: ndcsscotland@ndcs.org.uk

See main entry above.

Network 81

10 Boleyn Way
West Clacton
Essex CO15 2NJ
Tel: 0845 077 4056 (Admin)
Helpline: 0845 077 4055
Fax: 0845 077 4058
Email: Network81@hotmail.co.uk
Website: www.network81.org.uk

Network 81 offers practical help and support to parents throughout all stages of assessment and statementing as outlined in the Education Act 1996. Their national helpline offers an individual service to parents linked to a national network of local contacts.

NIACE – National Learning and Work Institute

4th Floor, Arnhem House
31 Waterloo Way
Leicester LE1 6LP
Tel: 0116 204 4200
Fax: 0116 204 6988
Email: enquiries@learningandwork.org.uk
Website: www.learningandwork.org.uk
Twitter: @LearnWorkUK
Facebook: @festivaloflearning

Works across sectors and age groups to raise national standards and encourage adults in achieving literacy, numeracy and language skills. You can follow them on Twitter.

NOFAS – UK (National Organisation for Fetal Alcohol Syndrome)

022 Southbank House
Black Prince Road, Lambeth
London SE1 7SJ
Tel: 0208 458 5951
Email: info@nofas-uk.org
Website: www.nofas-uk.org
Twitter: @NOFASUK
Facebook: @nofasuk

Offers advice, support and information about Foetal Alcohol Spectrum Disorder.

Paget Gorman Signed Speech

PGS Administrative Secretary
43 Westover Road
Fleet GU51 3DB
Tel: 01252 621 183
Website: www.pagetgorman.org

Advice and information for parents and professionals concerned with speech and language-impaired children.

Physically Disabled and Able Bodied (PHAB Ltd)

Summit House
50 Wandle Road
Croydon
CR0 1DF
Tel: 020 8667 9443
Fax: 020 8681 1399
Email: info@phab.org.uk
Website: www.phab.org.uk
Twitter: @phab_charity
Facebook: @PhabCharity

A charity that works to promote and encourage people with and without physical disabilities to work together to achieve inclusion for all in the wider community.

Potential Plus UK

Suite 1-2
Challenge House
Sherwood Drive
Bletchley
Milton Keynes MK3 6DP
Tel: 01908 646433
Fax: 0870 770 3219
Email: amazingchildren@potentialplusuk.org
Website: www.potentialplusuk.org
Twitter: @PPUK_
Facebook: @PotentialPlusUK

A mutually supportive self-help organisation offering services both through local branches and nationally. Membership is open to individuals, families, education professionals and schools.

Royal National Institute of Blind People (RNIB)

105 Judd Street
London WC1H 9NE
Helpline: 0303 123 9999
Email: helpline@rnib.org.uk
Website: www.rnib.org.uk
Twitter: @RNIB
Facebook: @rnibuk

We're RNIB, one of the UK's leading sight loss charities and the largest community of blind and partially sighted people.

We recognise everyone's unique experience of sight loss and offer help and support for blind and partially sighted people – this can be anything from practical and emotional support, campaigning for change, reading services and the products we offer in our online shop.

For blind and partially sighted children and young people, including those with complex needs, we offer:
- Specialist advice and guidance
- Family, early years and transitions support
- Shape and Share events to connect with other families
- Information and networks
- Products, toys and games
- Books, magazines and curriculum materials

We look forward to hearing from you soon.

Scope

6 Market Road
London N7 9PW
Helpline: 0808 800 3333 (Scope response)
Tel: 020 7619 7100
Text SCOPE plus message to 80039
Email: helpline@scope.org.uk
Website: www.scope.org.uk
Twitter: @Scope
Facebook: @Scope

Scope is a national disability organisation whose focus is people with cerebral palsy. We provide a range of support, information and campaigning services both locally and nationally in addition to providing opportunities in early years, education, employment and daily living. For more information about cerebral palsy and Scope services, contact Scope Response, which provides free information, advice and initial counselling. Open 9am-7pm weekdays and 10am-2pm Saturdays.

Scope Cymru

4 Ty Nant Court
Morganstown
Cardiff CF15 8LW
Tel: 029 20 815 450
Email: helpline@scope.org.uk

See main entry above.

Scottish Society for Autism

Hilton House,
Alloa Business Park
Whins Road
Alloa FK10 3SA
Tel: 01259 720044
Advice line: 01259 222022
Twitter: @scottishautism
Email: autism@scottishautism.org
Website: www.scottishautism.org
Twitter: @scottishautism
Facebook: @scottishautism

The Scottish Society for Autism is a registered charity established in 1968. They aim to work with individuals of all ages with autism spectrum disorder (ASD), their families and carers, to provide and promote exemplary services and training in education, care, support and life opportunities.

Sense – The National Deafblind Charity

101 Pentonville Road
London N1 9LG
Tel: 0300 330 9250
Textphone: 0300 330 9252
Fax: 0300 330 9251
Email: info@sense.org.uk
Website: www.sense.org.uk
Twitter: @sensecharity
Facebook: @sensecharity

Sense is the leading national charity that supports and campaigns for children and adults who are deafblind. They provide expert advice and information as well as specialist services to deafblind people, their families, carers and the professionals who work with them. They support people who have sensory impairments with additional disabilities.

Services include on-going support for deafblind people and families. These range from day services where deafblind people have the opportunity to learn new skills and Sense-run houses in the community – where people are supported to live as independently as possible. They provide leading specialist advice, for example on education options and assistive technology.

Shine

42 Park Road
Peterborough PE1 2UQ
Tel: 01733 555988
Fax: 01733 555985
Email: info@shinecharity.org.uk
Website: www.shinecharity.org.uk
Twitter: @SHINEUKCharity
Facebook: @ShineUKCharity

The new name for the Association for Spina Bifida and Hydrocephalus (ASBAH). Europe's largest organisation dedicated to supporting individuals and families as they face the challenges arising from spina bifida and hydrocephalus. Advisers are available to explain the problems associated with spina bifida and or hydrocephalus and may be able to arrange visits to schools and colleges to discuss difficulties. Has a Facebook page and you can follow them on Twitter.

Signature

Mersey House
Mandale Business Park
Belmont
Country Durham DH1 1TH
Tel: 0191 383 1155
Text: 07974 121594
Fax: 0191 3837914
Email: enquiries@signature.org.uk
Website: www.signature.org.uk
Twitter: @SignatureDeaf
Facebook: @SignatureDeaf

Association promoting communication with deaf and deafblind people.

SNAP-CYMRU

Head Office
10 Coopers Yard
Curran Road
Cardiff CF10 5NB
Tel: 02920 348 990
Helpline: 0808 801 0608
Textphone: 0345 120 3730
Fax: 029 2034 8998
Email: enquiries@snapcymru.org
Website: www.snapcymru.org
Twitter: @SNAPcymru
Facebook: @SNAPCymru

An all-Wales service for children and families, which provides: accurate information and impartial advice and support for parents, carers, and young people in relation to special educational needs and disability; disagreement resolution service; casework service; independent parental support service; advocacy for children and young people in receipt of services; training for parents, carers, young people; training for professionals in relation to SEN/disability. Has a Facebook page.

Spinal Injuries Association

SIA House
2 Trueman Place
Oldbrook
Milton Keynes MK6 2HH
Tel: 01908 604 191
Adviceline: 0800 980 0501
Text: 81025
Email: sia@spinal.co.uk
Website: www.spinal.co.uk
Twitter: @spinalinjuries
Facebook: @SpinalInjuriesAssociation

Set up to provide services for people with spinal cord injuries.

The Ace Centre

Hollinwood Business Centre,
Albert Street
Oldham OL8 3QL
Tel: 0161 358 0151
Fax: 0161 358 6152
Helpline: 0800 080 3115
Email: enquiries@acecentre.org.uk
Website: www.acecentre.org.uk
Twitter: @AceCentre
Facebook: @AceCentre.uk

The centre offers independent advice and information, assessments and training in the use of assistive technology for individuals with physical and communication disabilities across the north of England.

The Alliance for Inclusive Education

336 Brixton Road
London SW9 7AA
Tel: 020 7737 6030
Email: info@allfie.org.uk
Website: www.allfie.org.uk
Twitter: @ALLFIEUK
Facebook: @ALLFIEUK

National network campaigning for the rights of disabled children in education.

The Brittle Bone Society

Grant-Paterson House
30 Guthrie Street
Dundee DD1 5BS
Tel: 01382 204446
Fax: 01382 206771
Email: bbs@brittlebone.org
Website: www.brittlebone.org
Twitter: @BrittleBoneUK
Facebook: @brittlebonesociety

A UK registered charity providing support for people affected by Osteogenesis Imperfecta (OI).

The Disability Law Service

The Foundry, 17 Oval Way,
London, SE11 5RR
Tel: 020 7791 9800
Fax: 020 7791 9802
Email: advice@dls.org.uk
Website: www.dls.org.uk
Twitter: @DLS_law
Facebook: @disabilitylawservice

The Disability Law Service (DLS) offers free, confidential legal advice to disabled people in the following areas: benefits; children; community care; consumer/contract; discrimination; further and higher education; and employment.

In some cases they are able to offer legal representation. The Disability Law Service is made up of solicitors, advisers and trained volunteers who provide up-to-date, informed legal advice for disabled people, their families, enablers and carers.

The Fragile X Society

Rood End House
6 Stortford Road
Great Dunmow,
Essex CM6 1DA
Tel: 01371 875 100
Fax: 01371 859 915
Email: info@fragilex.org.uk
Website: www.fragilex.org.uk
Twitter: @fragilexuk
Facebook: @thefragilexsociety

The aims of The Fragile X Society are to provide support and comprehensive information to families whose children and adult relatives have fragile X syndrome, to raise awareness of fragile X and to encourage research. There is a link network of family contacts, national helplines for statementing, benefits and family support for epilepsy. They publish information booklets, leaflets, a publications list, video and three newsletters a year. There are also national conferences four times a year. Family membership (UK) is free. Welcomes associate membership from interested professionals.

The Guide Dogs for the Blind Association

Hillfields
Burghfield Common
Reading
Berkshire RG7 3YG
Tel: 0118 983 5555
Fax: 0118 983 5433
Email: guidedogs@guidedogs.org.uk
Website: www.guidedogs.org.uk
Twitter: @guidedogs

Blind Children UK and Guide Dogs have fully integrated into one charity to become The Guide Dogs for the Blind Association, building on their existing services to support more children with sight loss and the issues they face. The Guide Dogs for the Blind Association provides guide dogs, mobility and other rehabilitation services to blind and partially sighted people.

The Haemophilia Society

Willcox House,
140 – 148 Borough High Street
London, SE1 1LB
Tel: 0207 939 0780
Email: info@haemophilia.org.uk
Website: www.haemophilia.org.uk
Twitter: @HaemoSocUK
Facebook: @HaemophiliaSocietyUK

Founded in 1950, this registered charity has over 4000 members and a network throughout the UK providing information, advice and support services to sufferers of haemophilia, von Willebrand's and related bleeding disorders. You can follow them on Twitter.

The Hyperactive Children's Support Group (HACSG)

71 Whyke Lane
Chichester
Sussex PO19 7PD
Tel: 01243 539966
Email: hacsg@hacsg.org.uk
Website: www.hacsg.org.uk

Support group. Will send information pack if you send a large SAE.

The Makaton Charity

Westmead House
Farnborough
Hampshire GU14 7LP
Tel: 01276 606760
Fax: 01276 36725
Email: info@makaton.org
Website: www.makaton.org
Twitter: @MakatonCharity
Facebook: @TheMakatonCharity

Makaton vocabulary is a language programme using speech, signs and symbols to provide basic means of communication and encourage language and literacy skills to develop in children and adults with communication and learning difficulties. Training workshops, courses and a variety of resource materials are available and there is a family support helpline too.

The Planned Environment Therapy Trust (PETT)

Archive and Study Centre
Church Lane
Toddington
Cheltenham
Gloucestershire GL54 5DQ
Tel: 01242 621200
Fax: 01242 620125
Website: www.pettrust.org.uk
Twitter: @pettconnect

Founded to promote effective treatment for those with emotional and psychological disorders.

The Social, Emotional and Behavioural Difficulties Association (SEBDA)

The Panorama Building
Park Street
Ashford
Kent TN24 8DF
Tel: 01233 527044
Email: admin@sebda.org
Website: www.sebda.org
Twitter: @SebdaOrg

SEBDA exists to campaign on behalf of and to provide information, training and a support service to professionals who work with children and young people with social, emotional and behavioural difficulties. Please note: they do not provide any services to parents.

The Speech and Language Communcation Company

42-44 Castle Street
Dundee DD1 3AQ
Tel: 01382 250060
Fax: 01382 568391
Email:
info@speech-language-communication-company.uk
Website:
www.speech-language-communication-company.uk

SLCo are a Scottish registered charity which represents the interests of children and young people who have lived experience of speech, language and communication impairments.

Useful associations and websites

The Stroke Association

Stroke House
240 City Road
London EC1V 2PR
Tel: 020 7566 0300
Helpline: 0303 3033 100
Fax: 020 7490 2686
Email: info@stroke.org.uk
Website: www.stroke.org.uk
Twitter: @thestrokeassoc
Facebook: @TheStrokeAssociation

More than 250,000 people in the UK live with the disabilities caused by a stroke. The association's website provides information and advice for free.

The Talent Development Programmes

Brunel University
School of Sport & Education,
Kingston Lane
Uxbridge, Middlesex UB8 3PH
Tel: 01895 267152
Fax: 01895 269806
Email: catherina.emery@brunel.ac.uk
Website: www.brunel.ac.uk/cbass/education/research/bace

Conducts research into all aspects of identification and provision for able and exceptionally able children. The centre has been involved in supporting the education of able children in inner city schools for a number of years. A number of courses are run for teachers to train them to make effective provision for able pupils.

The Thalidomide Society

Tel: 020 8464 9048
Email: info@thalidomidesociety.org
Website: www.thalidomidesociety.org
Twitter: @ThalSociety

Created in 1962. A support group for impaired adults whose disabilities are a result of the drug Thalidomide.

Together for Short Lives

New Bond House,
Bond Street
Bristol, BS2 9AG
Tel: 0117 989 7820
Helpline: 0808 8088 100
Email: info@togetherforshortlives.org
Website: www.togetherforshortlives.org.uk
Twitter: @Tog4ShortLives
Facebook: @togetherforshortlives

The new name for the Association for Children's Palliative Care (ACT). Helps families with children who have life-limiting or life threatening conditions.

Tourette's Action

The Meads Business Centre,
19 Kingsmead, Farnborough,
Hampshire, GU14 7SR
Tel: 0300 777 8427
Email: admin@tourettes-action.org.uk
Website: www.tourettes-action.org.uk
Twitter: @tourettesaction
Facebook: @TourettesAction

Registered charity offering support and information about Tourette's.

WheelPower – British Wheelchair Sport

Stoke Mandeville Stadium
Guttman Road
Stoke Mandeville
Buckinghamshire HP21 9PP
Tel: 01296 395995
Fax: 01296 424171
Email: info@wheelpower.org.uk
Website: www.wheelpower.org.uk
Twitter: @wheelpower
Facebook: @wheelchairsport

The British Wheelchair Sports Foundation is the national organisation for wheelchair sport in the UK and exists to provide, promote and develop opportunities for men, women and children with disabilities to participate in recreational and competitive wheelchair sport.

Young Minds

Suite 11
Baden Place
Crosby Row
London SE1 1YW
Tel: 020 7089 5050
Parent Hotline: 0808 802 5544
Fax: 020 7407 8887
Website: www.youngminds.org.uk
Email: ymenquiries@youngminds.org.uk
Twitter: @youngmindsuk
Facebook: @youngmindsuk

National charity committed to improving the mental health of young people and children in the UK. Their website has advice, information and details of how you can help.

WEBSITES

www.abilitynet.org.uk

Ability Net is a charity that provides impartial, expert advice about computer technology for disabled people. You can follow them on Twitter.

www.abilityonline.org

Disability information and news and views online.

www.actionondisability.org.uk

Formerly HAFAD – Hammersmith and Fuham Action tor Disability. Campaigning for rights of disabled people, the site is managed and controlled by disabled people.

www.amyandfriends.org

Website set up to support those families affected by Cockayne Syndrome in the UK.

www.cae.org.uk

Centre for Accessible Environments is the leading authority on providing a built enviroment that is accessible for everyone, including disabled people.

www.choicesandrights.org.uk

CRDC – Choices and Rights Disability Coalition. Run for and by disabled people in the Kingston upon Hull and East Riding of Yorkshire area.

www.deafcouncil.org.uk

UK Council on Deafness. Has interesting list of member websites.

www.disabilitynow.wordpress.com

Disability Now – award winning online newspaper for everyone with an interest in disability.

www.direct.gov.uk/disabledpeople

The UK government's web page for disabled people..

www.focusondisability.org.uk

Focus on Disability – resource of general information regarding disability in the UK.

www.heartnsoul.co.uk

Heart 'n' Soul Music Theatre – a leading disability arts group. Has a Facebook page.

www.ncil.org

National Centre for Independent Living. A resource on independent living and direct payments for disabled people and others working in the field.

www.peoplefirstinfo.org.uk

WELDIS – an online information resource of services in and around Westminster for older people, adults and children with disabilities and their carers.

www.qef.org.uk

Queen Elizabeth's Foundation – a national charity supporting over 20,000 physically disabled people annually.

www.revitalise.org.uk

Revitalise (formerly The Winged Fellowship Trust) provides respite care for disabled children, adults and their carers.

www.ssc.education.ed.ac.uk

Scottish Sensory Centre – for everyone who is involved in the education of children and young people with sensory impairment.

www.theark.org.uk

A registered charity set up to enhance the lives of people with multi-sensory impairment, learning difficulties and physical disabilities.

www.tuberous-sclerosis.org

Tuberous Sclerosis Association of Great Britain. Website provides information and support for people and families affected by TSC.

www.youreable.com

Information, products and services for the disabled community including news, shopping, pen pals and discussion forums.

Glossary

ACLD	Autism, Communication and Associated Learning Difficulties
ADD	Attention Deficit Order
ADHD	Attention Deficit and Hyperactive Disorder (Hyperkinetic Disorder)
AdvDip SpecEduc	Advanced Diploma in Special Education
AFBPS	Associate Fellow of the British Psychological Society
ALAN	Adult Literacy and Numeracy
ALCM	Associate of the London College of Music
ALL	Accreditation of Lifelong Learning
AOC	Association of Colleges
AQA	Assessment and Qualification Alliance/ Northern Examinations and Assessment Board
ASC	Autistic Spectrum Conditions
ASD	Autistic Spectrum Disorder
ASDAN	Qualifications for 11-16 age range
ASP	Asperger syndrome
AUT	Autism
AWCEBD	now SEBDA
BA	Bachelor of Arts
BDA	British Dyslexic Association
BESD	Behavioural, Emotional and Social Difficulties
BMET	Biomedical Engineering Technologist
BPhil	Bachelor of Philosophy
BSc	Bachelor of Science
BSL	British Sign Language
BTEC	Range of practical work-related programmes; which lead to qualifications equivalent to GCSEs and A levels (awarded by Edexcel)
C & G	City & Guilds Examination
C(Ed) Psychol	Certificate in Educational Psychology
CACDP	Council for the Advancement of Communication with Deaf People
CAMHS	Child and Adolescent Mental Health Service
CB	Challenging Behaviour
CD	Communcation Difficulties
CertEd	Certificate of Education
CF	Cystic Fibrosis
CLAIT	Computer Literacy and Information Technology
CLD	Complex Learning Difficulties
CNS	Central Nervous System
COPE	Certificate of Personal Effectiveness
CP	Cerebral Palsy

CPD	Continuing Professional Development
CRB	Criminal Records Bureau
CReSTeD	Council for the Registration of Schools Teaching Dyslexic Pupils
CSSE	Consortium of Special Schools in Essex
CSSIW	Care and Social Services Inspectorate for Wales
CTEC	Computer-aided Training, Education and Communication
D	Deaf
DDA	Disability Discrimination Act
DEL	Delicate
DfE	Department for Education
DIDA	Diploma in Digital Applications
DipAppSS	Diploma in Applied Social Sciences
DipEd	Diploma of Education
DipSEN	Diploma in Speial Educational Needs
DipSpEd	Diploma in Special Education
DT	Design and Technology
DYC	Dyscalculia
DYSL	Dyslexia
DYSC	Dyscalculia
DYSP	Dyspraxia
EASIE	Exercise and Sound in Education
EBD	Emotional, Behavioural Difficulties
EBSD	Emotional, Behavioural and/or Social Difficulties
ECDL	European Computer Driving Licence
ECM	Every Child Matters (Government Green Paper)
EdMng	Educational Management
ELC	Early Learning Centre
ELQ	Equivalent or Lower Qualification
EPI	Epilepsy
EQUALS	Entitlement and Quality Education for Pupils with Learning Difficulties
FAS	Foetal Alcohol Syndrome
FLSE	Federation of Leaders in Special Education
FXS	Fragile X Syndrome
GLD	General Learning Difficulties
HA	High Ability
HANDLE	Holistic Approach to Newuro-DEvelopment and Learning Efficiency
HEA	Higher Educaiton Authority/Health Education Authority
HI	Hearing Impairment
HS	Hospital School
ICT	Information Communication Technology

Glossary

IEP	Individual Education Plan
IIP	Investors in People
IM	Idiopathic Myelofibrosis
ISI	Independent Schools Inspectorate
IT	Information Technology
KS	Key Stage
LA	Local Authority
LD	Learning Difficulties
LDD	Learning Difficulties and Disabilities
LISA	London International Schools Association
MA	Master of Arts
MAPA	Management of Actual or Potential Aggression
MBA	Master of Business Administration
MD	Muscular Dystrophy
MDT	Multidisciplinary Team
MEd	Master of Education
MLD	Moderate Learning Difficulties
MS	Multiple Sclerosis
MSc	Master of Science
MSI	Multi-sensory Impairment
NAES	National Association of EBD Schools
NAS	National Autistic Society
NASEN	Northern Association of Special Educational Needs
NASS	National Association of Independent Schools & Non-maintained Special Schools
NATSPEC	National Association of Specialist Colleges
NOCN	National Open College Network
NPQH	National Professional Qualification for Headship
NVQ	National Vocational Qualifications
OCD	Obsessive Compulsive Disorder
OCN	Open Course Network
ODD	Oppositional Defiant Disorder
OT	Occupational Therapist
P scales	method of recording the achievements of SEN students who are working towards the first levels of the National Curriculum
PACT	Parents Association of Children with Tumours
PACT	Parents and Children Together
PCMT	Professional and Clinical Multidisciplinary Team
PD	Physical Difficulties
PDA	Pathological Demand Avoidance
PE	Physical Education
PECS	Picture Exchange Communication System

PGCE	Post Graduate Certificate in Education
PGCertSpld	Post Graduate Certificate in Specific Learning Difficulties
PGTC	Post Graduate Teaching Certificate
PH	Physical Impairment
PhD	Doctor of Philosophy
Phe	Partially Hearing
PMLD	Profound and Multiple Learning Difficulties
PNI	Physical Neurological Impairment
PRU	Pupil Referral Unit
PSHCE	Personal Social Health, Citizenship and Economics
RE	Religious Education
SAT	Standard Asessment Test
SCD	Social and Communication Difficulties
SCLD	Severe and Complex Learning Difficulties
SEAL	Social and Emotional Aspects of Learning
SEBD	Severe Emotional and Behavioural Disorders
SEBDA	Social, Emotional and Behavioural Difficulties Association
SEBN	Social, Emotional and Behavioural Needs
SEMH	Social, Emotional and Mental Health Needs
SLCN	Speech, Language and Communicational Needs
SLD	Severe Learning Difficulties
SLI	Specific Language Impairment
SLT	Speech and Language Teacher
SP	Special Purpose/Speech Processing
SpEd	Special Education
SPLD	Specific Learning Difficulties
SP&LD	Speech and Language Difficulties
STREAM	Strong Therapeutic, Restoring Environment and Assesssment Model
SWALSS	South and West Association of Leaders in Special Schools
SWSF	Steiner Waldorf Schools Foundation
TAV	Therapeutic, Academic and Vocational
TEACCH	Treatment and Education of Autistic and related Communication Handicapped Children (also sometimes written as TEACHH)
TCI	Therapeutic Crisis Intervention
ToD	Teacher of the Deaf
TOU	Tourette syndrome
VB	Verbal Reasoning
VIS	Visually Impaired
VOCA	Voice Output Communication Aid

Index